I dedicate this book to the
Lord Jesus Christ,
my mentor and teacher

NOTICE TO THE READER

Mike Holt's Illustrated Guide to
Basic Electrical Theory
2nd Edition
Graphic Illustrations: Mike Culbreath
Cover Graphic: Marie P. Fore
Cover Design: Tracy Jette
Layout Design & Typesetting: Paul Wright, Cathleen Kwas, Tracy Jette

Printed January 2004.

1-932685-12-X

For more information, contact:
Mike Holt Enterprises, Inc.
7310 West McNab Road, Suite 201
Tamarac, Florida 33321
www.mikeholt.com

To request examination copies of this or other Mike Holt Publications, call or write to:

Mike Holt Enterprises, Inc.
7310 West McNab Road, Suite 201
Tamarac, Florida 33321
Phone: 1-888-NEC CODE • Fax: 1-954-720-7944

Mike Holt Online
www.NECcode.com
Sales@NECcode.com

You can download a sample PDF of all our publications by visiting www.NECcode.com

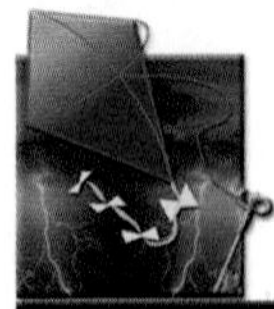

Table of Contents

Chapter 2
Basic Electricity

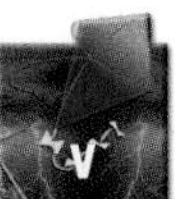

Chapter 3 Basic Electrical Circuits

Chapter 4 Electrical Systems and Protection

Chapter 5
Alternating Current

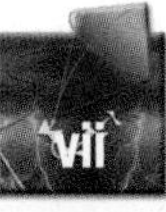

Chapter 6
Motors, Generators, and Transformers

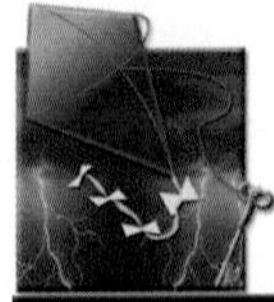

Preface

Introduction

Understanding electrical theory is critical for any person who desires to have a better understanding of the principles of electricity. The subjects contained in ***Basic Electrical Theory—2nd Edition*** should help you understand what electricity is, how it's produced and how it's used. You learn to perform basic electrical calculations critical for everyday use. Critical understanding of circuits will help you understand complicated circuits for controls, fire alarms, security and much more. In addition, the basics for understanding motors and transformers are clearly explained. The most important subject you will learn about is grounding!

This book/video program was developed so that you could understand all of the basic principles of electricity that a journeyman or master electrician would need to know to be qualified.

The writing style of this book is informal and relaxed, and the book contains clear graphics and examples that apply to the real world.

To get the most out of this book, you should answer the questions at the end of each unit. If you have difficulty with a question, skip it and go back to it later. You will find that the answer key contains detailed explanations for each question.

How To Use This Book

Each unit of this book contains an introduction, explanations with graphics, examples, and steps for calculations and formulas, along with conclusions and practice questions. As you read this book, review the author's comments, graphics, and examples.

Basic Electrical Theory—2nd Edition has been completely revised and printed in full color, with each chapter having its own color theme. Each unit contains an introduction, summary, conclusion and practice questions.

As you progress through this book, you will find some formulas, rules or comments that you don't understand. Don't get frustrated. Highlight the section in the book that you are having a problem with. Discuss it with your boss, inspector, coworker etc., and maybe they'll have some additional feedback. Once you've completed the book, review those highlighted sections again and see if you understand.

Errors

Any errors discovered, or revisions made after the publication date of this book will be posted at www.NECcode.com.

I have taken great care in researching this book, but I'm not perfect. If you feel that I've made an error, please let me know by contacting me directly at Mike@MikeHolt.com, or 1-888-NEC CODE (1-888-632-2633). In addition, you can visit www.NECcode.com for the most current answer key.

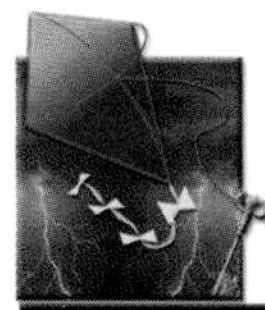

Mike Holt Enterprises Team

About the Author: Mike Holt

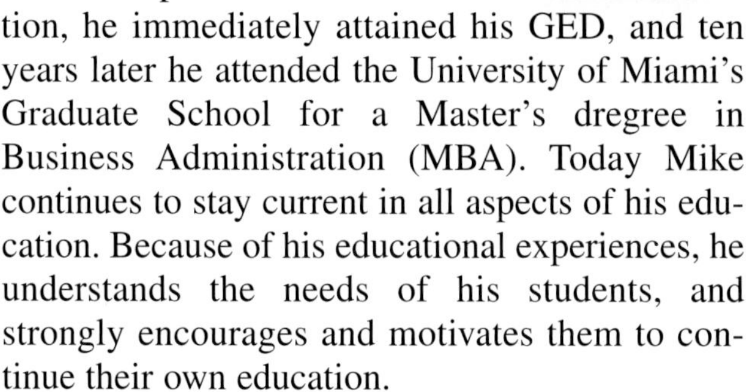

Mike Holt worked his way up through the electrical trade from apprentice electrician to master electrician and electrical inspector. Mike did not complete high school due to circumstances beyond his control. Realizing that success depends on one's education, he immediately attained his GED, and ten years later he attended the University of Miami's Graduate School for a Master's dregree in Business Administration (MBA). Today Mike continues to stay current in all aspects of his education. Because of his educational experiences, he understands the needs of his students, and strongly encourages and motivates them to continue their own education.

Mike is nationally recognized as one of America's most knowledgeable electrical trainers. He has touched the lives of many thousands of electricians, inspectors, contractors and engineers. His dynamic and animated teaching style is relaxed, direct and fun. Perhaps Mike's best quality is his ability to motivate his students to become successful.

Mike resides in Central Florida, is the father of seven children, and has many outside interests and activities. In 1988, he became the National Barefoot Waterskiing Champion. He has set five national records and, in 1999, he again captured the National Barefoot Waterskiing Championship. Mike also enjoys white-water rafting, racquetball, playing his guitar, motocross racing and his latest challenge, Mini Cup Racing (check it out at www.floridaminicup.com). But most of all, Mike enjoys spending time with his family. His commitment to God has helped him develop a lifestyle that balances God, family, career, and self.

In Memory Of...

On Saturday, October 4, 2003, my friend Paul Wright was killed in a terrible motorcycle accident. Paul was 47 years old and he loved his Harley.

Paul was a friend, a great guy, and team member of Mike Holt Enterprises for many years. You actually know him! You see, he's the one who did the ads in the magazines (like me standing with my arms stretched out), the catalogs, the graphics on the video/DVD boxes, etc. In addition, every MHE book you see is Paul's work.

Thank you Paul, for adding "Class and Market Presence" to our organization.

I just want to remind you that life is just a whisper away from death. I hope you live your life knowing that today could be your last. Let others know how much you love them, and do it today, not tomorrow! I pray that you have the right priorities—God first, family second, and your work last.

God Bless,

Educational Director

Sarina Snow was born and raised in "The Bronx" (Yankee Stadium Area), then moved to New Jersey with her husband Freddy where they raised their three children. They moved to Florida in 1979 and have totally loved the move to a warmer climate. Sarina has worked with Mike Holt for over twenty years and has literally learned the business from the ground up. She remembers typing Mike's books using carbon paper BC (Before Computers). She has developed a strong relationship with the industry by attending Mike's classes and seminars, and by accompanying Mike to many trade shows in various states to get a deeper understanding of the trade first-hand. Her love and devotion to Mike and Company (actually the original name of Mike Holt Enterprises) has given her the ability to be the "Mom" in the industry. "She Cares," sums it up.

Graphic Illustrator

Mike Culbreath devoted his career to the electrical industry and worked his way up from an apprentice electrician to master electrician. While working as a journeyman electrician, he suffered a serious on-the-job knee injury. With a keen interest in continuing education for electricians, and as part of his rehabilitation program, he completed courses at Mike Holt Enterprises, Inc. and then passed the exam to receive his Master Electrician's license.

In 1986, after attending classes at Mike Holt Enterprises, he joined the staff to update material and later studied computer graphics and began illustrating Mike Holt's textbooks and magazine articles. He's worked with Mike Holt Enterprises for over 15 years and, as Mike Holt has proudly acknowledged, has helped to transform his words and visions into lifelike graphics.

Mike Culbreath resides in northern Michigan with his wife Toni, and two children: Dawn and Mac. He is helping Toni fulfill her dream by helping her develop and build a quality horse boarding, training, and teaching facility. Mike enjoys working with children by coaching soccer, volunteering as a leader for a 4-H archery club, and assisting with the local 4-H horse club. He also enjoys fishing, gardening, and cooking.

Editorial

Toni Culbreath completed high school graduation requirements by the end of the first semester of her senior year. She went on to complete courses for computer programming at a trade school by March of that year, and then returned to participate in graduation ceremonies with her high school class.

Toni became associated with Mike Holt Enterprises in 1994 in the area of software support and training and enjoys the new challenges of editing Mike Holt's superb material. She recently earned certification as a therapeutic riding instructor and is extensively involved in Michigan's 4-H horse programs at both the county and state level.

Barbara Parks has been working for Mike Holt Enterprises for the past three years as a Writer's Assistant. She has edited most of Mike Holt's books and various projects over this period of time. She is a retired lady, working part time at home and thoroughly enjoys "keeping busy."

Cover Design

Tracy Jette has enjoyed working in the field of Graphic Design for over 10 years. She loves all aspects of design, and finds that spending time outdoors camping and hiking with her family and friends is a great inspiration. Tracy is very happy to have recently joined Mike Holt Enterprises and has found that working from home brings a harmony to her life with her 3 boys (10-year-old twins and a 7-year-old), her husband of 16 years, Mario, and her work life.

Layout Design and Production

Cathleen Kwas has been in the publishing industry for over 26 years. She's worn many hats–copy editor, desktop publisher, prepress manager, project coordinator, communications director, book designer and graphic artist.

Cathleen is very happily married to Michael and lives in beautiful Lake Mary, Florida with her large collection of teddy bears. Their only child, Derek, a 2003 graduate recently joined the Army.

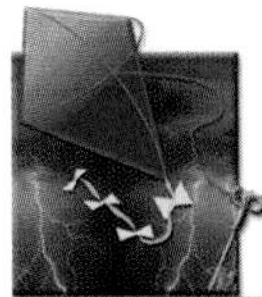

Special Acknowledgments

Acknowledgments

I would like to say thank you to all the people in my life who believed in me, even those who didn't. There are many people who played a role in the development and production of this book.

I will start with Mike Culbreath (Master Electrician), who helped me transform my words and visions into lifelike graphics. I could not have produced such a fine book without his help. Next, I would like to show my appreciation to Toni Culbreath and Barbara Parks for their editorial contribution. Working tirelessly through many sets of revisions, Toni and Barbara make sure my words are properly presented and easily understood.

On a Personal Note

Thanks to all those who helped me in the electrical industry, to the Electrical Construction and Maintenance magazine for my first "big break," and to Joe McPartland, "my mentor," who was there to help and encourage me. Joe, I'll never forget to help others as you've helped me.

In addition, I would like to thank Joe Salimando, the former publisher of Electrical Contractor Magazine, and Dan Walters of the National Electrical Contractors Association (NECA) for my second "big break," and for putting up with all of my crazy ideas.

A very special thank you goes to Marie Fore, my mother-in-law, who designed and created the illustration used in the cover design.

I would like to also thank James Stallcup, Dick Lloyd, Mark Ode, DJ Clements, Joe Ross, John Calloggero, Tony Silvestri, Morris Trimmer, and Marvin Weiss for being special people in my life.

The final personal thank you goes to Sarina, my long-time friend and office manager. Thank you for covering the office for me while I spend so much time writing books, doing seminars and producing videos and DVDs. Your love and concern for me has helped me through many difficult times.

Advisory Committee

I would also like to thank those individuals who reviewed the manuscript and offered invaluable suggestions and feedback. Their assistance is greatly appreciated.

Bob Huddleston, P.E.
Electrical Engineering
Eastman Chemical Co. Kingsport, Tennessee

Brooke Stauffer, NECA
National Electrical Contractors Association

Kurt A. Stout, Electrical Inspector
Plantation, Florida

Eric Stromberg, Electrical Engineering Specialist/Instructor
The Dow Checmical Company
Freeport, Texas

Elzy R. Williams, P.E.
Adjunct Professor at John Tyler Community College

A Very Special Thank You

To my beautiful wife, Linda, and my seven children: Belynda, Melissa, Autumn, Steven, Michael, Meghan, and Brittney—thank you for loving me so much.

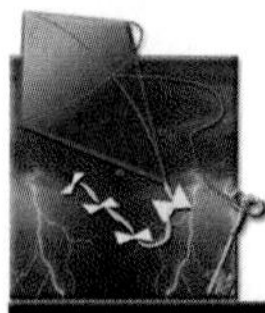

Video/DVD Team Members

Dr. Joe Engel was born and raised in Cincinnati. He earned a BS and MS in EE from the University of Cincinnati. As a co-op student, Joe first worked as an ac motor designer for Allis-Chalmers and later as a home electronic organ designer for Baldwin Piano. He moved to Pittsburgh where he earned a PhD from the University of Pittsburgh.

For 30 years Joe worked for Westinghouse and, most recently, 10 years for Eaton Cutler-Hammer as the manager of an electronics R&D group. This group focuses on electrical metering, control and protection products for the residential, commercial, industrial and utility markets. Awards include the Westinghouse Order of Merit (Westinghouse's highest honor) and an Inventor of the Year award; Joe has 90 U.S. Patents.

Joe has been married to his wife Mary for 44 years. They have raised eight children and have seven grandchildren. Joe loves to travel, usually with his children, and most recently back packed the Grand Canyon. Golf and bowling are his hobbies.

Bob Huddleston is a licensed Professional Engineer. He has a Bachelor's and Master's Degree in Electrical Engineering, and is currently employed by Eastman Chemical Company in Kingsport, Tennessee where he is responsible for the Electrical Safety Program.

Bob has served a number of roles in the electrical industry, including an engineering supervisor, maintenance supervisor, plant engineer, and an instructor of electrical and electronic theory for the U.S. Navy at the Naval Nuclear Power School.

Before completing his degrees, Bob served an 8,000 hour electrician apprenticeship at a Tennessee Valley Authority nuclear plant, and worked for approximately nine years as a construction electrician. He was recognized as the Electrical Apprentice of the Year during this time. Bob serves as an adjunct faculty member at a local technical community college, and is the Chairman of the Electrical Curriculum Advisory Council.

Bob enjoys boating, fishing, hunting, flying his Cessna 172, and serving the Lord.

Eric Stromberg enrolled in the University of Houston in 1976, with Electrical Engineering as his major. During the first part of his college years, Eric worked for a company that specialized in installing professional sound systems. Later, he worked for a small electrical company and eventually became a journeyman electrician. After graduation from college in 1982, Eric went to work for an electronics company that specialized in fire alarm systems for high-rise buildings. He became a state licensed fire alarm installation superintendent and was also a member of IBEW local union 716. In 1989, Eric began a career with The Dow Chemical Company as an Electrical Engineer designing power distribution systems for large industrial facilities. In 1997 Eric began teaching National Electric Code classes. Eric currently resides in Lake Jackson, Texas, with his wife Jane and three children: Ainsley, Austin, and Brieanna.

Ronald V. (Ron) Nelson is a Certified Engineering Technician. Born and raised in the Pacific Northwest, he was fascinated by the "miracle" of electricity from an early age. A hydro-electric plant was located nearby where Ron could see water being converted into electrical power.

Ron began his electrical engineering career in 1965 which included design for a power supply ranging from 120V through 69,000V; plus, street lighting design for Owensboro, Kentucky's municipal utility. After 21 years in engineering, he accepted a new position at Warren Rural Electric Cooperative in Bowling Green, Kentucky. Ron became the Technical Adviser to the agricultural, commercial and industrial customers for power quality issues and solutions. He retired in 2002 after serving the Cooperative as Vice President for 10 years.

Ron continues to provide technical services (including proper grounding/bonding), and training to the utility, electricians, vocational schools, and customers in the region.

James E Jones Jr. is the Director of Education & Training/ Instructor for Mills Electrical Contractors in Dallas, TX. He has been in the electrical construction/ maintenance industry since 1979 when he joined the U.S. Air Force right after graduating high school.

During his 21 year Air Force career he worked as a high voltage lineman, electrical instructor, and electrician. Going to school at night and on weekends, he received a Baccalaureate of Science Degree, with Honors, in Occupational Education, with specialization in Corporate Training Development, Electric Power Systems, and Computer Business Information Systems. He is a licensed Master Electrician and teaches several electrical, computer, and NEC courses. He is on the Electrical Advisory Board for the local apprenticeship programs. "Opportunity is waiting for whomever is ready to take advantage of it."

Notes

Chapter 1
Electrical Fundamentals

Unit 1 – Matter

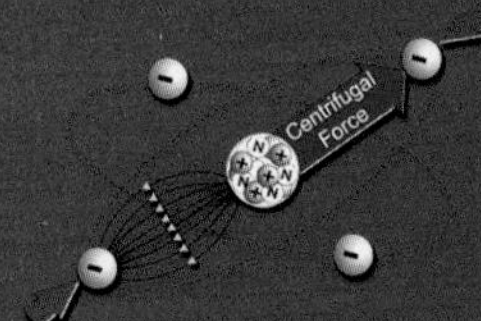

Unit 2 – Electron Theory

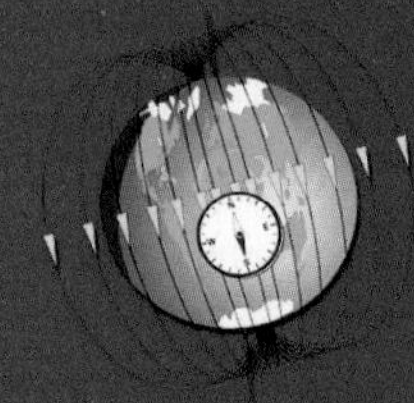

Unit 3 – Magnetism

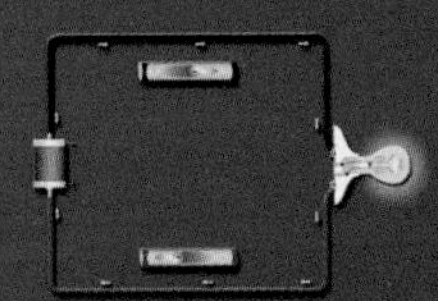

Unit 4 – Electricity

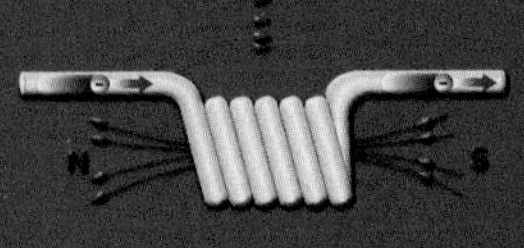

Unit 5 – Electromagnetism

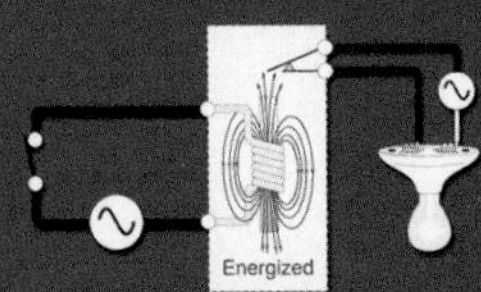

Unit 6 – Uses of Electromagnetism

Notes

UNIT

Matter

Introduction

Do you know where electricity comes from? To be able to say yes to that question, you must understand a bit about the physics of matter. What value does a brief study of the nature of matter have for the student of electrical theory? The understanding that comes from that study lays the foundation for understanding electrical theory. Only when you know the theory can you truly have confidence in the practical aspects of your electrical work.

Don't discount the role of physics in electrical theory and application. Many of the electrical innovations of the 20th Century—things such as radar—originated with physicists, not electrical engineers.

When people have a hard time understanding and applying the *National Electrical Code (NEC),* the root cause is often a lack of knowledge of the basic physics behind electricity. When you know the physics, then you can understand the rules, codes, and laws that arise from it.

1.1 Matter

Everything on earth that has weight and occupies space is called matter, which is made up of atoms of elements. When the atoms of elements combine, they produce compounds. The smallest particle of a compound is called a molecule. Figure 1–1

1.2 Atomic Theory

An atom contains three types of subatomic particles: electrons, protons, and neutrons. The central part of the atom is called the nucleus and it contains protons (positive charge) and neutrons (no charge). Electrons (negative charge) orbit around the nucleus. Figure 1–2

Electrons—Electrons are much smaller than protons and they are 1,840 times lighter. Because of their light weight and mobility (ease of separation from the atom), electrons actively participate in the transfer, or flow, of electrical energy.

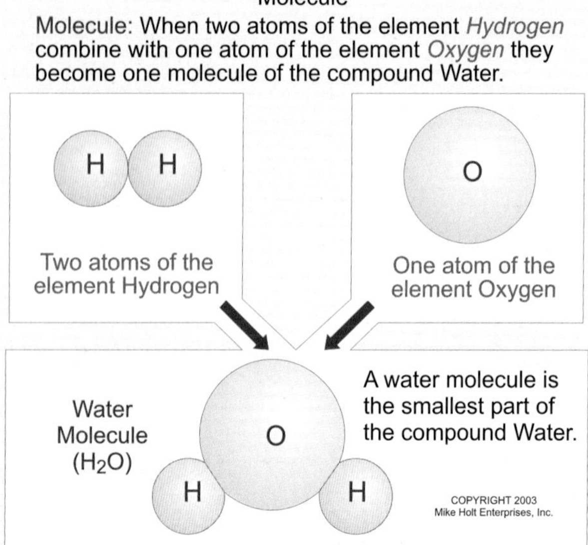

Molecule
Molecule: When two atoms of the element Hydrogen combine with one atom of the element Oxygen they become one molecule of the compound Water.
H H
Two atoms of the element Hydrogen
O
One atom of the element Oxygen
Water Molecule (H_2O)
O
H H
A water molecule is the smallest part of the compound Water.
COPYRIGHT 2003 Mike Holt Enterprises, Inc.

Figure 1–1

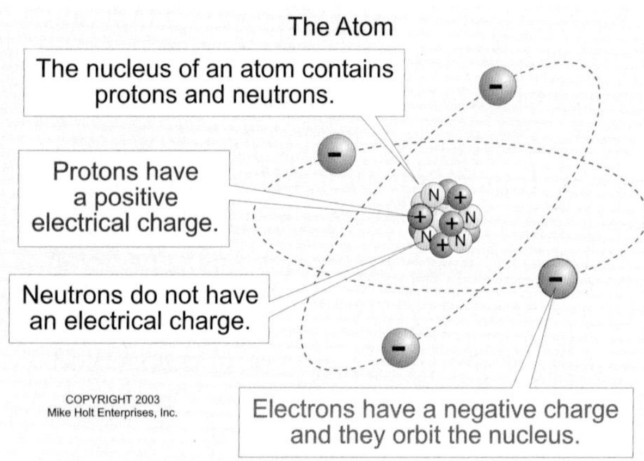

Figure 1–2

Electrons have a negative electrical charge that is visualized as lines of force coming straight into the electron from all sides. Figure 1–3

Protons—Protons are the same size as neutrons and have nearly the same mass (1,840 times as heavy as an electron), therefore they don't actively participate in the flow of electrical energy. Protons have a positive electrical charge with lines of force going straight out in all directions. Figure 1–3

Neutrons—Neutrons have a neutral electrical charge, no lines of force, and do not take an active role in the flow or transfer of electrical energy. Figure 1–3

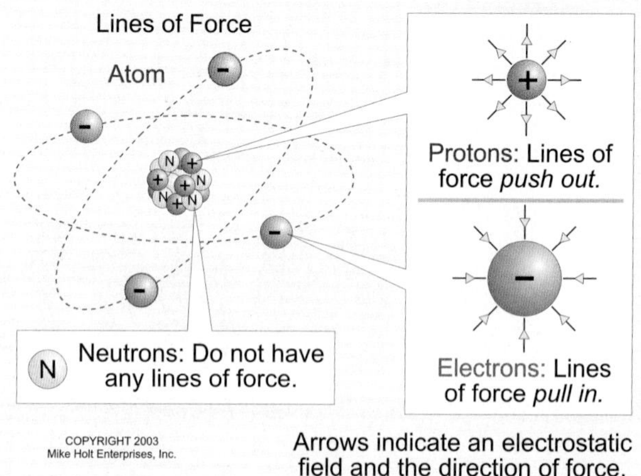

Lines of Force
Atom
Protons: Lines of force push out.
Electrons: Lines of force pull in.
N
Neutrons: Do not have any lines of force.
COPYRIGHT 2003 Mike Holt Enterprises, Inc.
Arrows indicate an electrostatic field and the direction of force.

Figure 1–3

1.3 Law of Electrical Charges

Subatomic particles that attract or repel other subatomic particles follow the Law of Electrical Charges. The Law of Electrical Charges states that "subatomic particles with like charges repel each other and particles with unlike charges attract each other." Therefore, electrons repel electrons and protons repel protons, but electrons and protons are attracted to each other. Figure 1–4

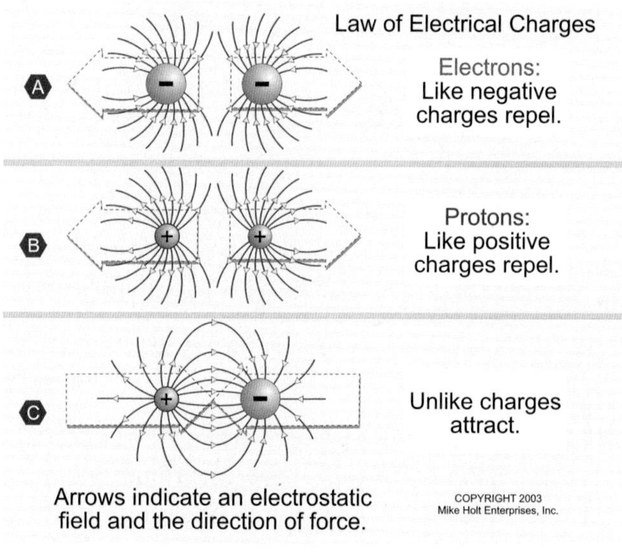

Law of Electrical Charges
A
Electrons: Like negative charges repel.
B
Protons: Like positive charges repel.
C
Unlike charges attract.
Arrows indicate an electrostatic field and the direction of force.
COPYRIGHT 2003 Mike Holt Enterprises, Inc.

Figure 1–4

AUTHOR'S COMMENT: This attracting and repelling force on subatomic particles (charged materials) is sometimes called the electrostatic field.

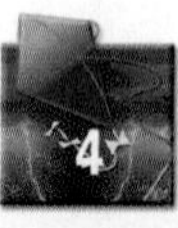

1.4 Law of Atomic Charges

Most of the time, the electrical charge of an atom is balanced or neutral; there are an equal number of positive and negative charges within the atom (the number of electrons equal the number of protons). Under this condition, the atom has no electrical charge. Figure 1–5A

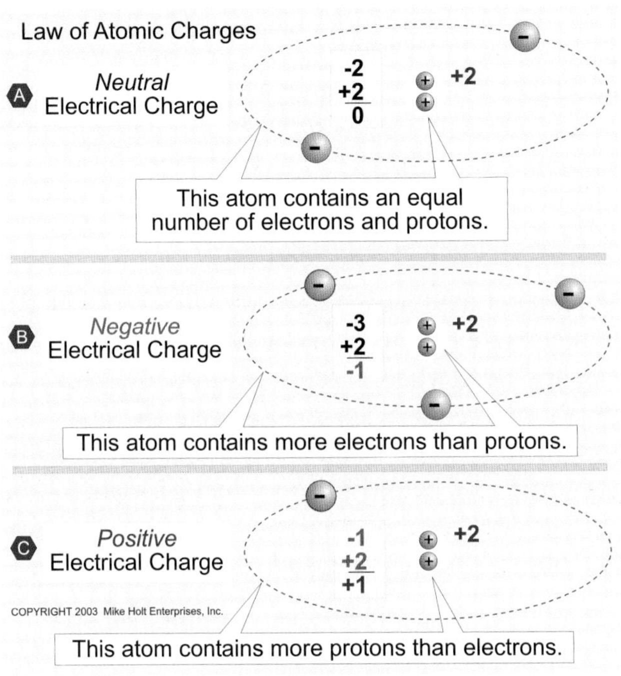

Figure 1–5

Negative Atomic Charge

However, if an atom contains more electrons than protons, then the atom has a negative atomic charge. This would occur if an atom picked up an additional electron or two and stored them in its electron cloud. Figure 1–5B

Positive Atomic Charge

If an atom contains more protons than electrons, then the atom will have a positive atomic charge. This would be the case if an atom lost an electron or two from its electron cloud. Charged atoms are called ions and they are either positively or negatively charged. Figure 1–5C

1.5 Charged Material (Static Charge)

If two conductive materials in contact with each other are separated, most of the electrons will return to the original surface before the separation is complete.

When unlike insulated materials are in intimate contact, electrons from one material move across the interface to the surface of the other, but the protons remain on the first surface. When the bodies are quickly separated, both will display a charge because one material will have an excess of electrons (negative charge) while the other will have fewer electrons (positive charge). Static charge is due to an excess of, or a deficiency of, electrons between objects that have been separated. Figure 1–6

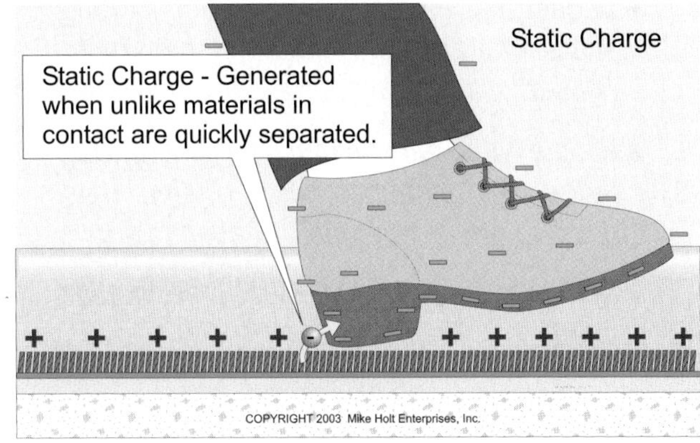

Figure 1–6

The human body in a low-humidity area may accumulate a dangerous static charge of several thousand volts by contact of shoes with floor coverings or by working closely to machinery that generates static electricity.

> **AUTHOR'S COMMENT:** An object can become positively or negatively charged depending on whether it loses or gains electrons.

Static Voltage

The voltage developed is related to the amount of charge deposited on a body and to the capacitance of this body with respect to its surroundings. This voltage can continue to grow on an insulating body under the influence of continuous charge generation. If leakage of charge from the surface of the insulating body is not rapid enough, a sparking voltage can be reached and a high-voltage static discharge can occur.

DANGER: ***The high-voltage static discharge introduces:***

- ***Danger in an area where flammable or explosive liquids, gases, dusts, or fibers are present.*** Figure 1–7
- ***Danger that a person subjected to a static shock may fall or accidentally come into contact with a piece of moving equipment.***
- ***People with heart rhythmic sensitivity may suffer dysfunctional heart rhythm thus causing great discomfort or even injury.***
- ***Damage to sensitive electronic equipment.***
- ***Loss of electronically stored data.***

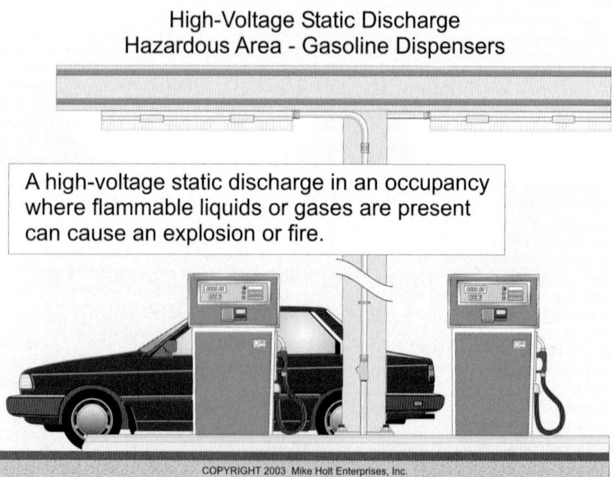

High-Voltage Static Discharge
Hazardous Area - Gasoline Dispensers
A high-voltage static discharge in an occupancy where flammable liquids or gases are present can cause an explosion or fire.
COPYRIGHT 2003 Mike Holt Enterprises, Inc.

Figure 1–7

Reducing Static Charge

Providing a path to the earth can often reduce the electrostatic charge between objects. In addition, cotton clothing, ion generators, and humidifiers, as well as antistatic furniture, walls, and flooring are used to reduce this charge. For more information on solving problems associated with static electricity, see *IEEE 142—Recommended Practice for Grounding of Industrial and Commercial Power Systems, NFPA 77-2000—Recommended Practice on Static Electricity,* and *API RP 2003-1998—Protection Against Ignitions Arising Out of Static Lightning and Stray Currents.*

1.6 Neutralizing a Charge

Because of the Law of Electrical Charges [1.3], the build up of electrons on a negatively charged object can discharge when it comes close enough to a positively charged or uncharged object. The discharge is sometimes seen as an arc, and the distance that the spark can jump is determined in part by the voltage and dielectric between the bodies. The temperature of the arc is dependent on the amperage.

Figure 1–8 shows how electrons picked up by a person walking across a carpet in a low humidity environment can arc to the positively charged surface of the metal doorknob.

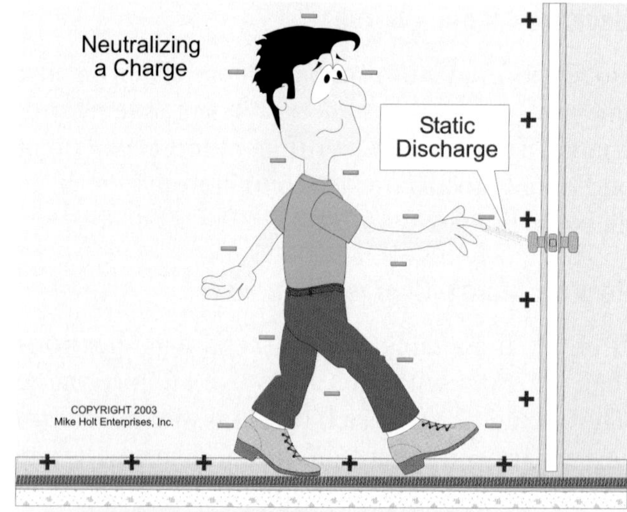

The build up of electrons can be "discharged" when a negatively charged object comes close to a positively charged object.

Figure 1–8

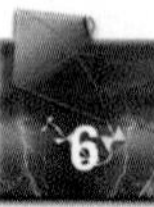

1.7 Lightning

Lightning is the discharging of high-voltage cells (usually negatively charged) within clouds to each other, to the earth, and sometimes to space. These charged cells in clouds normally attract charges of opposite polarity on high objects located on the earth. When the cell charge reaches a critical level (when the insulation between cloud and earth breaks down), it develops a "stepped leader" ionized path resulting in a high-current discharge (stroke), which temporarily neutralizes the positive and negative charges between the objects. **Figure 1–9**

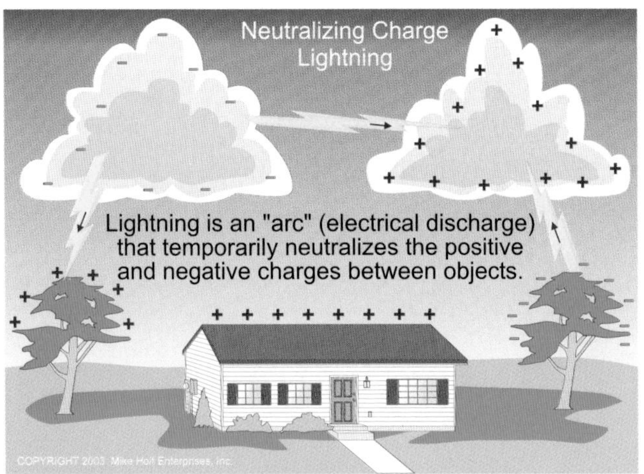

Figure 1–9

AUTHOR'S COMMENT: "High-voltage cells" are simply areas within clouds that have built-up charges through friction associated with air movement. "Stepped" paths are just ionized paths that zigzag toward the earth.

CAUTION: *The lightning stroke frequently terminates to a point of some elevation, such as a tree, a building, a transmission line, or similar raised structures, like a human body. Contrary to popular belief, lightning strikes both metallic and nonmetallic objects with the same frequency.*

The temperature at the terminal of the stroke, or at any high-resistance point in the path over which the current flows en route to ground, is likely to ignite combustible materials. **Figure 1–10**

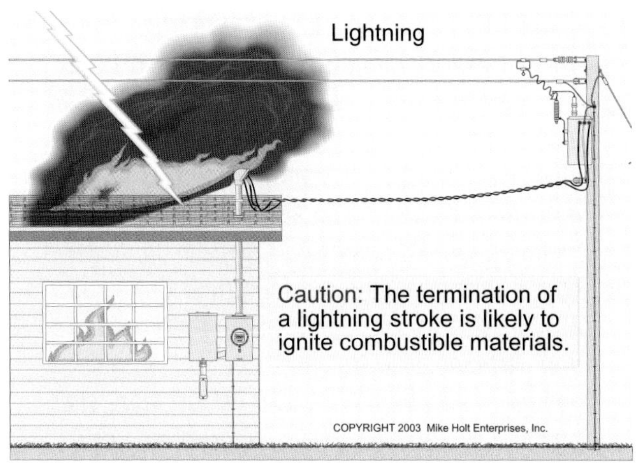

Figure 1–10

DANGER: ***Over 100 deaths, 250 injuries, and billions of dollars in property damage are caused each year in the United States because of lightning. A single bolt of lightning can have a voltage as high as thirty million volts and over twenty thousand amperes (20,000A).***

1.8 Lightning Protection

To protect property such as building structures from a lightning discharge, air terminals (connected together and to the earth by larger conductors) should be placed on top of the structure so that lightning can be harmlessly directed from the structure into the earth. **Figure 1–11**

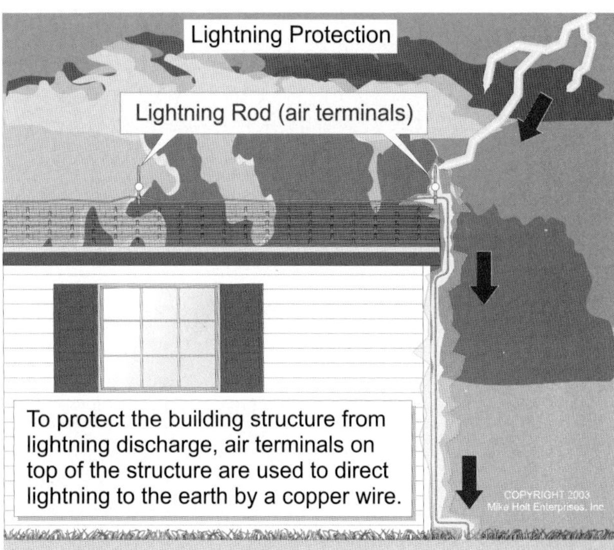

Figure 1–11

CAUTION: *Lightning protection is intended to protect the building structure itself; it is not intended to protect electrical equipment on or inside the building structure. If protection of electrical equipment from lightning is important, then surge-protection devices must be installed on the electrical system in accordance with the* National Electrical Code. *See Article 280 for Surge Arrester requirements and Article 285 for the rule on transient voltage protection. For more information, visit http://www.leviton.com/pdfs/spdrefman.pdf.* Figure 1–12

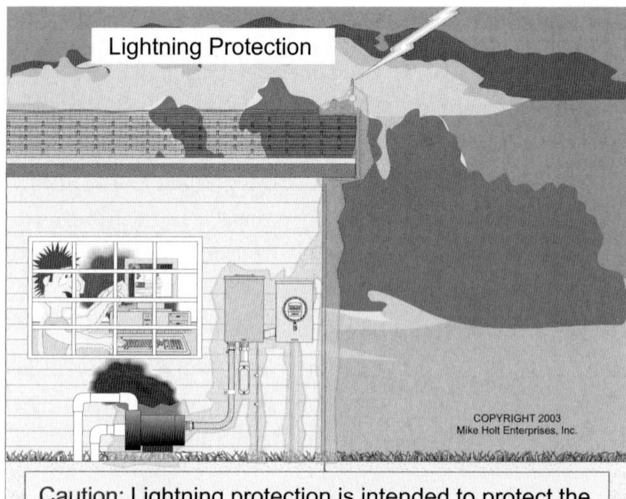

Figure 1–12

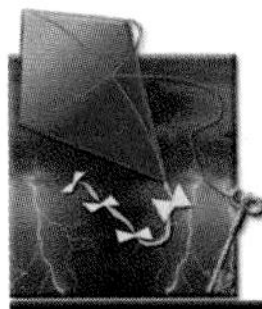

Unit 1 Summary

1.1 Matter

When the atoms of elements combine, they produce compounds. The smallest particle of a compound is called a molecule.

1.2 Atomic Theory

An atom contains three types of subatomic particles: electrons, protons, and neutrons. Electrons are much smaller than protons and they actively participate in the transfer, or flow, of electrical energy.

1.3 Law of Electrical Charges

The Law of Electrical Charges states that "subatomic particles with like charges repel each other and particles with unlike charges attract each other." Therefore, electrons repel electrons and electrons and protons are attracted to each other.

1.4 Law of Atomic Charges

Most of the time, the electrical charge of an atom is balanced or neutral. Under this condition, the atom has no electrical charge. If an atom contains more electrons than protons, then the atom has a negative atomic charge.

1.5 Charged Material (Static Charge)

Static charge is due to an excess of, or a deficiency of, electrons between objects that have been separated. An object can become positively or negatively charged depending on whether it loses or gains electrons.

Static Voltage

The voltage developed is related to the amount of charge deposited on a body and to the capacitance of this body with respect to its surroundings. If leakage of charge from the surface of the insulating body is not rapid enough, a sparking voltage can be reached, and a high-voltage static discharge can occur.

Reducing Static Charge

Providing a path to the earth can often reduce the electrostatic charge between objects. In addition, cotton clothing, ion generators, and humidifiers, as well as antistatic furniture, walls, and flooring are used to reduce this charge.

1.6 Neutralizing a Charge

Because of the Law of Electrical Charges [1.3], the build up of electrons on a negatively charged object can discharge when it comes close enough to a positively charged or uncharged object.

1.7 Lightning

Lightning is the discharging of high-voltage cells within clouds to each other, to the earth, and sometimes to space. When the cell charge reaches a critical level, it develops a "stepped leader" ionized path resulting in a high-current discharge, which temporarily neutralizes the positive and negative charges between the objects.

CAUTION: *Contrary to popular belief, lightning strikes both metallic and nonmetallic objects with the same frequency.*

DANGER: ***Over 100 deaths, 250 injuries, and billions of dollars in property damage are caused each year in the United States because of lightning.***

1.8 Lightning Protection

To protect property, air terminals connected together and to the earth by larger conductors should be placed on top of the structure so that lightning can be harmlessly directed from the structure into the earth.

CAUTION: *Lightning protection is intended to protect the building structure itself. If protection of electrical equipment from lightning is important, then surge-protection devices must be installed on the electrical system in accordance with the* National Electrical Code.

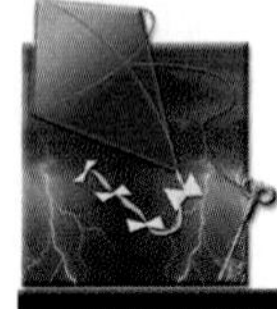

Unit 1 Conclusion

Understanding a bit about the physics of matter is essential to understanding the principles behind electrical theory. The movement of the electrons in the atoms that make up the matter of our universe is what gives us electricity. Understanding this movement allows us to harness electricity and even protect ourselves from undesirable electricity such as lightning.

A strong knowledge of electrical theory has important practical implications. For example, every now and then someone comes out with a product that allegedly makes standard lightning protection or grounding systems no longer necessary. With your knowledge of electrical theory, you won't be fooled by these claims. However, developing that knowledge begins with a solid foundation in the physics of matter. Test your foundation with the following questions.

Words to Live By: *The grass may look greener on the other side, but it still needs to be mowed.*

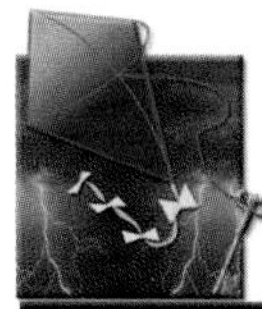

Unit 1 Practice Questions

1.1 Matter

1. Everything on earth that has weight and occupies space is called _____, which is/are made up of atoms of elements.

   (a) matter (b) elements (c) energy (d) compounds

2. When the atoms of elements combine, they produce _____. The smallest particle of a(n) _____ is called a molecule.

   (a) matter (b) element(s) (c) energy (d) compound(s)

1.2 Atomic Theory

3. Atoms contain three types of subatomic particles: electrons, protons, and neutrons. The _____ orbit around the nucleus.

   (a) electrons (b) protons (c) neutrons (d) nucleus

4. Because of their light weight, _____ actively participate in the transfer of energy.

   (a) electrons (b) protons (c) neutrons (d) nuclei

5. _____ do not participate in the flow of energy and they have a positive electrical charge with lines of force going straight out in all directions.

   (a) Electrons (b) Protons (c) Neutrons (d) Nuclei

1.3 Law of Electrical Charges

6. The Law of Electrical Charges states that subatomic particles with like charges repel each other.

   (a) True (b) False

7. The Law of Electrical Charges states that subatomic particles with unlike charges repel each other.

   (a) True (b) False

1.4 Law of Atomic Charges

8. If an atom contains more electrons than protons, the atom has a negative atomic charge.

   (a) True (b) False

1.5 Charged Material (Static Charge)

9. If two conductive materials in contact with each other are separated, most of the electrons will return to the original surface before the separation is complete.

(a) True (b) False

10. When insulated materials are in contact with each other, electrons move to the surface of each other, but the protons remain on the original surface.

(a) True (b) False

11. When insulated bodies are quickly separated, both will display an electrostatic charge because one surface will have an excess of electrons while the other surface has fewer electrons.

(a) True (b) False

12. Electrostatic charge is due to an excess of, or a deficiency of, electrons between objects that have been separated.

(a) True (b) False

13. The human body in a low-humidity area may accumulate a dangerous electrostatic charge of several thousand volts.

(a) True (b) False

14. Providing a path to the earth often helps reduce electrostatic charge.

(a) True (b) False

1.6 Neutralizing a Charge

15. The discharge of electrons from a negatively charged object is sometimes seen as an arc, and the arc distance is a function of the _____ between the bodies.

(a) static voltage
(b) dielectric between the bodies
(c) a and b
(d) a or b

1.7 Lightning

16. Lightning is the discharging of high-voltage cells within clouds to each other, to the earth, and sometimes to space.

(a) True (b) False

17. The high-current discharge from the negatively charged cloud to a positively charged object permanently neutralizes the cloud.

(a) True (b) False

18. Lightning frequently terminates to a point of elevation and it strikes nonmetallic as well as metallic objects with the same frequency.

(a) True (b) False

19. The termination of the lightning stroke is unlikely to ignite combustible materials.

(a) True (b) False

20. Over 100 deaths, 250 injuries, and billions of dollars in property damage are caused each year in the U.S. because of lightning.

(a) True (b) False

1.8 Lightning Protection

21. Lightning protection is intended to protect the building structure itself, as well as the electrical equipment on or inside the building structure.

(a) True (b) False

22. If protection of electrical equipment from lightning is desired, then a listed surge-protection device must be installed on the electrical system in accordance with the *NEC*.

(a) True (b) False

UNIT 2 Electron Theory

Introduction

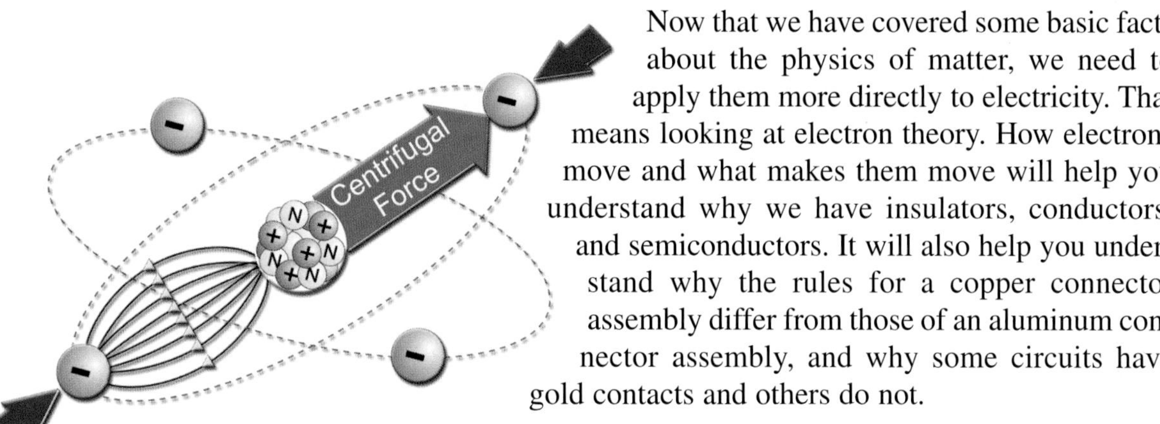
Centrifugal Force

Now that we have covered some basic facts about the physics of matter, we need to apply them more directly to electricity. That means looking at electron theory. How electrons move and what makes them move will help you understand why we have insulators, conductors, and semiconductors. It will also help you understand why the rules for a copper connector assembly differ from those of an aluminum connector assembly, and why some circuits have gold contacts and others do not.

2.1 Electron Orbits

Electrons revolve at high speeds in an orbit around an atom's nucleus. The high-speed orbits of the electrons tend to throw the electron out of orbit due to centrifugal force. However, according to the Law of Electrical Charges [1.3], the attraction between the positive charge of the protons and the negative charge of the electrons keeps the electrons from breaking out of their orbit. **Figure 2–1**

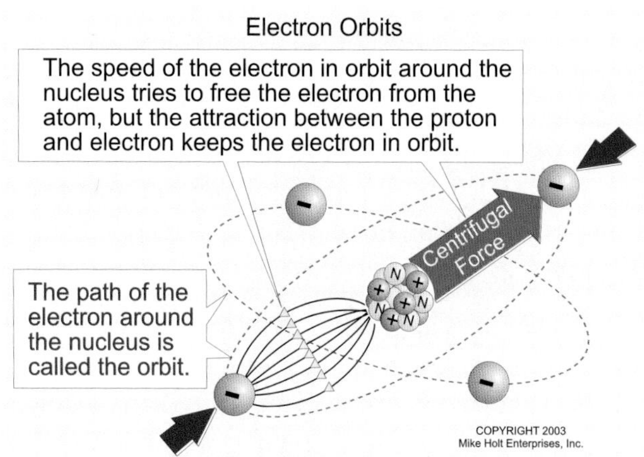
Electron Orbits
The speed of the electron in orbit around the nucleus tries to free the electron from the atom, but the attraction between the proton and electron keeps the electron in orbit.
The path of the electron around the nucleus is called the orbit.
Centrifugal Force
COPYRIGHT 2003 Mike Holt Enterprises, Inc.

Figure 2–1

2.2 Valence Electrons

Electrons orbit in one of seven possible shells around the nucleus of an atom. The outermost shell (orbit) is called the valence shell and electrons in this shell are called valence electrons. The maximum number of electrons in the valence shell is eight. Figure 2–2

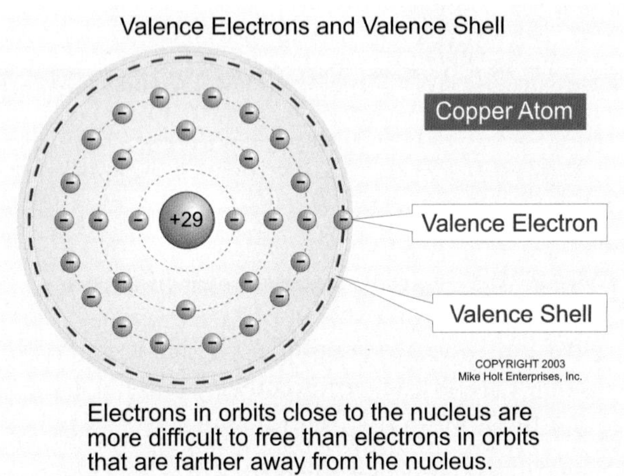

Figure 2–2

2.3 Freeing Electrons from an Atom

Because the strength of the electrostatic field (attractive force between the proton and electron) falls off with the square of distance from their sources, the attractive force of the protons is greater on electrons that are closest to the nucleus.

Electrons in the orbits farthest away from the nucleus, like the valence electrons, have less energy and this is one of the reasons they are more readily separated from their atomic structure. If sufficient energy is applied to break an electron out of the valence shell, it will no longer be bound to the atom. The electron will either move (or flow) toward a positive charge, or away from a negative charge.

When energy is applied to the valence electrons of an atom, the energy is distributed evenly among all the valence electrons. Thus, if there are fewer valence electrons for a given amount of energy, each valence electron receives more of the available energy. Figure 2–3

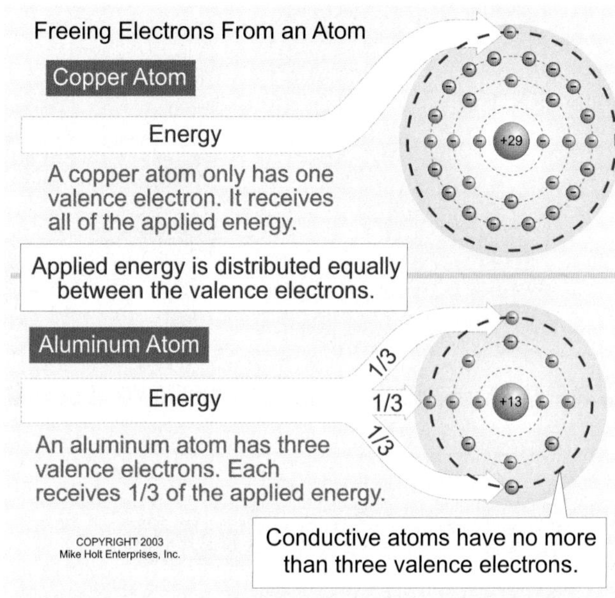

Freeing Electrons From an Atom
Copper Atom
Energy
+29
A copper atom only has one valence electron. It receives all of the applied energy.
Applied energy is distributed equally between the valence electrons.
Aluminum Atom
Energy
1/3
1/3
1/3
+13
An aluminum atom has three valence electrons. Each receives 1/3 of the applied energy.
COPYRIGHT 2003
Mike Holt Enterprises, Inc.
Conductive atoms have no more than three valence electrons.

Figure 2–3

AUTHOR'S COMMENT: The movement of electrons from their atoms is the basis of current flow (electricity), which will be explained in Unit 5.

2.4 Conductors

Conductive materials are made of elements that have one, two, or three valence electrons. Elements that have one valence electron, such as silver, copper, and gold, make the best electrical conductors. Copper is a better conductor than aluminum because the single copper valence electron receives all of the energy while each of the three aluminum electrons only receive one-third of the energy. Figure 2–3

Aluminum is not as good a conductor as copper, but its light weight and low cost offer advantages for its use in certain applications, such as in bus bars and high-voltage transmission lines (utility power lines).

AUTHOR'S COMMENT: To prevent corrosion from forming on low-voltage electronic circuitry connectors, gold plating is often placed on copper cable terminals.

2.5 Insulators

An atom is completely stable when its outer valence shell is completely filled with eight electrons. Insulators are atoms that have six to eight valence electrons. The valence electrons in insulator atoms are very difficult to free. Atoms that have seven valence electrons actively try to become stable (eight valence electrons), and they make the best electrical insulators. **Figure 2–4**

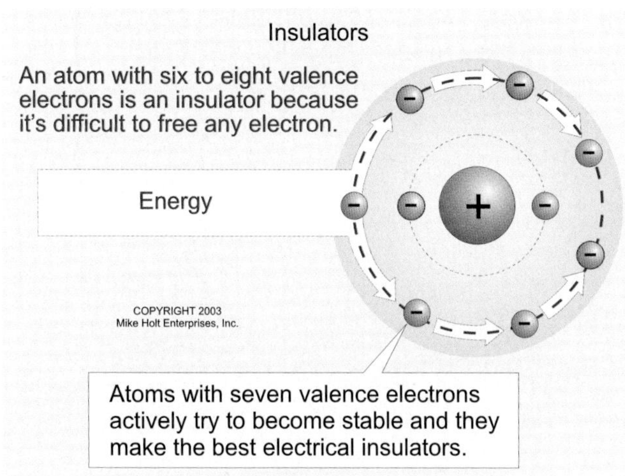

Figure 2–4

2.6 Semiconductors

Semiconductor atoms contain four or five valence electrons. Semiconducting materials used in electronic components such as diodes and transistors can act like conductors or insulators, depending on circumstances that can be precisely controlled.

2.7 Atomic Bonding

Atoms strive for chemical stability, which is the condition where the valence shell is completely filled (eight valence electrons). This is often accomplished by atomic bonding (combining atoms together). An example of atomic bonding is the formation of the compound water (H_2O), where two hydrogen atoms (one valence electron each) bond with one oxygen atom (six valence electrons). The atomic bonding of hydrogen and oxygen results in the stable compound (water), which has eight valence electrons.

AUTHOR'S COMMENT: Water (H_2O) is an insulator because it has eight valence electrons. However, minerals, salts and other impurities in the water can make this compound a little conductive.

2.8 Compounds

Compounds (the results of atomic bonding of two or more atoms) can change the electrical characteristics of the individual atoms. For example, two atoms of copper (one valence electron each) combined with one atom of oxygen (six valence electrons) will result in the compound copper-oxide (Cu_2O). The copper-oxide compound has a stable valence shell of eight electrons, which makes it an insulator. **Figure 2–5**

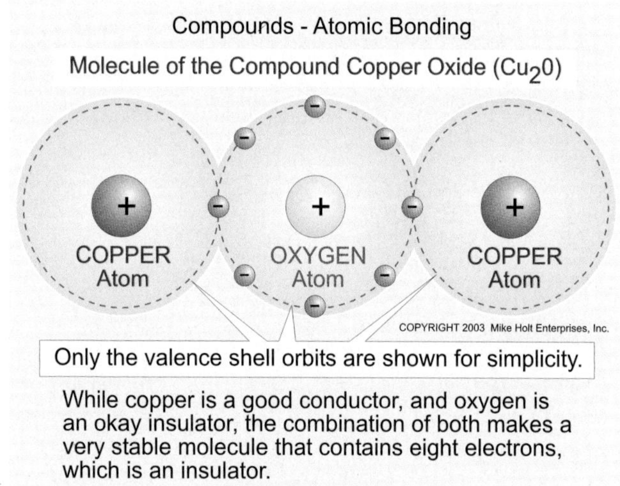

Compounds - Atomic Bonding
Molecule of the Compound Copper Oxide (Cu_20)
COPPER Atom
OXYGEN Atom
COPPER Atom
COPYRIGHT 2003 Mike Holt Enterprises, Inc.
Only the valence shell orbits are shown for simplicity.
While copper is a good conductor, and oxygen is an okay insulator, the combination of both makes a very stable molecule that contains eight electrons, which is an insulator.

Figure 2–5

Fresh stripped copper wire will be bright and shiny, but after some time, the oxygen element bonds with the copper element and it creates the compound copper-oxide on the surface of the copper conductor.

CAUTION: *Copper—The insulation compound "copper-oxide" is very soft and the standard pressure of a pressure connector can break it. In industrial areas where there are large quantities of sulfur gas (or hydrogen sulfide), copper turns black and the oxide coating is not conductive.*

Aluminum—The insulating compound "aluminum-oxide" is very difficult to break and it often results in the overheating of aluminum conductors at their terminals. The application of an antioxidant on aluminum is desirable because of its rapid oxidation (much faster than copper). The manufacturer of the antioxidant product suggests that the surface of the aluminum conductor be scratched once the product has been applied. This method works to prevent the newly revealed surfaces from becoming instantly oxidized.

AUTHOR'S COMMENT: According to NECA/AA 104-2000 *Recommended Practice for Installing Aluminum Building Wire and Cables*, Section 3.2, aluminum conductor terminations should use a listed anti-oxide joint compound to retard oxidation at the termination. The joint compound is applied after the exposed conductor has been wire brushed.

AUTHOR'S COMMENT: Gold plating on copper terminals is used in high reliability connections in electronic circuits because it does not oxidize and it ensures a reliable connection over time.

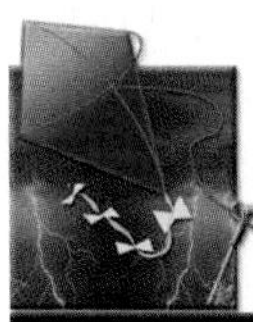

Unit 2 Summary

2.1 Electron Orbits

Electrons revolve at high speeds in an orbit around an atom's nucleus. However, according to the Law of Electrical Charges, the attraction between the positive charge of the protons and the negative charge of the electrons keeps the electrons from breaking out of their orbit.

2.2 Valence Electrons

The outermost shell (orbit) is called the valence shell and electrons in this shell are called valence electrons. The maximum number of electrons in the valence shell is eight.

2.3 Freeing Electrons from an Atom

The attractive force of the protons is greater on electrons that are closest to the nucleus. Electrons in the orbits farthest away from the nucleus have less energy and they are more readily separated from their atomic structure.

When energy is applied to the valence electrons of an atom, the energy is distributed evenly among all the valence electrons. Thus, if there are fewer valence electrons for a given amount of energy, each valence electron receives more of the available energy.

The movement of electrons from their atoms is the basis of current flow and is also known as "electricity."

2.4 Conductors

Elements that have one valence electron, such as silver, copper, and gold, make the best electrical conductors. Copper is a better conductor than aluminum because the single copper valence electron receives all of the energy, while each of the three aluminum electrons only receive one-third of the energy.

To prevent corrosion from forming on low-voltage electronic circuitry connectors, gold or silver plating is often placed on copper cable terminals.

2.5 Insulators

An atom is completely stable when its outer valence shell is completely filled with eight electrons. Insulators are atoms that have six to eight valence electrons. Atoms that have seven valence electrons actively try to become stable (eight valence electrons), and they make the best electrical insulators.

2.6 Semiconductors

Semiconductor atoms contain four or five valence electrons and can act like conductors or insulators, depending on circumstances that can be precisely controlled.

2.7 Atomic Bonding

Atoms strive for chemical stability, which is the condition where the valence shell is completely filled with eight valence electrons. The atomic bonding of hydrogen and oxygen results in the stable compound water (H_2O), which has eight valence electrons.

H_2O is an insulator because it has eight valence electrons. However, minerals, salts and other impurities in the water can make this compound a little conductive.

2.8 Compounds

Compounds, the atomic bonding of two or more atoms, can change the electrical characteristics of the individual atoms. For example, two atoms of copper (one valence electron each) combined with one atom of oxygen (six valence electrons) will result in the compound copper-oxide (Cu_2O).

Copper—The insulation compound "copper-oxide" is very soft and it can be broken by the standard pressure of a pressure connector, but in areas where sulfur gas (or hydrogen sulfide) is present, copper turns black and the oxide coating is not conductive.

Aluminum—The insulating compound "aluminum-oxide" is very difficult to break and it often results in the overheating of terminals. The application of an antioxidant on aluminum is desirable because of its rapid oxidation.

Gold and silver plating on copper terminals is used because it does not oxidize and it ensures a reliable connection over time.

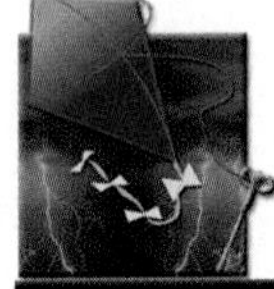

Unit 2 Conclusion

Now you know how electrons move and what makes them move. You understand why we have insulators, conductors, and semiconductors. You also know certain things about the most important materials used in the practical application of electricity.

Other useful knowledge you've gained here are such things as the reason the rules for a copper connector assembly differ from those of an aluminum connector assembly, and why some circuits have gold contacts while others do not.

Words to Live By: *If at first you don't succeed, try reading the instructions.*

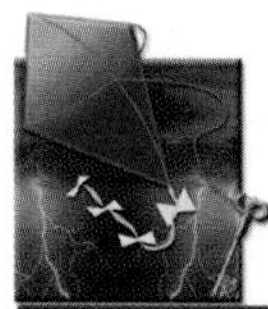

Unit 2 Practice Questions

2.1 Electron Orbits

1. The attraction between the positive charge of the protons and the negative charge of the electrons keeps the electrons from breaking out of their orbit.

   (a) True (b) False

2.2 Valence Electrons

2. The outermost shell is called the valence shell and electrons in this shell are called valence electrons. The maximum number of electrons in the valence shell is _____.

   (a) 1 (b) 3 (c) 6 (d) 8

2.3 Freeing Electrons from an Atom

3. Because the attractive force of the protons is greater on electrons that are closest to the nucleus, electrons in the orbits farthest away from the nucleus are more readily separated from their atomic structure.

   (a) True (b) False

4. When energy is applied to the valence electrons, the energy is distributed evenly among all the valence electrons.

   (a) True (b) False

2.4 Conductors

5. Conductive materials have one, two, or three valence electrons. Elements with one valence electron, such as silver, copper, and gold, make the best electrical conductors.

   (a) True (b) False

6. To prevent corrosion from forming on low-voltage electronic circuitry connectors, _____ plating is often placed on copper cable terminals.

   (a) silver (b) gold (c) aluminum (d) none of these

2.5 Insulators

7. Insulators have four to five valence electrons. Atoms that have seven valence electrons make the best electrical insulators.

    (a) True (b) False

2.6 Semiconductors

8. Semiconductors contain more than six valence electrons.

    (a) True (b) False

2.7 Atomic Bonding

9. Atoms strive for chemical stability, which is the condition where the valence shell is completely filled. This is often accomplished by combining atoms together to produce a compound atom.

    (a) True (b) False

2.8 Compounds

10. Compounds can change the electrical characteristics of an individual atom. For example, the insulating aluminum-oxide compound is very difficult to break and it often results in the overheating of aluminum conductors at their terminals.

    (a) True (b) False

UNIT 3

Magnetism

Introduction

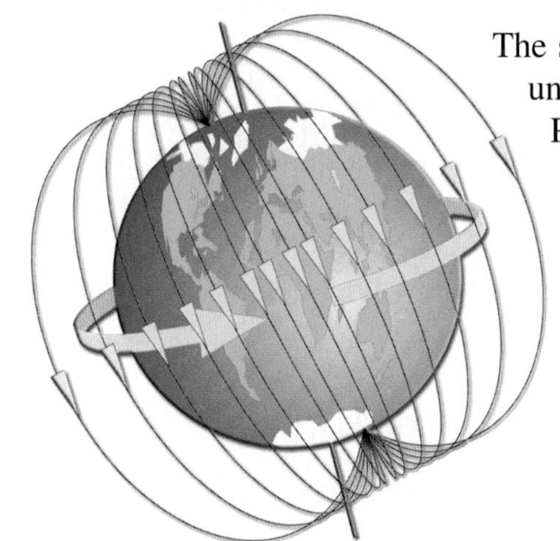

The study of magnetism provides the background necessary to understand electromagnetism, which is the key to electricity. Practically every piece of electrical apparatus uses magnetism for some part of its operation.

3.1 The Natural Magnet

Thousands of years ago the ancient Greeks and Chinese discovered that certain rare stones, called loadestones, were naturally magnetized. These stones could attract small pieces of iron in a magical way, and were found to always point in the same direction when allowed to swing freely suspended by a piece of string. The name "magnet" comes from Magnesia, a district in Thessaly, Greece.

3.2 Magnetic Polarities

The north end of a magnet can be determined by hanging a magnet by a string and allowing it to swing freely. The magnet will align itself with the earth's magnetic field. The end of the magnet that points to the north is called the north-seeking pole, and the opposite end of the magnet is the south-seeking pole.

3.3 Magnetic Compass

It is believed that about 2,000 years ago, the Greek people discovered that a suspended piece of lodestone would align itself to the earth's magnetic field, thus acting as a compass. The compass was not generally used until about 1200 A.D., when it was discovered that it was an excellent navigational tool.

A compass is made with a tiny magnet that is freely pivoted so it can easily keep itself aligned to the earth's magnetic North Pole, which is in the area of Baffin's Bay in the Arctic. Regardless of how the compass is turned, the magnetic needle points to the earth's magnetic North Pole. Figure 3–1.

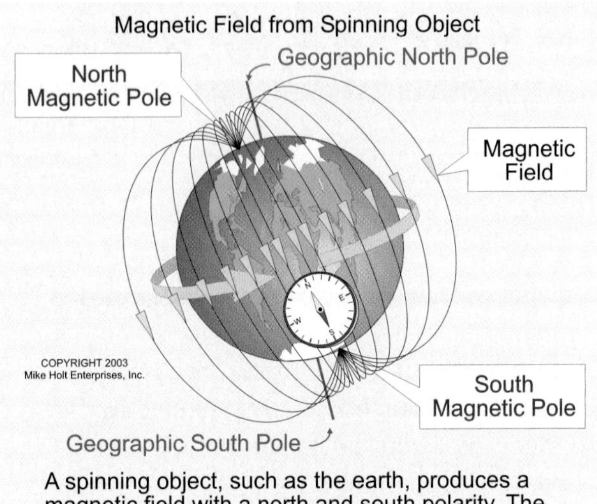

Figure 3–1

AUTHOR'S COMMENT: It is interesting to note that the magnetic North Pole is some distance from the axis of rotation of the earth (the top of the globe).

CAUTION: *If a compass is brought near a magnet, the north-seeking pole of the compass needle will be attracted to the south-seeking pole of the adjacent magnet.*

3.4 Magnetic Molecule

It is not definitely known just what magnetism is, but many theories have been advanced. The generally accepted theory is that magnetic materials are made up of a very large number of small magnets (spinning molecules). If molecules in metal are arranged so that their magnetic poles are pointing in the same direction, their magnetic fields will add together and the metal is then considered magnetized. Figure 3–2

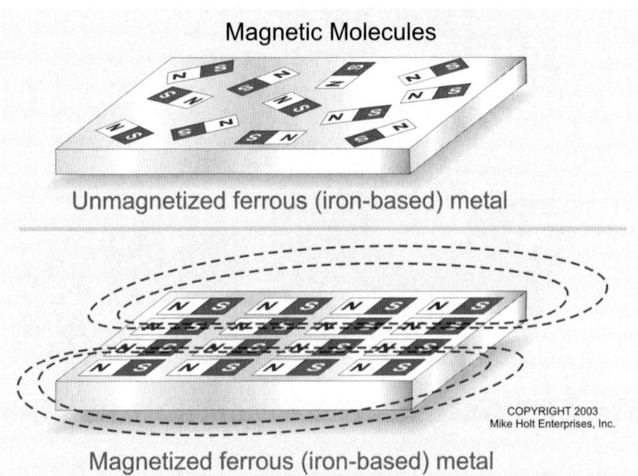

Figure 3–2

The reason most metals are not magnetic is because their atoms tend to pair off in orbits with opposite spins so that their magnetic fields cancel each other.

3.5 Magnetic Properties

Only ferrous (iron-based) metals, such as iron and steel, have magnetic properties. Nonmagnetic metals, such as copper and aluminum are nonferrous, meaning they do not contain any iron, therefore they cannot be magnetized.

3.6 How to Magnetize Iron

Based on the generally accepted theory of magnetism, if a magnetizing force is applied to the end of an iron bar, the magnetic field of many of the ferrous molecule electrons will align with each other and the bar will demonstrate magnetic properties. Magnetizing force can also be applied by stroking magnetizable material with a magnet or by applying an electrical current.

3.7 Permanent and Temporary Magnets

All magnets, other than lodestones which occur naturally, are artificial magnets.

When a magnetized material keeps its magnetic field for a long time, it is a permanent magnet. If it loses its magnetism quickly, it is a temporary magnet. Hard iron or steel is used to make permanent magnets. Soft iron is used for temporary magnets.

The most common artificial magnet is the permanent magnet, which is made by placing tempered steel within a strong magnetic coil. The bar and horseshoe magnets are good examples of permanent magnets, which are generally used for electric measuring instruments.

3.8 Demagnetizing Magnets

To demagnetize a magnet, the magnetic fields of the ferrous material must be disarranged so that the molecules return to their original random positions. If a permanent magnet is struck with a hammer, it will lose some of its magnetism; each subsequent blow helps the molecules return to their original random positions.

> **CAUTION:** *Because permanent magnets are often used in electronic equipment such as testers, be careful when handling this type of equipment. Don't drop it.*

Another method of demagnetizing a magnet is to apply heat to excite the molecules out of alignment. The concept is that when heat is applied, the molecules in the magnetic field will be made to move rapidly and they will return to their original random positions.

Finally, placing a permanent magnet in a reversing magnetic field will demagnetize the magnet.

3.9 Magnetic Lines of Force

The magnetic field of a magnet is visualized as lines of force that radiate from the magnetic North Pole to the South Pole. Magnetic lines of force cannot cross each other and the closer the lines and the greater the number of force lines, the stronger the magnetic field they represent. These force lines are called flux lines and are measured in number of lines of force per unit area. Figure 3–3

> **AUTHOR'S COMMENT:** The magnetic lines of force become wider apart the farther they are from the magnet.

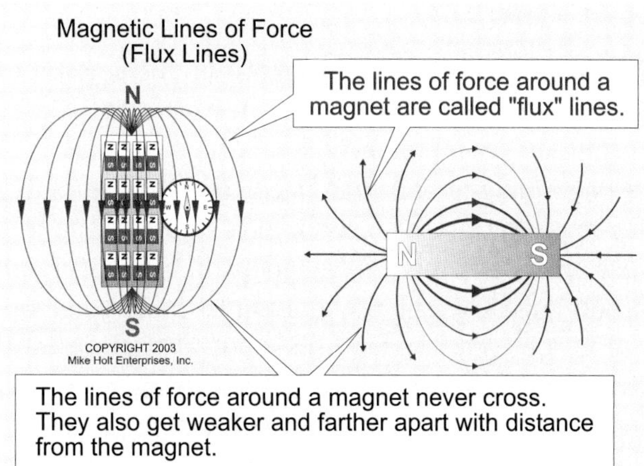

Magnetic Lines of Force
(Flux Lines)
The lines of force around a magnet are called "flux" lines.
N
S
N
S
COPYRIGHT 2003
Mike Holt Enterprises, Inc.
The lines of force around a magnet never cross. They also get weaker and farther apart with distance from the magnet.

Figure 3–3

3.10 Magnetic Materials

Materials that are good conductors of magnetic force, such as iron and steel, are called magnetic materials. Materials that are poor conductors of magnetism are called nonmagnetic materials.

Examples of nonmagnetic materials are copper, zinc, glass, and paper. If a piece of iron is placed in a magnetic field, more lines of force will pass through the iron than through the air. Iron is several hundred times better as a conductor of magnetism than air is.

3.11 Law of Attraction and Repulsion

The Law of Attraction and Repulsion of magnets states that like poles repel and unlike poles attract each other. Figure 3–4

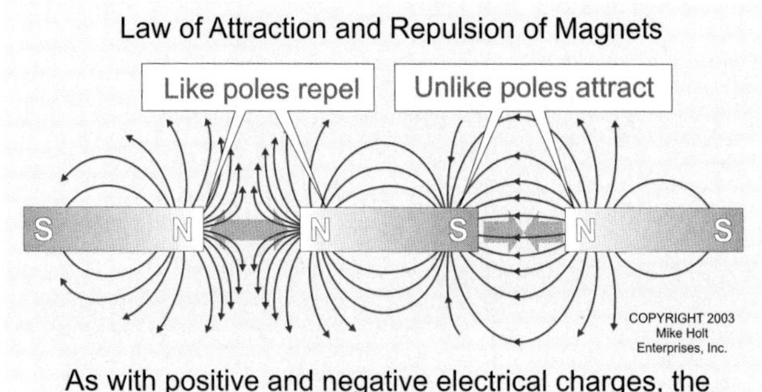

Figure 3–4

3.12 Retentivity

Magnetic materials differ greatly in the amount of magnetism they will retain; stated differently, they differ in their retentivity. Soft iron makes a stronger magnet than hard steel, but the instant that the magnetizing force is removed, the soft iron will lose practically all of its magnetism. Hard steel will retain a relatively large amount of its magnetism, but it does not have the magnetic strength of soft iron. Soft iron is used for temporary magnets and hard steel is always used for permanent magnets.

3.13 Permeability

Permeability is the term used to describe the relative ease with which a material can be magnetized (orientation of the molecular structure to that of a magnet). Soft iron is easy to magnetize (high permeability), whereas hard steel is hard to magnetize (low permeability).

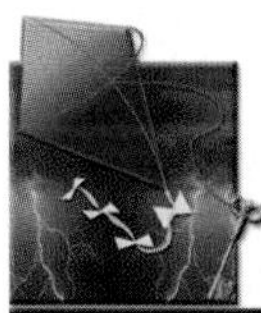

Unit 3 Summary

Introduction

The study of magnetism is the foundation of understanding electricity. A large number of electrical apparatuses use magnetism for their operation.

3.1 The Natural Magnet

Lodestone is a naturally occurring rock that has magnetic properties.

3.2 Magnetic Polarities

The north end of a magnet can be determined by hanging the magnet by a string and allowing it to swing freely. The magnet will align itself with the earth's magnetic field. The end of the magnet that points to the north is called the north-seeking pole and the opposite end is the south-seeking pole.

3.3 Magnetic Compass

A compass is made with a tiny magnet that is freely pivoted so that it will easily align to the earth's magnetic North Pole. Regardless of how the compass is turned, the magnetic needle will point to the magnetic North Pole.

If a compass needle is brought near a magnet, the compass is affected. This shows that there is a field surrounding the magnet in which magnetism is present. This is called the magnetic field.

3.4 Magnetic Molecule

The generally accepted theory is that magnetic materials are made up of a very large number of small magnets. If molecules in an iron-based metal are arranged so that they are pointing in the same direction, their magnetic fields add together and the metal is then magnetized. The greater the alignment, the greater the magnetic field.

3.5 Magnetic Properties

Steel and iron-based (ferrous) metals have magnetic properties.

3.6 How to Magnetize Iron

If a magnetizing force is applied to the magnetic field of each molecule, forcing it into alignment with the other molecules, we will find evidence of magnetism. This force can be applied by magnetic stroking or by the magnetic field associated with electric current.

3.7 Permanent and Temporary Magnets

All magnets, other than lodestones, are artificial magnets. The most common artificial magnet is the permanent magnet, which is a piece of hard steel that has been magnetized and retains its magnetism indefinitely.

If a magnet loses its magnetism quickly, it is called a temporary magnet. Soft iron is used for temporary magnets.

3.8 Demagnetizing Magnets

To demagnetize a magnet, the magnetic field must be disarranged so that the molecules return to their original orientations. This can be done by a hard blow, with heat, or by the use of an alternating-current field.

3.9 Magnetic Lines of Force

The magnetic field of a magnet is visualized as lines of force, called flux lines, which extend out into space from the magnetic North Pole to the South Pole. Magnetic lines of force do not cross, and actually spread wider apart the farther they are from the magnet. The closer the lines and the greater the number of force lines, the stronger the magnetic field.

3.10 Magnetic Materials

Ferrous (iron) materials are several hundred times better conductors of magnetism than air is.

3.11 Law of Attraction and Repulsion

The Law of Attraction and Repulsion of magnets states that like poles repel each other and unlike poles attract.

3.12 Retentivity

Magnetic materials differ greatly in the amount of magnetism they will retain (retentivity). A bar of soft iron makes a stronger magnet than a bar of hard steel, but the instant the magnetizing force is removed, the soft iron loses practically all of its magnetism while the hard steel retains a relatively large amount. Soft iron is used for temporary magnets and hard steel is used for permanent magnets.

3.13 Permeability

Permeability is the term used to describe the relative ease with which a material can be magnetized. Soft iron is easy to magnetize (high permeability), whereas steel is harder to magnetize (low permeability).

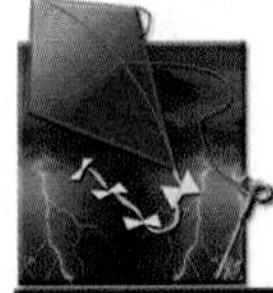

Unit 3 Conclusion

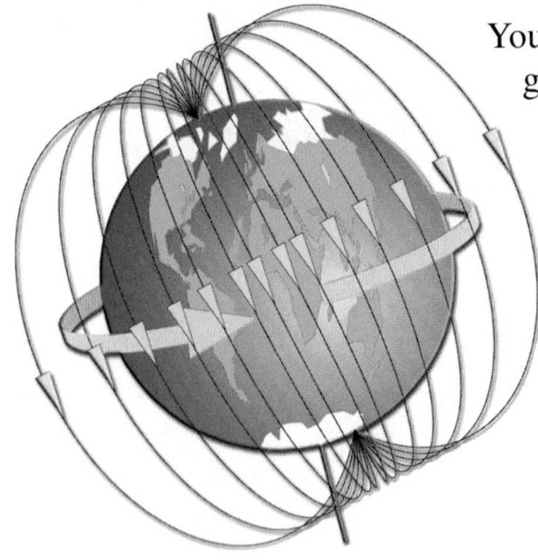

Your knowledge of magnetism provides you with the background for the study of electromagnetism—a key knowledge area for people who work with electricity. You've learned which materials make good magnets and which don't. You also know the difference between permanent magnets and temporary magnets, and you know about magnetic fields. Such knowledge is essential for learning motor and generator theory, and for understanding the reasons for Chapter 3 wiring methods in the *National Electrical Code*.

Words to Live By: *Your friends are like the buttons on an elevator. They will either take you up or they will take you down.*

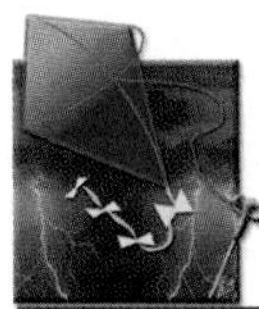

Unit 3 Practice Questions

3.1 The Natural Magnet

1. When loadestone were suspended by a piece of string, they always pointed in the same direction.

   (a) True (b) False

3.2 Magnetic Polarities

2. The north end of a magnet can be determined by hanging a magnet by a string and allowing it to swing freely.

   (a) True (b) False

3.3 Magnetic Compass

3. The end of the magnet that points to the north is called the south-seeking pole, and the opposite end of the magnet is the north-seeking pole.

   (a) True (b) False

4. The north end of the compass needle is actually the south pole of the compass needle seeking the earth's magnetic north pole.

   (a) True (b) False

3.4 Magnetic Molecule

5. The reason most metals are not magnetic is because their atoms tend to pair off in orbits with opposite spins so that their magnetic fields cancel each other.

   (a) True (b) False

3.5 Magnetic Properties

6. Nonmagnetic metals are ferrous, meaning they do not contain any iron, and cannot be magnetized.

   (a) True (b) False

3.6 How to Magnetize Iron

7. If a magnetizing force is applied to the end of an iron bar, the magnetic field of many of the ferrous molecule electrons will align with each other and the bar will demonstrate magnetic properties.

   (a) True (b) False

3.7 Permanent and Temporary Magnets

8. When a magnetized material keeps its magnetic field for a long time, it is a permanent magnet. Hard iron or steel is used for permanent magnets.

   (a) True (b) False

9. If a metal loses its magnetism quickly, it is a temporary magnet. Soft iron is used for temporary magnets.

   (a) True (b) False

3.8 Demagnetizing Magnets

10. If a permanent magnet is struck with a hammer, it will lose some of its magnetism; each subsequent blow helps the molecules return to their original random positions.

    (a) True (b) False

3.9 Magnetic Lines of Force

11. Magnetic lines of force can cross each other and they are called flux lines.

    (a) True (b) False

3.10 Magnetic Materials

12. The law of attraction and repulsion of magnets states that like poles attract and unlike poles oppose each other.

    (a) True (b) False

3.12 Retentivity

13. Soft iron can be used to make a stronger magnet than hard steel, but the instant the magnetizing force is removed, the soft iron loses all of its magnetism.

    (a) True (b) False

14. Hard steel will retain a relatively large amount of its magnetism, but it does not have the magnetic strength of soft iron.

    (a) True (b) False

3.13 Permeability

15. Permeability describes the relative ease with which a material can be magnetized.

    (a) True (b) False

16. Soft iron has high permeability, whereas hard steel is hard to magnetize, which means it has low permeability.

    (a) True (b) False

UNIT 4 Electricity

Introduction

A solid understanding of electron theory will help you master such widely misunderstood topics as grounding, ampacity, and electrical safety.

4.1 Electrical Current Flow (Electricity)

Electrical current flow is one of the many types of energy that we use daily in our lives. For the purpose of this book, we will call the movement of electrons for the purpose of transferring energy to perform useful functions "Electricity."

Electrical current is the unseen movement of electrons that flow from the power source through the electrical circuit of the appliance or equipment and then return to the power source. The complete path the electrons take is called an electrical circuit. Figure 4–1

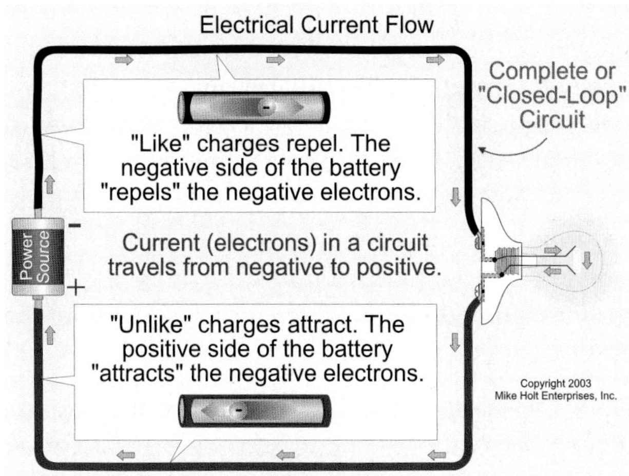
Electrical Current Flow
Complete or "Closed-Loop" Circuit
"Like" charges repel. The negative side of the battery "repels" the negative electrons.
Current (electrons) in a circuit travels from negative to positive.
"Unlike" charges attract. The positive side of the battery "attracts" the negative electrons.
Power Source
-
+
Copyright 2003 Mike Holt Enterprises, Inc.

Figure 4–1

Electric current is produced by forcing billions upon billions of electrons to move through an electrical circuit. A power source accomplishes this by applying a negative charge at one end of the circuit (repels electrons from the source), and a positive charge to the other end (attracts the electrons to the source). Figure 4–1

For current to flow from the power source through the load (appliance/equipment) and then back to the power source, the current flow path must be conductive. Since copper is a very good conductor (only one valence electron), it is the most common wire used for this purpose.

4.2 Electricity

To force electrons to move (create a current flow), some form of energy must be applied to the electrons to cause them to leave their atom; this energy can be supplied by chemical activity, magnetism, light, heat, or pressure.

Chemical Activity (Electrochemistry)

When chemicals combine in a controlled manner, they can provide the energy needed to move electrons out of the atom's orbit. This is the principle of the electrical battery and fuel cell.

When electricity is created by chemical activity, the electron flow will be in one given direction. This is called direct current (dc).

Battery—A battery is a power source where voltaic cells are combined in a series arrangement, positive terminal to negative terminal, so that the voltage of one cell will be added to the voltage of the other cells. Voltaic cells are chambers in which two dissimilar solid conductors (called electrodes) are immersed in a conducting liquid/paste (electrolyte). The combination of electrodes and electrolytes support chemical reactions to generate the energy for current flow.

By changing the quantities and types of materials used in a cell, the manufacturer can increase, change, or control the current producing capacity and other operating characteristics of the battery for a specific application. Figure 4–2

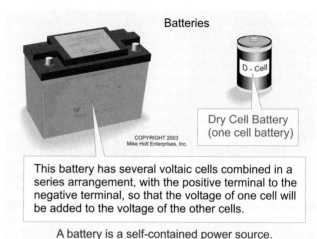

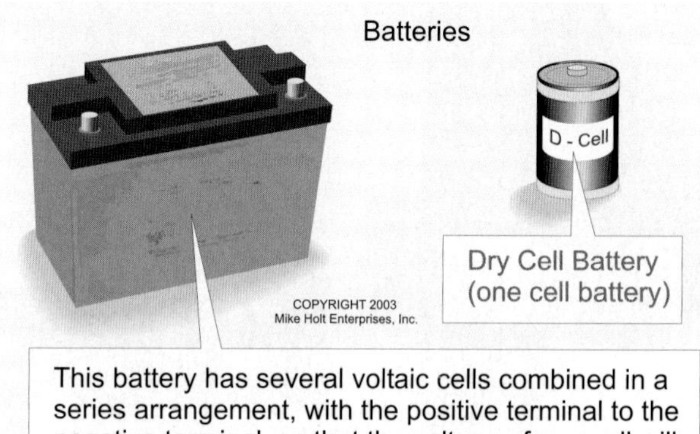

Batteries
D - Cell
Dry Cell Battery
(one cell battery)
COPYRIGHT 2003
Mike Holt Enterprises, Inc.
This battery has several voltaic cells combined in a series arrangement, with the positive terminal to the negative terminal, so that the voltage of one cell will be added to the voltage of the other cells.

A battery is a self-contained power source.

Figure 4–2

AUTHOR'S COMMENT: Technically, a battery is comprised of two or more voltaic cells, but everyone calls a single cell a battery.

Fuel Cells—Fuel cells use an advanced electrochemical process to convert a gaseous fuel, such as natural gas or propane, into electrical energy. Fuel cells are virtually pollution free, very quiet when compared to other means of electric power generation, and can operate at high efficiency levels using relatively inexpensive alternative fuels such as natural gas and LP gas.

Magnetism (Magnetoelectricity)

The vast majority of the electrical energy utilized today is created in power plants that rotate a magnetic field through a conductor. Moving a magnetic field through a conductor provides the energy needed to cause the valence electrons in the conductor to flow in a given direction. Moving the magnetic field in the opposite direction relative to the conductor will cause the current to flow in the opposite direction. This is the principle of alternating current (ac). Figure 4–3

It was the development of alternating-current systems and transformers and motors by Mr. Tesla that led to the explosion in the use of electricity. It is extremely doubtful that our society would have advanced as rapidly as it has in the last one hundred years without it.

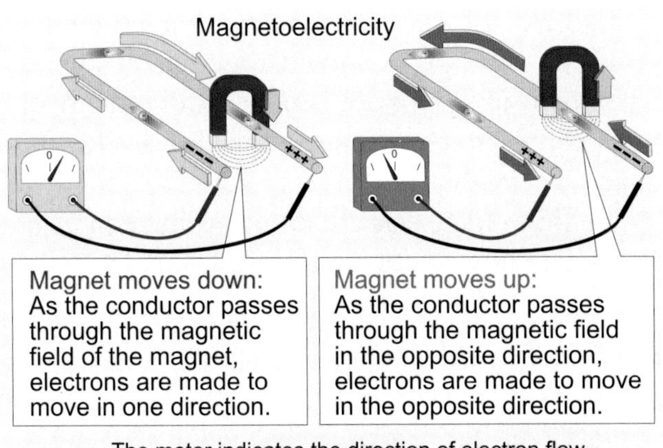

Magnetoelectricity
Magnet moves down:
As the conductor passes through the magnetic field of the magnet, electrons are made to move in one direction.
Magnet moves up:
As the conductor passes through the magnetic field in the opposite direction, electrons are made to move in the opposite direction.
The meter indicates the direction of electron flow.
COPYRIGHT 2003 Mike Holt Enterprises, Inc.

Figure 4–3

AUTHOR'S COMMENT: It is not the force of a magnetic field through a conductor that produces electricity, it is the relative motion of the magnetic field to the electrons within the conductor. The moving magnetic field literally pulls or pushes the valence electrons through the circuit. If there is no movement of the magnetic field relative to the electrons within the conductor, there is no electron flow, no matter how strong the magnetic field.

Electromagnetic Field—Interestingly, current flow (movement of electrons) creates its own electromagnetic field at right angles to the current flow of the electrons. This is the principle of induction, which is the foundation of the electric motor and transformer.

Light (Photoelectricity)

Photoelectricity works on the principle that light (photons) striking a semiconducting plate causes the plate to release electrons to another semiconducting plate. Early photovoltaic systems were able to produce only minor quantities of electrical power from photoelectricity which limited their use to low-power applications, such as a photo eye for lighting, and to other light sensing and measuring applications, as in a camera light meter.

With the advent of the transistor and accompanying semiconductor technology, the efficiency of photovoltaic power has increased dramatically. Now that solar power and high-capacity batteries have come along, people can live in remote areas without paying large fees to have the utility company run power to their homes. Today there are many homes that are virtually self-sufficient with solar power. Figure 4–4

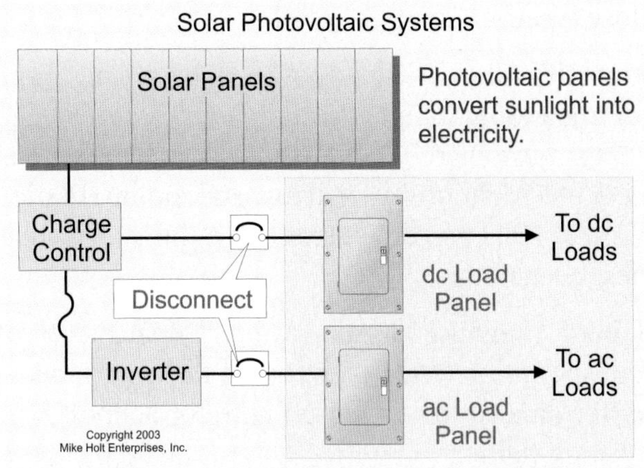

Figure 4–4

AUTHOR'S COMMENT: Some conditions limiting solar power are hours of direct sun exposure and electric power demand.

With government funding and with improvements in photovoltaic cells and batteries, the initial cost of these systems is being dramatically reduced each year. Other examples of the use of photoelectricity are:

Billboard Signs—The billboard industry uses photoelectricity to illuminate remote signs for a few hours a day; for example, during the early evening hours while there is still heavy traffic with many prospective viewers.

Interstate Call Boxes—Many of our interstate highways have roadside assistance aid devices, such as battery-powered phone systems where solar cells are used to recharge the systems' batteries.

Navigational Markers/Buoys—Navigational markers and buoys often have a solar panel connected with storage batteries. These markers and buoys aid navigation through waterways and inlets (going from the ocean into port or vice-versa), or marking entrances to marinas.

Photo Cells—These devices "sense and react" to specific light levels to open or close switch contacts in order to turn equipment (often lights) on at night and off at daylight. These photoelectric devices produce very small amounts of power in a closed, self-contained circuit.

Roadside Signs—Solar power is becoming more common to light highway directional, caution, and safety signs, thereby eliminating dependence upon local electrical utility systems, and the installation of other local power generation equipment such as diesel generators.

School Warning Signs—Many Departments of Transportation (DOTs) are using these systems to power small traffic signal lights for school zone warning lights.

Telecommunications—When telecommunications equipment and systems are needed in remote or economically expensive areas, such as mountaintops, solar electrical power generation systems have proven to be economical and reliable.

Weather Stations—Remote weather gathering stations for stream flow, rain and snowfall data are often powered by solar cells.

AUTHOR'S COMMENT: Visit this URL: http://www.solarexpert.com/Photovoltaics.html for more information.

Thermo Energy (Thermoelectricity)

When the temperature decreases, the molecules move or bounce off each other relatively slowly. At the temperature of absolute zero (-459°F), the movement of atoms stops. As a material is heated, the molecules move and/or bounce off each other more rapidly.

The thermoelectric effect is the process where heat is applied to dissimilar metals that are joined together to produce about $^{5}/_{1,000}$ to $^{30}/_{1,000}$ of a volt.

A common application of thermoelectricity is the thermocouple, which is based upon the findings of Thomas Johann Seebeck (1821) who showed that a small electric current will flow in a circuit composed of two alloys joined together at one end when their junctions are kept at different temperatures. At room temperatures, the current flow produced by the thermocouple is very low, but as the temperature increases the output voltage increases linearly relative to absolute zero (-459°F)

A thermocouple can be used to generate the energy needed to provide sufficient circuit voltage to control the gas shut-off valve for gas appliances. It operates on the principle that when the thermocouple is in the flame of the pilot, it generates sufficient energy to keep the gas shut-off valve relay energized. If the pilot goes out, the thermocouple cools down resulting in a reduction of the output voltage to the point that the control relay is de-energized, resulting in the shutting off of the gas supply to the appliance. **Figure 4–5**

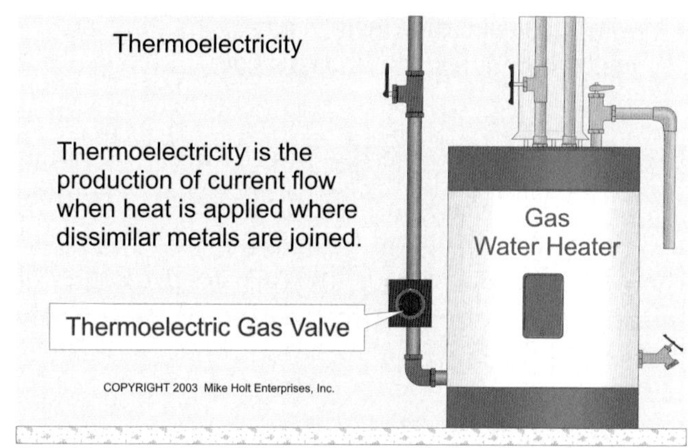

Figure 4–5

Pressure (Piezoelectricity)

Some crystalline materials produce a small electrical voltage when bending or twisting pressure is applied to them. The piezoelectric effect is commonly used in sensing elements such as strain gauges and vibration pickup sensors. The amount and frequency of the voltage can be calibrated to the pressure, force, strain or vibration levels when used as a sensor. Modern audio equipment tends to avoid piezoelectric devices because they are easily destroyed by high temperature or overvoltage.

However, piezoelectric devices are commonly used in ultrasonic alarms, as well as in certain radar and sonar systems. Another example of piezoelectricity would be the little red button on the gas grill. By physically applying pressure to the button, high-voltage electrical energy will travel over a wire and through a ceramic spark plug located near the gas burner, which ignites the gas fuel. Figure 4–6

Pressure Spark Device

Current flow can be created by bending or twisting pressure on crystals.

COPYRIGHT 2003
Mike Holt Enterprises, Inc.

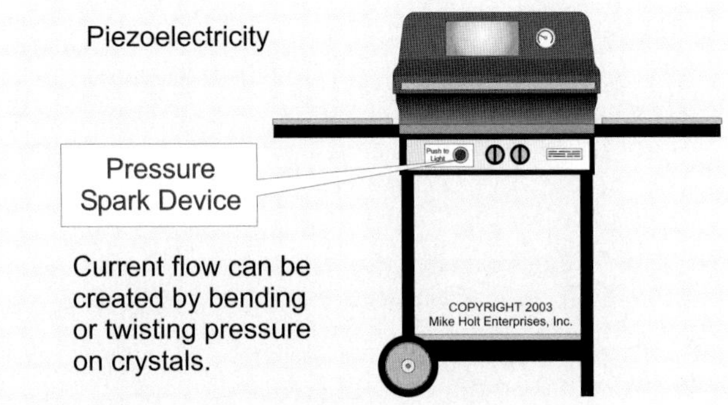

Figure 4–6

4.3 Useful Purposes of Electricity

Electricity, the transfer of energy via the movement of electrons, can be used for electrochemistry, electromagnetism, heating, and illumination.

Electrochemistry

Electrical current can be used to alter the effects of chemical bonding so as to separate or encourage the formation of new compounds. This is the basis of electroplating and electrolysis. Both electroplating and electrolysis are forms of corrosion, one being controlled and the other not.

Electroplating—Electroplating is a commercial-industrial process intended to make some improvement to the plated surface. Electroplating is building up layers of metal on one surface and removing the same metal from another by the chemical action of an electrical current in a solution. This process is commonly used for coating relatively inexpensive jewelry with gold, silver, or copper. Another application is the gold plating of contact surfaces of copper terminals for computer cables to prevent the forming of an oxide compound on the terminals.

AUTHOR'S COMMENT: Gold plating is added to electronic circuitry connectors to prevent corrosion from forming because gold will not chemically bond with other elements to produce an insulating oxide. When an electrical connector carries low current (less than 1/100 of an ampere) at low voltages (less than 12V dc), there is not enough energy to break through a corrosion oxide film that often forms on the surface of the copper terminals. This results in an undesirable open or intermittent connection for electronic equipment circuits.

Electrolysis—Electrolysis is a decomposition action where metal from one surface is removed to another surface because of a chemical action caused by electrical current. Electrolysis is a very expensive problem for boats and ships when they are at shore because rudders, shafts and propellers can disintegrate due to stray electrical current.

Electromagnetism

Alternating current is used to produce an alternating electromagnetic field that is necessary for the operation of a transformer. In addition, electromagnetic fields, from both ac and dc circuits, are necessary for the operation of electric motors and electric relays. Figure 4–7

Electricity is used to produce electromagnetism for the operation of transformers, motors, etc.

Relay

Transformer

Motor

COPYRIGHT 2003
Mike Holt
Enterprises, Inc.

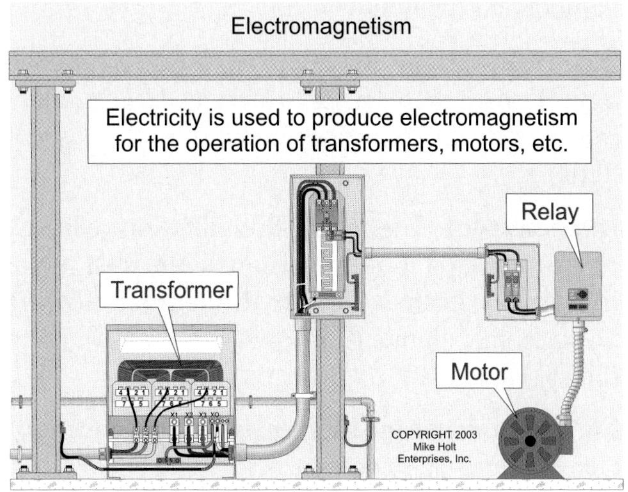

Figure 4–7

Heat (Resistance)

Electrical current flowing through a high-resistance heating element will produce heat (as well as a glow) as the electrons flow through the circuit. This is the principle for most electrical resistance-heating appliances such as toasters, ranges, ovens, water heaters, clothes dryers, flat irons, etc. Figure 4–8

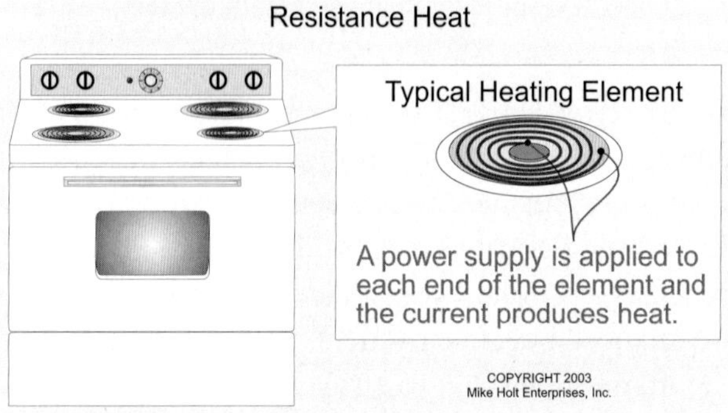

Resistance Heat
Typical Heating Element
A power supply is applied to each end of the element and the current produces heat.
COPYRIGHT 2003 Mike Holt Enterprises, Inc.

Resistance heating elements are often made out of nichrome wire which is enclosed in an insulating material.

Figure 4–8

AUTHOR'S COMMENT: Heat can also be produced by inductive heating (electromagnetism), but that is beyond the scope of this book.

Illumination (Lighting)

Electrical current flow can be used to produce light through the principles of incandescent, electroluminescent, phosphorescent and fluorescent lighting.

Incandescent Lighting—Illumination can be produced when a high-resistance tungsten metal filament is heated (due to the current flowing through the element) in a vacuum glass lamp (bulb). Figure 4–9

Electroluminescent Lighting—Light can be produced when an electrical arc flows through a charged gas lamp.

Examples would include neon lighting, as well as sodium, mercury vapor and metal-halide lighting. Figure 4–10

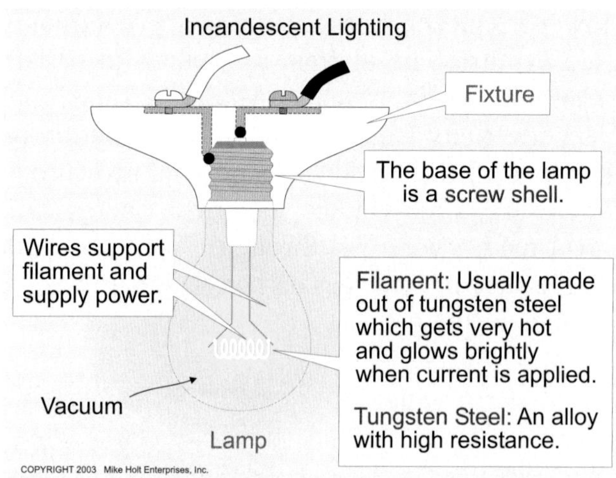

Figure 4–9

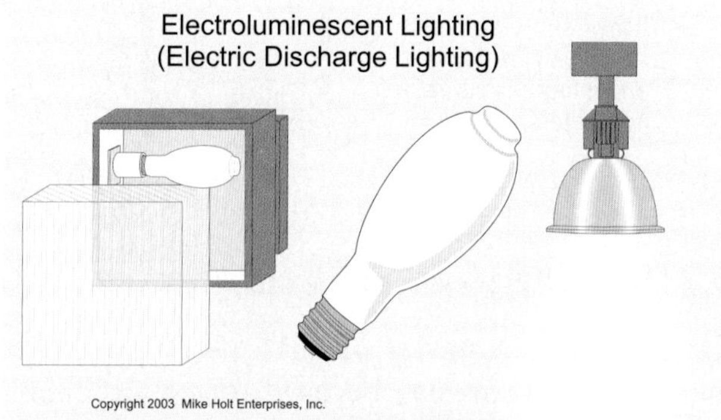

Electroluminescent lighting is the production of light from an electrical arc in charged gas. Examples include neon, high and low-pressure sodium, and mercury vapor.

Figure 4–10

Phosphorescent Illumination—Illumination can be produced when a source of energy strikes phosphorous materials.

Examples of phosphorescence include televisions and computer monitors. Figure 4–11

Fluorescent Lighting—Illumination results from the combination of electroluminescence and phosphorescence when electrical current flows through a charged gas or vapor. This causes emission of invisible, ultraviolet radiation, which strikes a phosphorescent coating. Figure 4–12

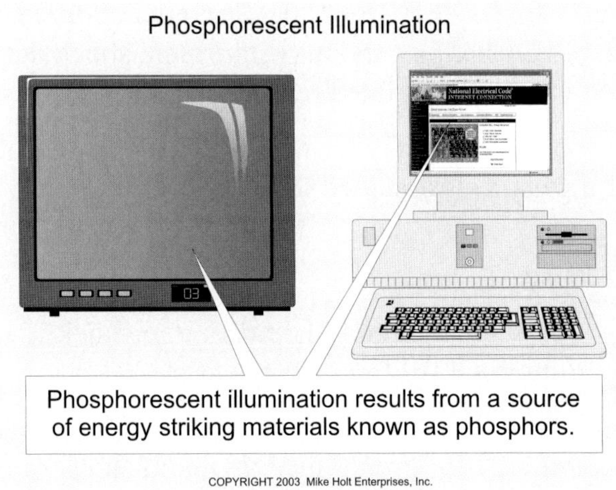

Phosphorescent Illumination
Phosphorescent illumination results from a source of energy striking materials known as phosphors.
COPYRIGHT 2003 Mike Holt Enterprises, Inc.

Figure 4–11

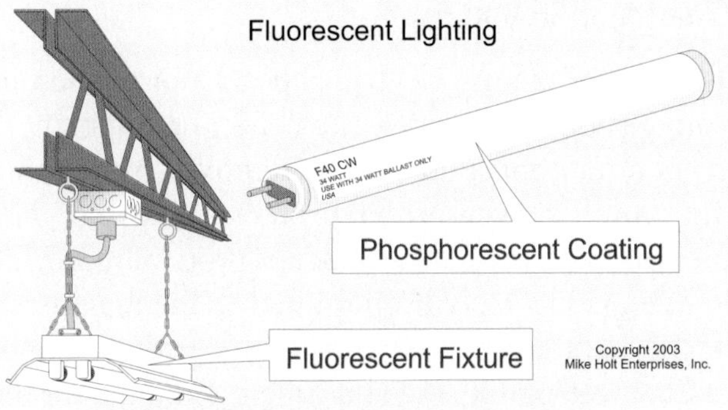

Figure 4–12

4.4 Danger of Electricity

If an electrical system is not properly designed and wired, people can be subjected to electrical shock, or death, by electrocution or fire.

Understanding Electrical Shock Hazard

If an electrical system is not properly wired to remove dangerous voltage from a ground fault, persons can be subjected to electrical shock, which can result in injury or death. The National Safety Council estimates that approximately 300 people in the United States die each year because of an electrical shock from 120V and 277V circuits. People become injured and death occurs when voltage pushes electrons through the human body, particularly through the heart. An electrical shock from as little as 30V alternating current for as little as one second can disrupt the heart's electrical circuitry, causing it to go into ventricular fibrillation. Ventricular fibrillation prevents the blood from circulating through the brain, resulting in death in a matter of minutes. **Figure 4–13**

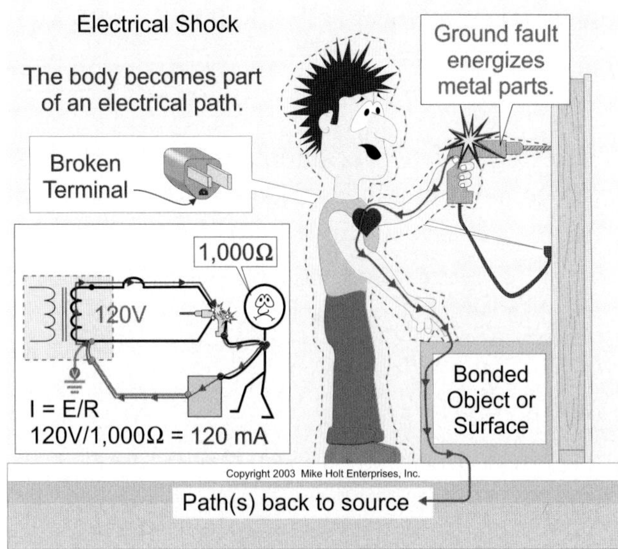

Figure 4–13

AUTHOR'S COMMENT: According to the American Heart Association, ventricular fibrillation (VF) is a life-threatening condition in which the heart no longer beats but "quivers" or fibrillates very rapidly — 350 times per minute or more. To avoid sudden cardiac death, the person must be treated with a defibrillator immediately. Cardiopulmonary resuscitation (CPR) provides some extra time, but defibrillation is essential for surviving ventricular fibrillation.

What Determines the Severity of Electrical Shock?

The severity of an electrical shock is dependent on the current flowing through the body, which is impacted by the electromotive force (E), measured in volts, and the contact resistance (R), measured in ohms (Ω). Current can be determined by the formula I = E/R.

The typical resistances of individual elements of human circuits include:

	Dry	Wet
Foot Immersed in Water		100Ω
Hand Immersed in Water		300Ω
Hand Around 1.5 in. Pipe	1,000Ω	500Ω
Hand Holding Pliers	8,000Ω	1,000Ω
Finger-Thumb Grasp	30,000Ω	8,000Ω
Finger Touch	100,000Ω	12,000Ω

The effects of 60 Hz alternating current on an average human includes: **Figure 4–14**

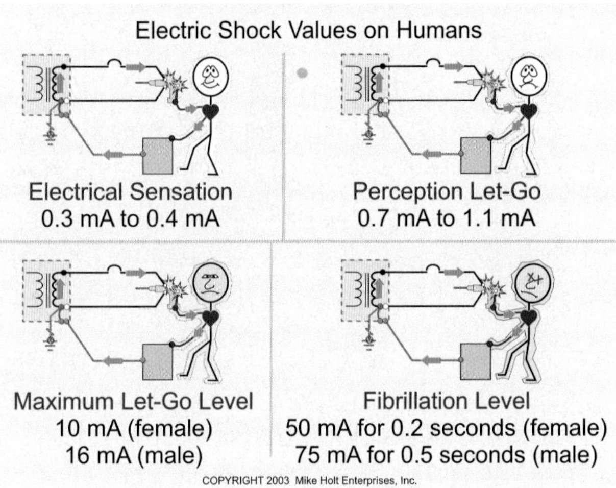

Figure 4–14

- Electrical Sensation. Tingle sensation occurs at about 0.3 mA for an adult female and 0.4 mA for an adult male.
- Perception Let-Go. Current over 0.7—1.1 mA is very uncomfortable to both sexes.
- Maximum Let-Go Level. The maximum let-go threshold level for a female is approximately 10 mA and for a male it is about 16 mA.

  The "let-go threshold" is the current level where we lose control of our muscles and the electricity causes muscles to contract until the current is removed.

- Fibrillation Level—50 mA for 0.2 seconds (female) and 75 mA for 0.5 seconds (male).

According to IEEE Std. 80, *IEEE Guide for Safety in AC Substations,* the maximum safe shock duration can be determined by the formula:

Seconds = 0.116/(E/R), where "R" (the resistance of a person) is assumed to be 1,000Ω.

Example:

For a 120V circuit, the maximum shock duration = 0.116/(120V/1,000Ω) = 1 second.

For a 277V circuit, the maximum shock duration = 0.116/(277V/1,000Ω) = 0.43 seconds.

Clearing a Ground Fault

To protect against electric shock from dangerous voltages on metal parts of electrical equipment, a ground fault must quickly be removed by opening the circuit's overcurrent protection device. The time it takes for an overcurrent protection device to open is inversely proportional to the magnitude of the fault current. Thus, the higher the ground-fault current value, the less time it will take for the protection device to open and clear the fault. For example, a 20A circuit with an overload of 40A (two times the rating) would trip a breaker in 25 to 150 seconds. At 100A (five times the rating) the breaker would trip in 5 to 20 seconds. **Figure 4-15**

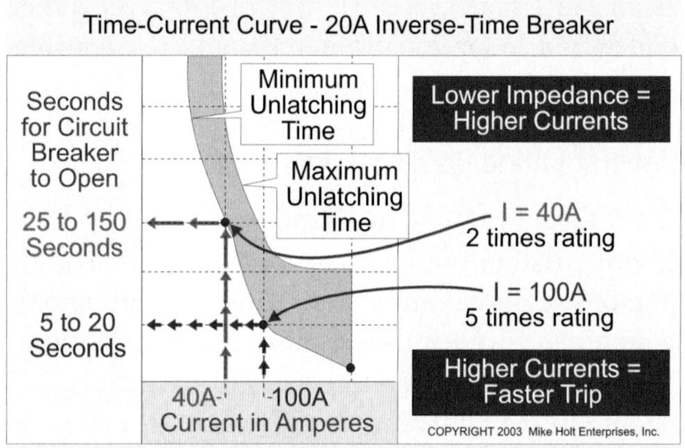

Figure 4–15

To remove dangerous touch voltage on metal parts from a ground fault, the fault-current path must have sufficiently low impedance to allow the fault current to quickly rise to facilitate the opening of the branch-circuit overcurrent protection device.

Example:

Approximately how much ground-fault current can flow in a 100A circuit which consists of:

- Ungrounded Conductors—200 ft of 3 AWG at 0.05Ω
- Equipment Grounding (bonding) Conductor—200 ft of 8 AWG at 0.156Ω

(a) 100A (b) 200A
(c) 600A (d) 800A

- Answer: (c) 600A

$$\text{Fault Current} = \frac{E}{Z}$$

$$E = 120V$$

$$Z = 0.05\Omega + 0.156\Omega = 0.206\Omega$$

$$\text{Fault Current} = \frac{120V}{0.206\Omega} = 583A$$

Fire

Each year, fires from electrical faults result in billions of dollars of property damage, not to mention the loss of many lives. A fire can be generated by electrical energy when current from an electrical fault (often an arc fault) ignites adjacent combustible materials. Figure 4–16

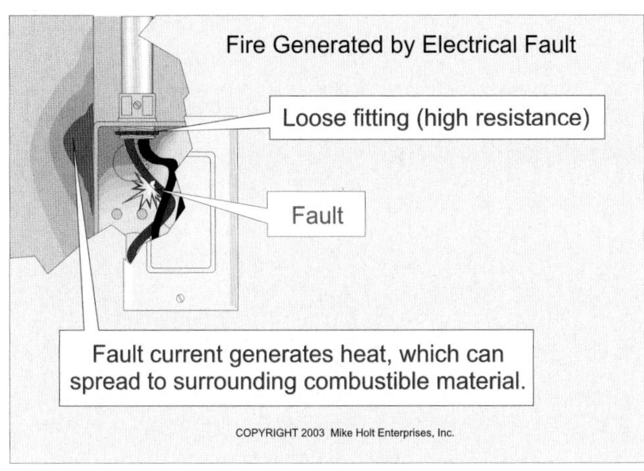

Figure 4–16

Electrical Arc Blast

In addition to electrical shock, a sudden movement from an energized object has caused many people to move conductive metal objects into energized parts, resulting in a phase-to-phase or ground fault. The fault can cause a severe arc-blast, which can approach 30,000°F. This vaporizes metal parts and produces an explosive pressure wave of molten metals which can kill or severely injure those in close proximity.

An electrical arc blast can also occur when electrical equipment malfunctions. NFPA 70E (*Standard for Electrical Safety Requirements for Employee Workplaces, 2000 edition*) dictates the requirements for employees whose work requires them to enter into the "flash boundary"—the distance that determines whether 2nd degree burns to the skin will occur. Figure 4–17

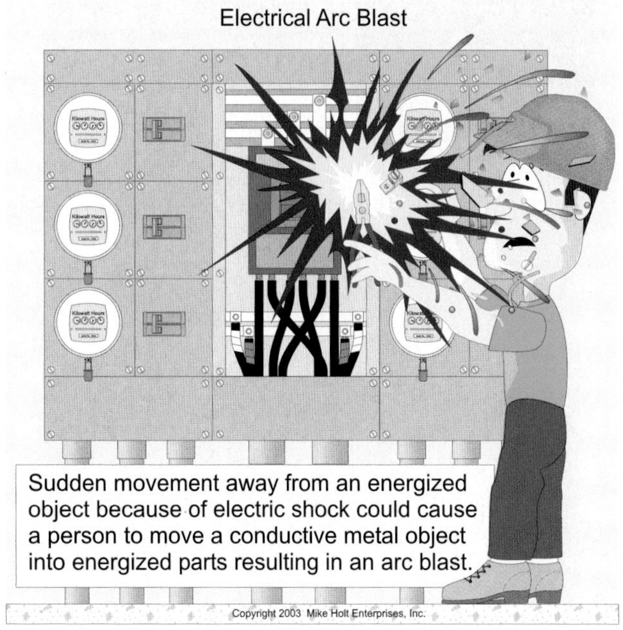

Electrical Arc Blast
Sudden movement away from an energized object because of electric shock could cause a person to move a conductive metal object into energized parts resulting in an arc blast.
Copyright 2003 Mike Holt Enterprises, Inc.

Figure 4–17

AUTHOR'S COMMENT: For more information about electrical shock, electrocution, and arc blast see *Bussmann Safety Basics* book and video, which are available at www.bussmann.com.

4.5 National Electrical Code

To ensure the minimum practical safeguarding of persons and property from the use of electricity, all wiring must be installed in accordance with the *National Electrical Code* (*NEC*). The *NEC* is a safety standard that contains rules necessary for a safe electrical installation. Installing electrical systems in accordance with the *NEC*, and providing proper maintenance for the electrical system, should result in an installation that is essentially free from an electrical hazard [90.1]. **Figure 4–18**

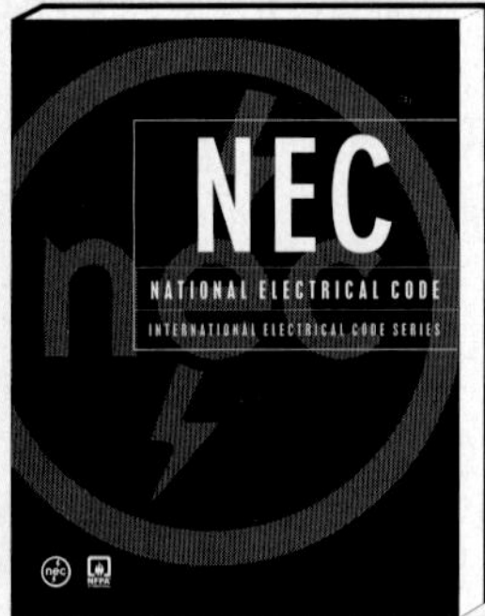

Figure 4–18

Hazards from the use of electricity often occur when the electrical system was not installed in accordance with the *NEC* and/or the initial wiring did not provide for the future increased use of electricity. **Figure 4–19**

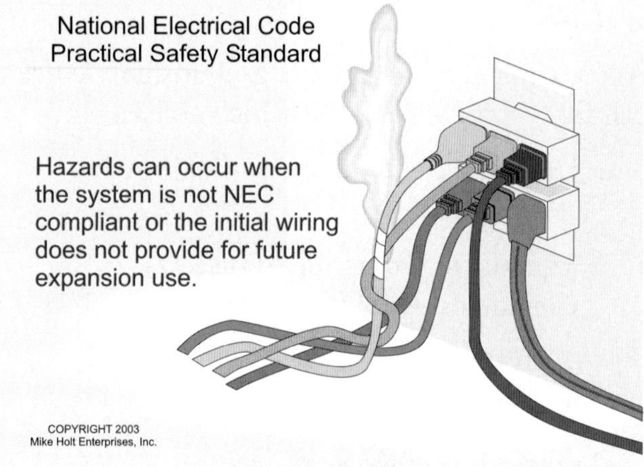

National Electrical Code
Practical Safety Standard
Hazards can occur when the system is not NEC compliant or the initial wiring does not provide for future expansion use.
COPYRIGHT 2003
Mike Holt Enterprises, Inc.

Figure 4–19

AUTHOR'S COMMENT: The *NEC* is a document and it is not written so that it can be used as an instruction manual. Learning to use and understand the *NEC* takes years of study, but many of the rules are based on the principles of electrical theory.

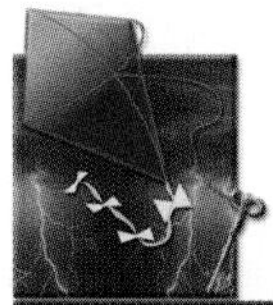

Unit 4 Summary

4.1 Electrical Current Flow (Electricity)

Electrical current flow is used daily in our lives. We call the movement of electrons for the purpose of transferring energy to perform useful functions "Electricity."

Electrical current is the movement of electrons from the power source through the electrical circuit and then back to the power source. Forcing electrons to move through an electrical circuit by a power source that applies a negative charge at one end of the circuit and a positive charge to the other end produces electric current.

For current to flow from the power source through the load and then back to the power source, the path must be conductive. Since copper is a very good conductor, it is the most common wire used for this purpose.

4.2 Electricity

To force electrons to move, energy must be applied to the electrons to cause them to leave their atom.

Chemical Activity (Electrochemistry)

When chemicals combine in a controlled manner, they can provide the energy needed to move electrons out of the atom's orbit. This is the principle of the electrical battery and fuel cell.

Battery—A battery is a power source where voltaic cells are combined in a series arrangement, positive terminal to negative terminal, so that the voltage of one cell will be added to the voltage of the other cells.

Fuel Cells—Fuel cells use an advanced electrochemical process to convert a gaseous fuel, such as natural gas or propane, into electrical energy.

Magnetism (Magnetoelectricity)

The vast majority of the electrical energy utilized today is created in power plants that rotate a magnetic field through a conductor.

It is not the force of a magnetic field moving through a conductor that produces electricity, it is the relative motion of the magnetic field to the electrons within the conductor. The moving magnetic field literally pulls or pushes the valence electrons through the circuit. If there is no movement of the magnetic field relative to the electrons within the conductor, there is no electron flow, no matter how strong the magnetic field.

Light (Photoelectricity)

Photoelectricity works on the principle that light (photons) striking a semiconducting plate causes it to release electrons to another semi-conducting plate. Conditions limiting solar power are hours of direct sun exposure and electric power demand.

Thermo Energy (Thermoelectricity)

The thermoelectric effect is the process where heat is applied to dissimilar metals that are joined together to produce about $^{5}/_{1,000}$ to $^{30}/_{1,000}$ of a volt.

Pressure (Piezoelectricity)

Some crystalline materials produce a small electrical voltage when bending or twisting pressure is applied to them.

4.3 Useful Purposes of Electricity

Electricity, the transfer of energy via the movement of electrons, can be used for the following purposes:

Electrochemistry

Electrical current can be used to alter the effects of chemical bonding so as to separate or encourage the formation of new compounds. This is the basis of electroplating and electrolysis.

Electroplating—Electroplating is a commercial-industrial process intended to make some improvement to the plated surface. Electroplating is building up layers of metal on one surface and removing the same metal from another by the chemical action of an electrical current in a solution.

Gold plating is added to electronic circuitry connectors to prevent corrosion from forming because gold will not chemically bond with other elements to produce an insulating oxide.

Electrolysis—Electrolysis is a decomposition action where metal from one surface is removed to another surface because of a chemical action caused by electrical current.

Electromagnetism

Alternating current is used to produce an alternating electromagnetic field that is necessary for the operation of a motor, relay, and transformer.

Heat (Resistance)

Electrical current flowing through a high-resistance heating element will produce heat as the electrons flow through the circuit. This is the principle for most electrical resistance-heating appliances such as toasters, ranges, ovens, water heaters, clothes dryers, flat irons, etc.

Illumination Lighting

Electrical current flow can be used to produce light through the principles of incandescent, electroluminescent, phosphorescent and fluorescent lighting.

Incandescent Lighting—Illumination can be produced when a high-resistance tungsten metal filament is heated in a vacuum glass lamp (bulb).

Electroluminescent Lighting—Light can be produced when an electrical arc flows through a charged gas lamp.

Phosphorescent Illumination—Illumination can be produced when a source of energy strikes phosphorous materials.

Fluorescent Lighting—Illumination results from the combination of electroluminescence and phosphorescence when electrical current flows through a charged gas or vapor causing emission of invisible, ultraviolet radiation, which strikes a phosphorescent coating.

4.4 Danger of Electricity

If an electrical system is not properly designed and wired, people can be subjected to electrical shock or death by electrocution or fire.

Understanding Electrical Shock Hazard

People become injured and death occurs when voltage pushes electrons through the human body, particularly through the heart. An electrical shock from as little as 30V alternating current for as little as one second can disrupt the heart's electrical circuitry causing it to go into ventricular fibrillation.

According to the American Heart Association, ventricular fibrillation (VF) is a life-threatening condition in which the heart no longer beats but "quivers" or fibrillates very rapidly—350 times per minute or more. Cardiopulmonary resuscitation (CPR) provides some extra time, but defibrillation is essential for surviving ventricular fibrillation.

What Determines the Severity of Electrical Shock?

The severity of an electrical shock is dependent on the current flowing through the body, which is impacted by the electromotive force (E) measured in volts, and the contact resistance (R) measured in ohms. Current can be determined by the formula $I = E/R$.

- Tingle sensation occurs at about 0.3 mA for an adult female and 0.4 mA for an adult male.
- Current over 0.7—1.1 mA is very uncomfortable to both sexes.
- The maximum let-go threshold level for a female is approximately 10 mA and for a male it is about 16 mA.
- Fibrillation Level—50 mA for 0.2 seconds (female) or 75 mA for 0.5 seconds (male).

Fire

A fire can be generated by electrical energy when current from an electrical fault (often an arc fault) ignites adjacent combustible materials.

Electrical Arc Blast

An electrical fault can cause a severe arc blast (that can approach 30,000°F), which vaporizes metal parts and produces a pressure wave of molten metals which can kill or severely injure those in close proximity.

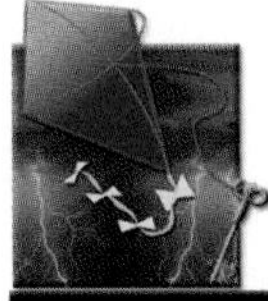

Unit 4 Conclusion

You now know what causes current flow, and you are familiar with some ways of applying energy to atoms to make the electrons move out of orbit. You are now aware of a large variety of ways we use electricity.

These various uses, however, do come with the dangers of shock, arc blast, and fire. Because of these dangers, the *National Electrical Code* prescribes specific requirements designed to protect people and property. The *NEC*, however, is not a simple document—it cannot be, because of the laws of physics that underlie it. But your knowledge of current flow will help you understand and apply the *NEC*.

Words to Live By: ***There is a name for people who are not excited about their work—unemployed.***

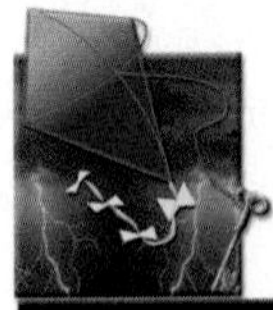

Unit 4 Practice Questions

4.1 Electrical Current Flow (Electricity)

1. The movement of electrons to perform a useful function is called static electricity.

   (a) True (b) False

2. For current to flow from the power source through the load and then back to the power source, the current path must be conductive.

   (a) True (b) False

4.2 Electricity

3. To force electrons to move, some form of energy must be applied to the electrons to cause them to leave their atom; this energy can only be supplied by magnetism.

   (a) True (b) False

4. When electricity is created by chemical activity, the electrons will flow in two directions, and this is called alternating current.

   (a) True (b) False

5. A battery is a power source where voltaic cells are combined in a series arrangement, positive terminal to negative terminal, so that the voltage of one cell will be added to the voltage of the other cells.

   (a) True (b) False

6. Moving a magnetic field through a conductor provides the energy needed to cause the valence electrons in the conductor to flow in a given direction.

   (a) True (b) False

7. It is not the force of the magnetic field through a conductor that produces electricity; it is the relative motion of the field to the electrons within the conductor that produces the movement of electrons.

   (a) True (b) False

8. Photoelectricity is the principle that photons striking a semiconducting plate cause the plate to release electrons to another semiconducting plate.

   (a) True (b) False

9. At _____, the movement of molecules stops.

(a) 32°F (b) 0°F (c) -459°F (d) none of these

10. The thermoelectric effect is the process where heat is applied to dissimilar metals joined together to produce about _____.

(a) 5 mV (b) 10 mV (c) 30 mV (d) all of these

11. A common application of thermoelectricity is the thermocouple.

(a) True (b) False

12. Some crystalline materials produce a small electrical voltage when bending or twisting pressure is applied to them. This is called piezoelectricity.

(a) True (b) False

4.3 Useful Purposes of Electricity

13. Electrolysis is a commercial-industrial process intended to make some improvement to the plated surface.

(a) True (b) False

14. Electroplating is a process where metal from one surface is removed to another surface because of a chemical action caused by electrical current.

(a) True (b) False

15. Electroluminescent lighting is the process of illumination where a high-resistance tungsten metal filament is heated due to the current flowing through the element in a vacuum glass lamp.

(a) True (b) False

16. Illumination can be produced when an electrical arc flows through a charged gas lamp.

(a) True (b) False

17. Fluorescent lighting is illumination that results from the combination of electroluminescence and phosphorescence.

(a) True (b) False

4.4 Danger of Electricity

18. The National Safety Council estimates that approximately _____ people in the United States die each year because of an electric shock from 120V and 277V circuits.

(a) 100 (b) 200 (c) 300 (d) 400

19. People become injured and death occurs when voltage pushes electrons through the human body, causing it to go into ventricular fibrillation.

    (a) True (b) False

20. Ventricular fibrillation causes the blood to circulate so fast through the brain that death can occur in a matter of minutes.

    (a) True (b) False

21. The severity of an electric shock is dependent on the current flowing through the body, which is impacted by circuit voltage and contact resistance.

    (a) True (b) False

22. The time it takes for an overcurrent protection device to open is directly proportional to the magnitude of the fault current.

    (a) True (b) False

23. A fire can be generated by electrical energy when _____ from an arcing electrical fault ignites adjacent combustible materials.

    (a) voltage (b) current (c) power (d) resistance

24. An electrical arc blast can approach _____, which vaporizes metal parts and produces an explosive, and deadly pressure wave.

    (a) 10,000°F (b) 15,000°F (c) 25,000°F (d) 30,000°F

4.5 National Electrical Code

25. To ensure the minimum practical safeguarding of persons and property from the use of electricity, all premises wiring must be installed in accordance with the *National Electrical Code (NEC).*

    (a) True (b) False

UNIT

5 Electromagnetism

Introduction

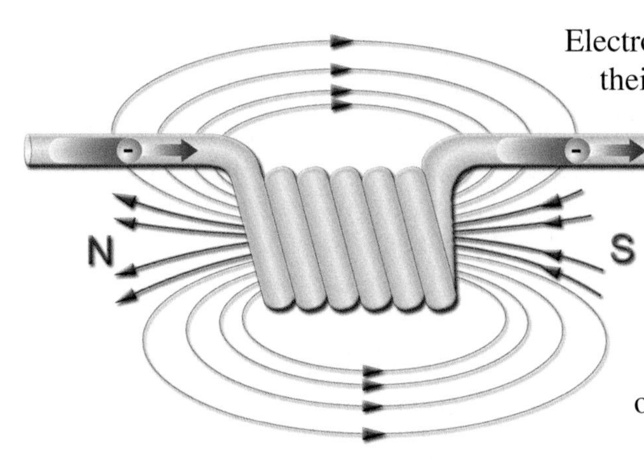

Electrons produce their own magnetic fields because of their orbital spin. When electrons move through a wire under a force (voltage), the magnetic fields of individual electrons add together.

The study of magnetic theory in Unit 3 gave you the basis for understanding electromagnetism theory in this unit. The concepts here will allow you to understand motors, generators, and the rationale behind the rules in Chapter 3 of the *National Electrical Code.*

5.1 Electromagnetism in a Wire

In 1819, Hans Oersted discovered the relationship between a compass and electrical current flowing through a conductor. He discovered that when current flowed through a conductor, an electromagnetic field would develop around the conductor. He also discovered that if the current in the conductor were reversed, the direction of the compass needle (next to the wire) would also reverse. The direction of the electromagnetic field around a conductor because of current flow is determined by the left-hand rule as it relates to "electron theory," or the right-hand rule as it relates to "conventional current flow theory," as discussed in section 7.3 of this book. Figure 5–1

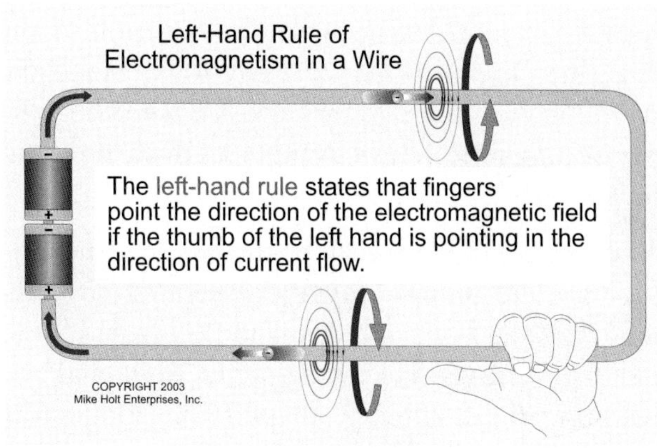

Left-Hand Rule of
Electromagnetism in a Wire
The left-hand rule states that fingers point the direction of the electromagnetic field if the thumb of the left hand is pointing in the direction of current flow.
COPYRIGHT 2003
Mike Holt Enterprises, Inc.

Figure 5–1

5.2 Field Intensity

The electromagnetic field intensity (lines of flux) increase with increased current flow, but they weaken as they get further from the conductor. Oersted demonstrated that as the current in the conductor increased, the compass needle was affected at a greater distance from the conductor. **Figure 5–2**

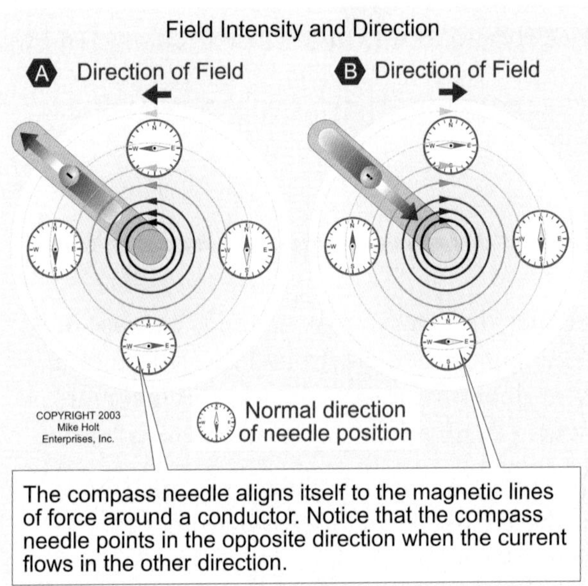

Figure 5–2

5.3 Field Interaction

If a conductor that carries current is placed next to another conductor that carries current in the opposite direction, their electromagnetic fields oppose one another because the direction of the flux lines are in opposite directions. Since the magnetic flux lines cannot cross each other, the electromagnetic field attempts to push the conductors apart. **Figure 5–3A**

When conductors carrying current in the same direction are brought together, their electromagnetic fields aid one another. The flux lines join to make a stronger electromagnetic field and the magnetic fields attempt to pull the conductors together. **Figure 5–3B**

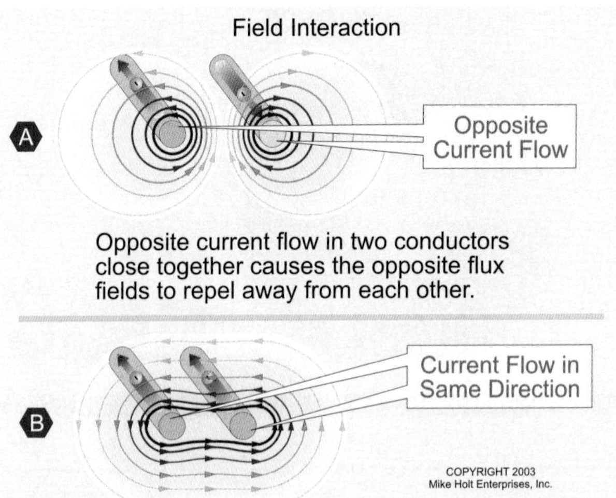

Field Interaction
A
Opposite Current Flow
Opposite current flow in two conductors close together causes the opposite flux fields to repel away from each other.
B
Current Flow in Same Direction
COPYRIGHT 2003 Mike Holt Enterprises, Inc.
The flux fields of two conductors that have current flowing in the same direction combine to make a single, stronger field. Adding additional conductors with the current flowing in the same direction will strengthen the field more.

Figure 5–3

5.4 Field Interaction of Loops

If a conductor is twisted to form a loop, the electromagnetic fields around the conductor are oriented in accordance with the left-hand rule, based on electron current flow theory, so they all flow into the loop on one side and out the other side. In the center of the loop, the flux lines are compressed to create a dense and strong electromagnetic field. The electromagnetic field in the center of the loop has a north-south polarity. **Figure 5–4**

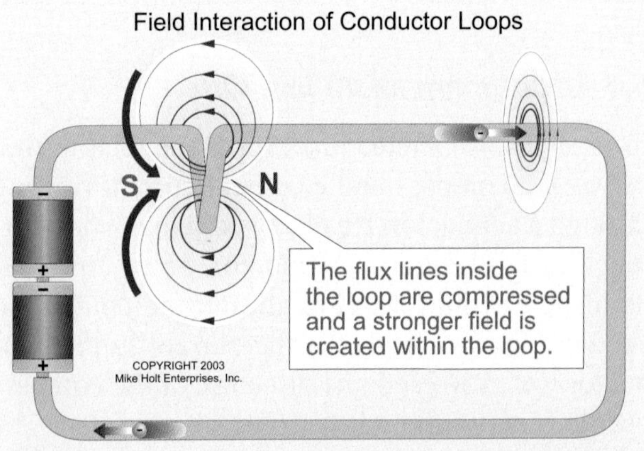

Field Interaction of Conductor Loops
S
N
The flux lines inside the loop are compressed and a stronger field is created within the loop.
COPYRIGHT 2003 Mike Holt Enterprises, Inc.
When a loop is formed in the wire, all the magnetic flux lines enter one side of the loop and come out the other side of the loop. This forms a north and south pole within the loop.

Figure 5–4

5.5 Electromagnetism in a Coil

If loops of a conductor are wound (coiled) in the same direction, the electromagnetic fields will add together. The more loops a conductor makes, the greater the electromagnetic field. If the conductor coil were compressed tightly, the electromagnetic fields would produce an even stronger electromagnetic field. Figure 5–5

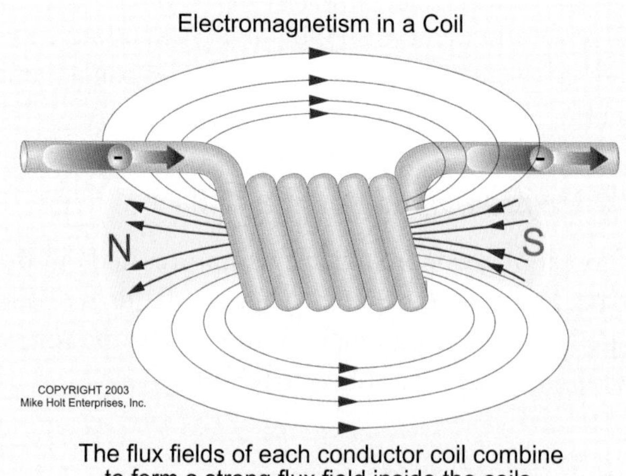

The flux fields of each conductor coil combine to form a strong flux field inside the coils.

Figure 5–5

5.6 Magnetic Core

The electromagnetic field of a coil can be made stronger by placing a soft iron core inside the coil windings. The iron core permits a higher concentration of magnetic flux lines than does air. Soft iron is used for the core because it has low retentivity but high permeability. Figure 5–6

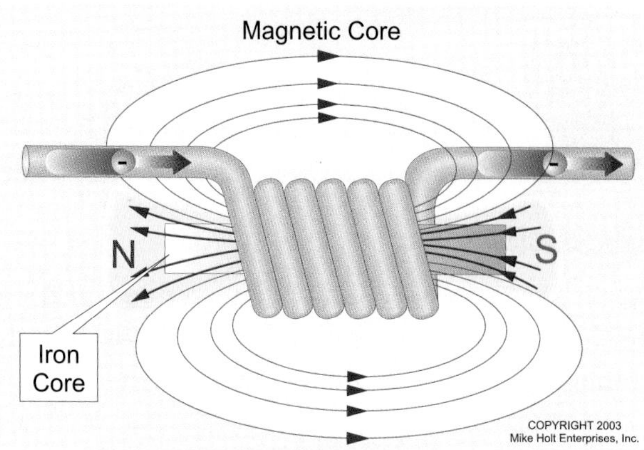

A soft iron core increases the density of the magnetic field inside the coils of wire.

Figure 5–6

5.7 Ampere and Turns

The strength of an electromagnetic field is dependent on the magnitude of the current and the number of turns in the electromagnet coil. A coil with 100 turns carrying 1A will produce the same electromagnetic field as a coil with 50 turns carrying 2A.

Electromagnetism is used in many electrical applications such as motors, transformers, generators, doorbells, and telephones, as well as thousands of other types of electrical equipment.

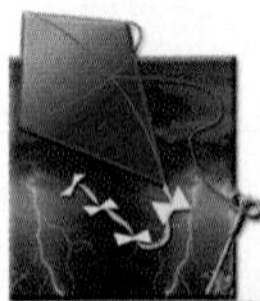

Unit 5 Summary

Introduction

When electrons are forced to move (current flow) through a conductor, the magnetic fields of individual electrons are said to add together.

5.1 Electromagnetism in a Wire

In 1819, Hans Oersted discovered that when current flowed through a conductor, an electromagnetic field would develop around the wire. He also discovered that if the current in the conductor were reversed, the direction of the compass needle (next to the wire) would also reverse.

The direction of the electromagnetic field is determined by the left-hand rule as it relates to "electron theory," or the right-hand rule as it relates to "conventional current flow theory."

5.2 Field Intensity

The field intensity (lines of flux) increase with increased current flow, but they weaken as they get further from the conductor.

5.3 Field Interaction

If a conductor that carries current is placed next to another conductor that carries current in the opposite direction, their electromagnetic fields oppose one another because the direction of the flux lines are in opposite directions. Since the magnetic flux lines cannot cross each other, the electromagnetic field attempts to push the conductors apart.

When conductors carrying current in the same direction are brought together, their flux lines join to make a stronger electromagnetic field and the magnetic fields attempt to pull the conductors together.

5.4 Field Interaction of Loops

If a conductor is twisted to form a loop, the electromagnetic fields around the conductor are oriented in accordance with the left-hand rule (electron current flow theory) so that the flux lines are compressed to create a dense and strong electromagnetic field.

5.5 Electromagnetism in a Coil

If loops of a conductor are wound (coiled) in the same direction, the electromagnetic fields will add together. The more loops, or the tighter the loops, the greater the electromagnetic field.

5.6 Magnetic Core

The electromagnetic field of a coil can be made stronger by placing a soft iron core inside the coil windings because the iron core permits a higher concentration of magnetic flux lines.

5.7 Ampere and Turns

The strength of an electromagnetic field is dependent on the magnitude of the current and the number of turns in the electromagnet coil.

Electromagnetism is used in many electrical applications such as motors, transformers, generators, doorbells, and telephones, as well as thousands of other types of electrical equipment.

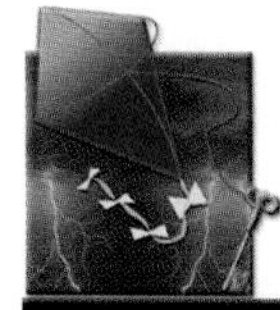

Unit 5 Conclusion

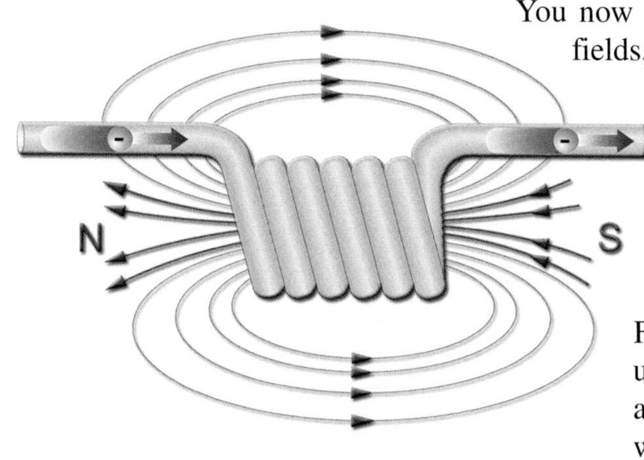

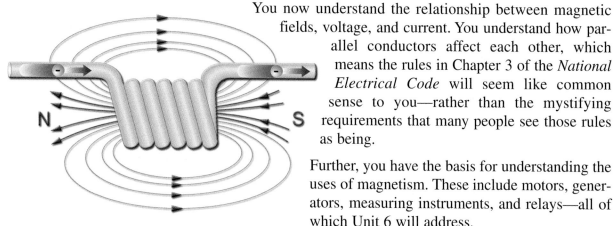

You now understand the relationship between magnetic fields, voltage, and current. You understand how parallel conductors affect each other, which means the rules in Chapter 3 of the *National Electrical Code* will seem like common sense to you—rather than the mystifying requirements that many people see those rules as being.

Further, you have the basis for understanding the uses of magnetism. These include motors, generators, measuring instruments, and relays—all of which Unit 6 will address.

Words to Live By: *Some people complain because there are thorns on roses, while others appreciate the roses among the thorns.*

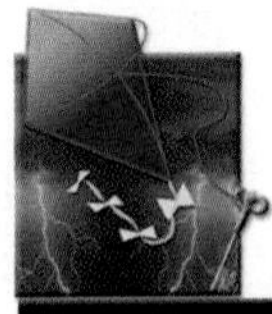

Unit 5 Practice Questions

Introduction

1. When electrons are forced to move through a conductor, the magnetic fields of individual electrons subtract and an electromagnetic field will develop around the conductor.

   (a) True (b) False

5.1 Electromagnetism in a Wire

2. The direction of the electromagnetic field around a conductor because of current flow is determined by the right-hand rule as it relates to electron theory.

   (a) True (b) False

5.2 Field Intensity

3. The field intensity around a conductor carrying current decreases with increased current flow, and is stronger the further the distance from the conductor.

   (a) True (b) False

5.3 Field Interaction

4. If a conductor carrying current is next to another conductor carrying current in the opposite direction, the electromagnetic field attempts to pull the conductors apart.

   (a) True (b) False

5. When conductors carrying current in the same direction are brought together, the electromagnetic fields attempt to push the conductors together.

   (a) True (b) False

5.4 Field Interaction of Loops

6. If a conductor is twisted to form a loop, the electromagnetic fields around the conductor are compressed to create a dense and strong electromagnetic field.

   (a) True (b) False

5.5 Electromagnetism in a Coil

7. If conductor loops are wound in the same direction, the conductor's electromagnetic fields add together.

   (a) True (b) False

5.6 Magnetic Core

8. The electromagnetic field of a coil can be made stronger by placing a soft iron core inside the coil windings.

   (a) True (b) False

5.7 Ampere and Turns

9. The strength of an electromagnetic field is dependent on the magnitude of the current and the number of turns in the electromagnet coil.

   (a) True (b) False

Notes

UNIT 6 Uses of Electromagnetism

Introduction

Anyone who does electrical work eventually works with motors, generators, or electro-mechanical relays.

We find motors in heating, ventilating and air-conditioning systems (HVAC), appliances, and industrial processes. Generators are becoming increasingly common as more facilities install their own onsite power sources for backup, peak load-shaving, and/or emergency power. Relays control everything from residential HVAC systems to industrial processes and commercial security systems.

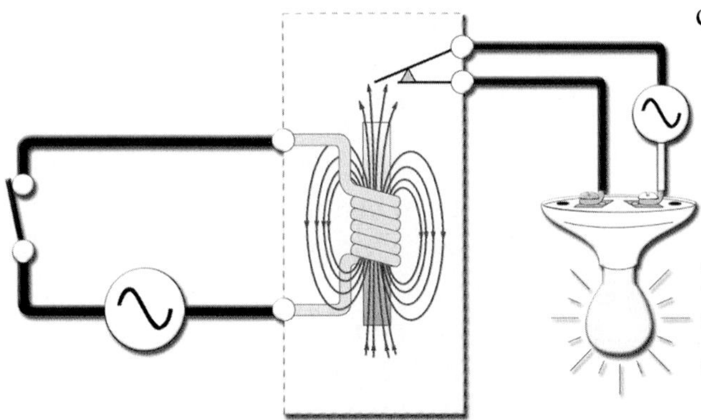

Everyone working with electricity should understand the basic functioning of these devices.

6.1 Basic Electric Meters

Electromechanical meters use a coil of wire around a soft iron core. This arrangement is immersed in a magnetic field that is provided by two permanent magnets. As current flows through the coil, the magnetic field created around this coil interacts with the permanent magnets along with the needle that is connected to the coil. This mechanism is referred to as a Galvanometer.

Some meters use a solenoid coil and a movable core to measure voltage, current, and resistance. A solenoid coil is a multiple-turn coil of wire that produces a strong magnetic field inside the coil when current flows through it.

Digital meters are commonly in use today. It is beyond the scope of this course to describe how they function. (Besides, they don't have any cool mechanical devices that you can look at and see move around like the old meters so they're not as much fun to talk about). Digital meters are used to measure ac voltage and current, dc voltage and current, and resistance.

Voltmeter

Voltmeters are used to measure both dc and ac voltage. An analog voltmeter has a resistor connected in series with a coil that allows a very small amount of current, produced by the voltage being measured across the resistance, to flow through the solenoid coil.

The purpose of the resistor in the meter is to limit the current flow through the meter to a very small amount. As current flows through the meter coil, the electromagnetic field of the coil exerts force on a soft iron bar that is in the center of the coil, causing it to move against spring tension and, in turn, causing the pointer attached to the bar to move.

The greater the voltage, the greater the current flow through the meter; the greater the magnetic field produced, the farther the iron bar is drawn into the coil and the greater the movement of the pointer. In the case of the Galvanometer, the current through the coil interacts with the permanent magnetic field and causes the loop of wire to pivot, thereby causing the meter needle to move with it.

DC Voltmeter

Voltmeters are connected in parallel with the circuit and measure the difference of potential between the two test leads, Figure 6–1. Place the red lead on the spot where you expect to measure positive dc voltage, and place the black lead on the location that you expect to show a negative potential, relative to where the red lead is placed.

If it is unknown which is more positive or negative, momentarily touch the leads to the circuit in the locations to measure the dc voltage; if the meter pegs to the left, simply reverse the leads so that deflection is in the correct direction.

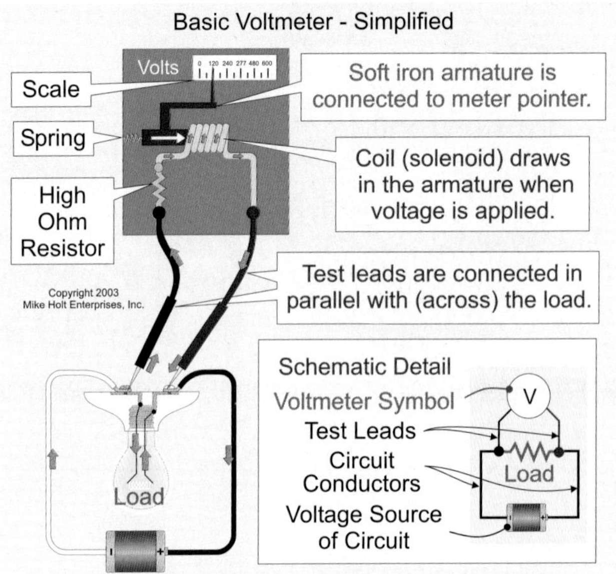

Figure 6–1

AUTHOR'S COMMENT: "Pegging" the meter means that the pointer on the meter is driven against the stop, (moving opposite of the intended direction). Pegging of the meter only occurs when the leads are incorrectly placed on a dc current with an electromechanical voltmeter.

DC Ammeter

DC ammeters are used to measure dc current (current that flows in one direction only). DC ammeters can be either for direct connection to the circuit, or they can be of the clamp-on variety. In meters that are built for direct connection, actual circuit current (or a portion of the actual circuit current) is connected in series with the meter coil.

As the full current of the circuit flows through the meter coil, the magnetic field causes the meter needle to deflect. The greater the current flow through the coil, the greater the magnetic field produced by the coil, and the greater the deflection of the needle.

There are also dc clamp-on ammeters. Whereas ac clamp-on meters operate on the principle that a fluctuating magnetic field will induce an alternating current in a conductive loop that is immersed in the field, dc clamp-on meters use a semiconductor effect called the "Hall Effect." A magnetic field will cause particle displacement within the semiconductor that is detectable and measurable.

Measuring currents larger than 10 milliamperes (mA) with a directly connected meter often requires the use of a resistor, called a shunt, in parallel with the meter movement's coil. The resistance of the shunt is a known value, in relation to the internal resistance of the meter, and so the current that travels through the shunt is a known multiple of the current that travels through the meter.

AUTHOR'S COMMENT: To shunt means to bypass. A dc ammeter is sometimes called a shunt meter.

DC ammeters of the direct connection type must be connected in series with the power source and the load, **Figure 6–2**. If a dc ammeter is accidentally connected in parallel with the load, the meter will operate at the source voltage and the current flowing through the meter will be extremely high. This will blow the internal fuse protecting the meter. However, if the meter does not have any internal fuse protection (inexpensive meter), it will likely destroy the meter.

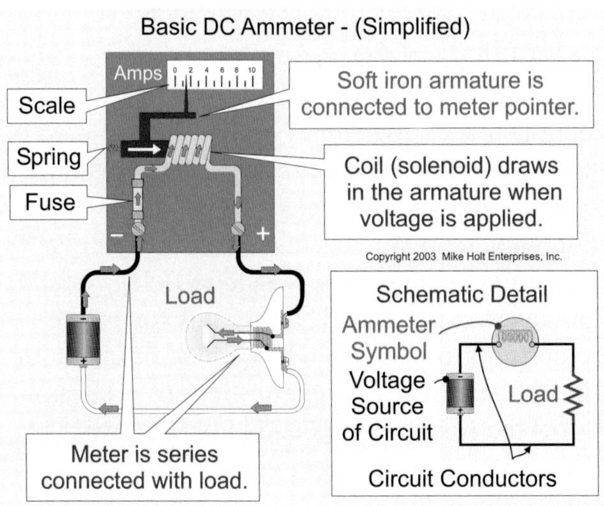

Figure 6–2

When dc ammeters are connected in series with the circuit, dc current polarity (+ or –) must be observed. If the meter is connected in reverse polarity, the meter coil will move in the opposite direction, pegging the meter in the negative direction and possibly damaging its delicate movement. Connect the red lead to the positive terminal of the voltage source, and the black lead should be connected to the negative terminal of the voltage source.

CAUTION: *To prevent damaging the meter from excessive current, do not connect a dc current meter of the direct connection type to a circuit unless you know the approximate maximum current flowing in the circuit. If you are unsure of the maximum current flow of the circuit, start with the highest possible ampere setting.*

Clamp-on AC Ammeter

Clamp-on ac ammeters are used to measure ac currents. A clamp-on ammeter has a coil that is clamped around the conductor and detects the rising and falling magnetic field being produced due to the alternating-current flow through the conductor. Clamp-on ac ammeters are used for measuring the circuit current without breaking the circuit.

AUTHOR'S COMMENT: The expanding and collapsing magnetic field around the conductor being tested induces a voltage in the sensing coil, which causes current to flow through the meter's coil.

To operate a clamp-on ammeter, the sensing coil of the meter is placed around the ac circuit conductor that carries current. The expanding and collapsing magnetic field around the conductor being measured induces a force in the soft iron movable core, causing electrons to flow in the meter circuit.

As current flows through the meter coil, the magnetic field draws in the soft iron bar against spring pressure. The greater the circuit current flow through the coil, the greater the electromagnetic field produced within the coil. This will result in greater induced current in the meter circuit. **Figure 6–3**

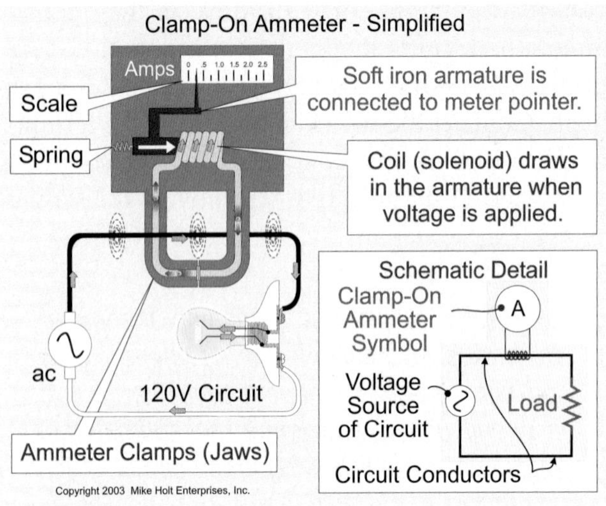

Figure 6–3

Ohmmeters

Ohmmeters are used to measure the resistance or opposition to current flow of a circuit or component. An ohmmeter has a moving coil and a dc power supply (battery) and it is connected in series with the resistor being measured.

As current flows through the coil of the ohmmeter, the magnetic field around the coil draws in the soft iron bar. The greater the current flow through the circuit, the greater the magnetic field produced inside the coil, and the farther the iron bar is drawn into the coil, moving the pointer further. **Figure 6–4**

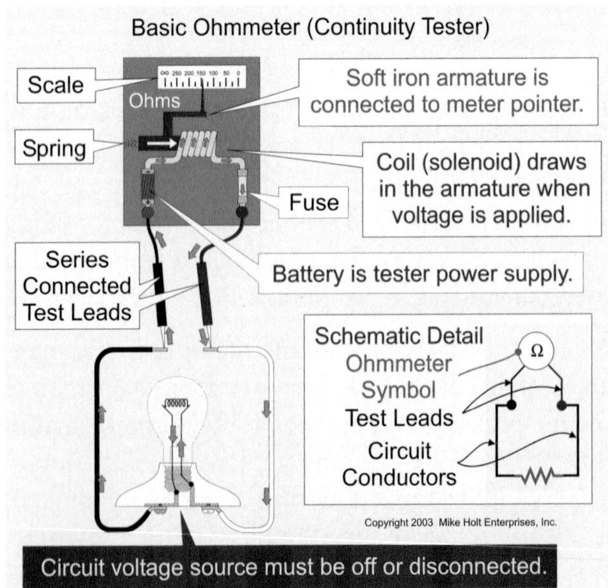

Figure 6–4

Wheatstone Bridge

The Wheatstone Bridge meter is used for extremely accurate resistance measurements. It consists of two known-value precision resistors, a precision variable resistor, a galvanometer (an ammeter that has its pointer in the center with no current flow through it), and an unknown resistor. When the bridge is "balanced," the galvanometer pointer is aimed straight up, indicating no current flow. To determine the value of the unknown resistor, the variable resistor is adjusted until the bridge is balanced. The unknown resistance is determined by the formula:

$$R = \frac{(S \times P)}{Q}$$

where S is the variable resistor's value, and P and Q are the precision resistors of known value.

Megohmmeter

The Megohmmeter, or Megger, is used to measure very high-resistance values, such as those found in cable insulation or between motor or transformer windings. Meggers use a relatively high voltage (500 to 1,000V) in order to determine the resistance in megohms (one million ohms).

A battery can power a Megger, or it may be hand-cranked to produce the desired voltage.

6.2 Electric Motor

The electric motor works on the principle of the attracting and repelling forces of a magnetic field. Motor action can take place when a free moving conductor carrying current is perpendicular to, and within, a stationary magnetic field. The electromagnetic field around the conductor, created by the current flow through the conductor interacting with the stationary magnetic field of a dc motor, causes the free moving conductor to move.

Motor Components

The stationary magnetic field of a dc motor will be either a permanent magnet or an electromagnet. This stationary component is called the "stator." The conductor that rotates between the stationary magnetic field poles of the stator is called the "rotor" or "armature."

AUTHOR'S COMMENT: The turning or repelling force between the stationary magnetic fields and the rotating magnetic fields is called torque. The amount of torque a motor can produce is dependent on the strength of the stator field (which is determined by the current flow through the stator and the number of turns in the stator winding), and the physical construction of the motor.

Understanding Motor Motion

According to the laws of attraction and repulsion, magnetic fields of similar polarity repel each other when brought close together and magnetic fields of opposite polarity attract each other. The repelling force of similar magnetic polarities and the attracting force of opposite polarities cause the armature of the motor to rotate.

AUTHOR'S COMMENT: The topic of Motors will be covered in greater detail in Unit 20.

Figure 6–5A shows the stationary magnetic field (stator).

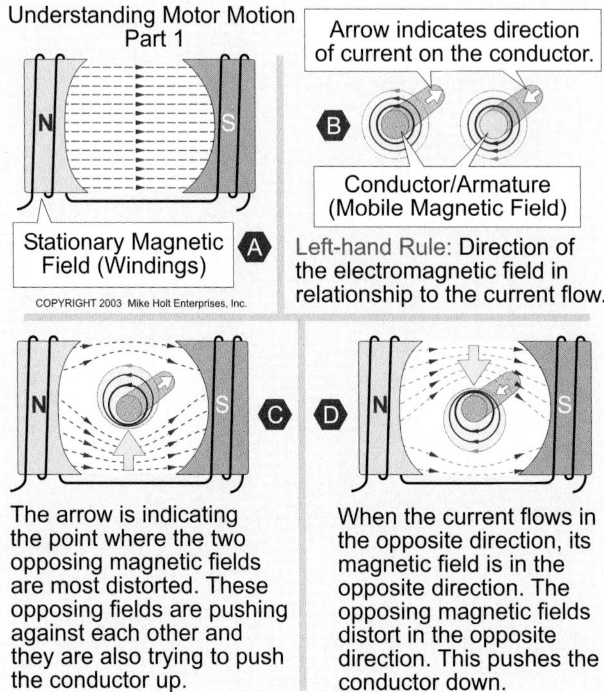

Figure 6–5

Figure 6–5B shows the magnetic field produced around a current-carrying conductor (rotor/armature).

Figure 6–5C and Figure 6–5D show the movement of the conductor (rotor/armature) due to the interaction of the conductor's electromagnetic field (rotor/armature) relative to the stationary magnetic field (stator).

Figure 6–6A shows the direction of the magnetic field as it relates to the direction of the current flow within a conductor that is looped (rotor/armature).

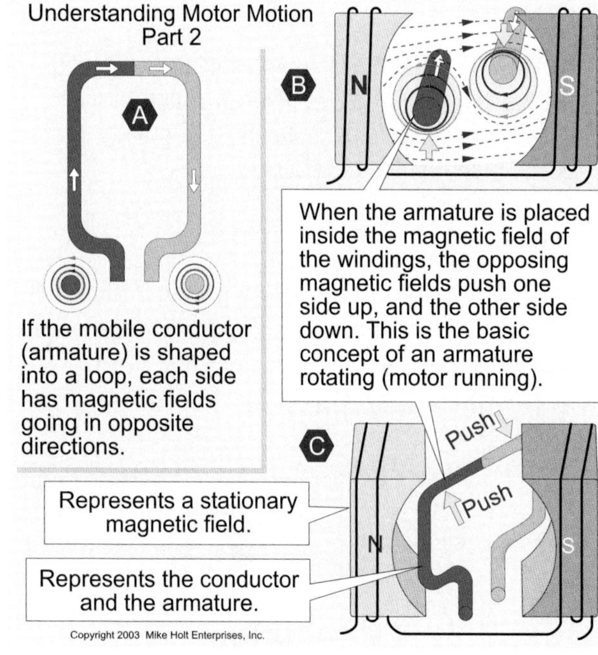

Figure 6–6

Figure 6–6B shows that if a looped conductor (rotor/armature) is placed inside a stationary magnetic field (stator), the opposing magnetic fields cause the conductor to rotate.

Figure 6–6C provides a perspective vision of the rotating armature (conductor loop).

AUTHOR'S COMMENT: For a dc motor to function properly so that the current flows in the same direction through the magnetic field, a device called a commutator is placed on the end of the conductor loop. The polarity of the loop is maintained so that the magnetic fields oppose each other to keep the rotor in motion.

6.3 Electrical Generator

The operation of an electrical generator is opposite that of a motor. That is to say that electrons are forced to move when there is relative motion between a conductor and a magnetic field. In a generator, the rotor (armature) is forced to rotate by a "prime mover," (diesel or gasoline engine, a steam turbine, or the wind) while it is being subjected to the magnetic field of the stator. The movement of the magnetic field through the conductor (rotor) forces the electrons in the conductor to move, thereby producing electrical potential or voltage. Figure 6–7

AUTHOR'S COMMENT: The greater the magnetic field in the generator, whether provided by field coils or by permanent magnets, the greater the power output of the generator.

DC Generator

A dc generator requires the magnetic field of the stationary field (stator) to be produced from a permanent magnetic or electromagnetic field that is always in the same direction. The dc output is taken from the rotating conductors of the rotor through a commutator.

The current that flows through the stationary field winding to produce the electromagnetic field is called the excitation current. This current can be supplied from a separate external dc voltage source, in which case the generator is called a separately excited generator; or it can originate from the output of the rotor, in which case the generator is called a self-excited generator.

AC Generator

The electromagnetic field of an ac generator is usually supplied by a dc or rectified (changed from ac to dc) power source.

AUTHOR'S COMMENT: In actual practice, the magnetic field is placed on the revolving part of the generator and the ac windings are stationary. This is in order not to have high-voltage ac on the collector rings. If the ac windings were allowed to revolve in 3-phase generators, it would be necessary to have three sets of collector rings.

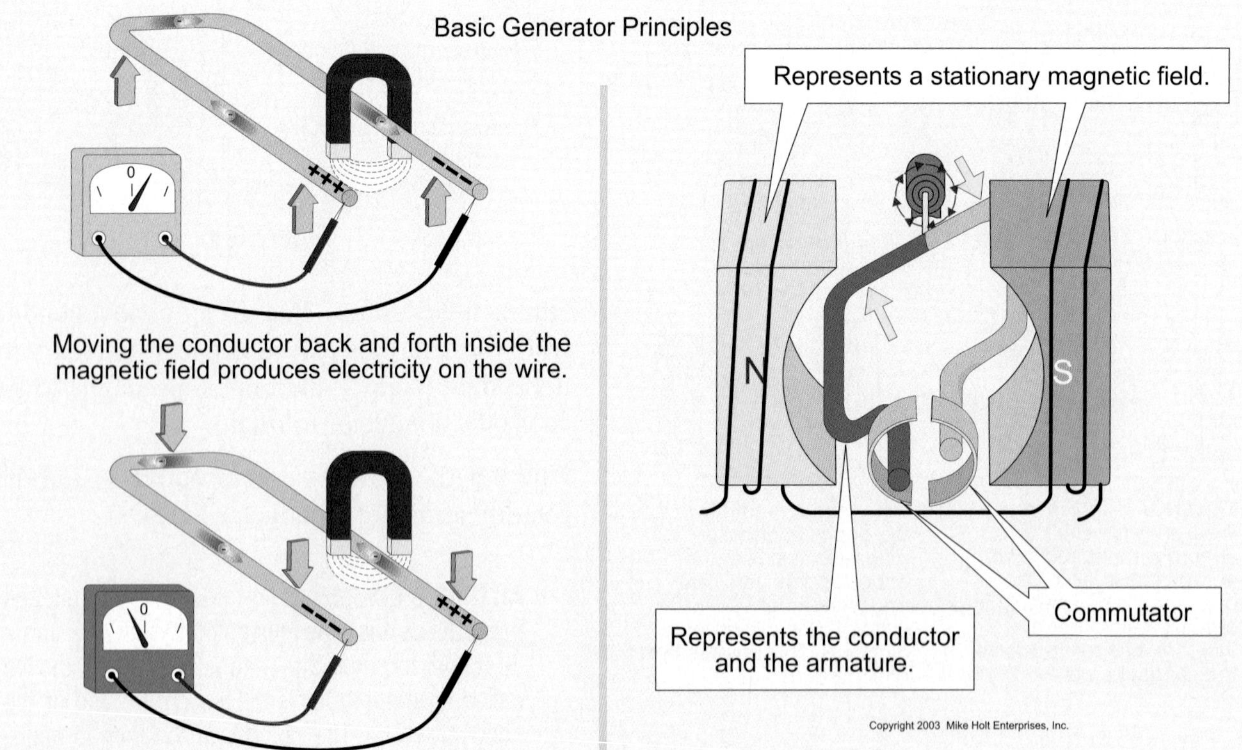
Basic Generator Principles
Moving the conductor back and forth inside the magnetic field produces electricity on the wire.
Represents a stationary magnetic field.
N
S
Commutator
Represents the conductor and the armature.
Copyright 2003 Mike Holt Enterprises, Inc.

Figure 6–7

AUTHOR'S COMMENT: The topic of generators will be covered in greater detail in Units 16 and 21.

6.4 Electromagnetic Relay

Electromagnetic relays are used in industry for many applications, including control circuits with complicated sequences and interlocks, as well as for interfacing between voltages (such as a 24V dc circuit used to start and stop a 480V ac pump motor).

An electromagnetic relay is simply a switch that uses an electromagnetic field to open or close a set of contacts. One part of the contact (switch) is fixed and the other part is moved by the attraction of the magnetic field. Figure 6–8

AUTHOR'S COMMENT: The moving element of the contact is called an armature.

Contacts

Contacts are either Normally Open (N.O.) or Normally Closed (N.C.). "Normally Open" means that the contacts are "open" (not touching each other) when power is not applied to the coil, but the contacts will close when the coil is energized, Figure 6–9A. "Normally closed" means that the contacts are closed when the coil is not energized, but will "open" when the coil is energized, Figure 6–9B. A single relay may contain both normally open and normally closed contacts. Figure 6–9C

AUTHOR'S COMMENT: *Contacts are sometimes referred to with a "Form" designation as follows:*

Form A—Normally Open
Form B—Normally Closed
Form C—Set of contacts that has one wiper arm, a normally open contact, and a normally closed contact.

On some schematics and spec sheets, contacts are sometimes referred to as simply "A" or "B" contacts.

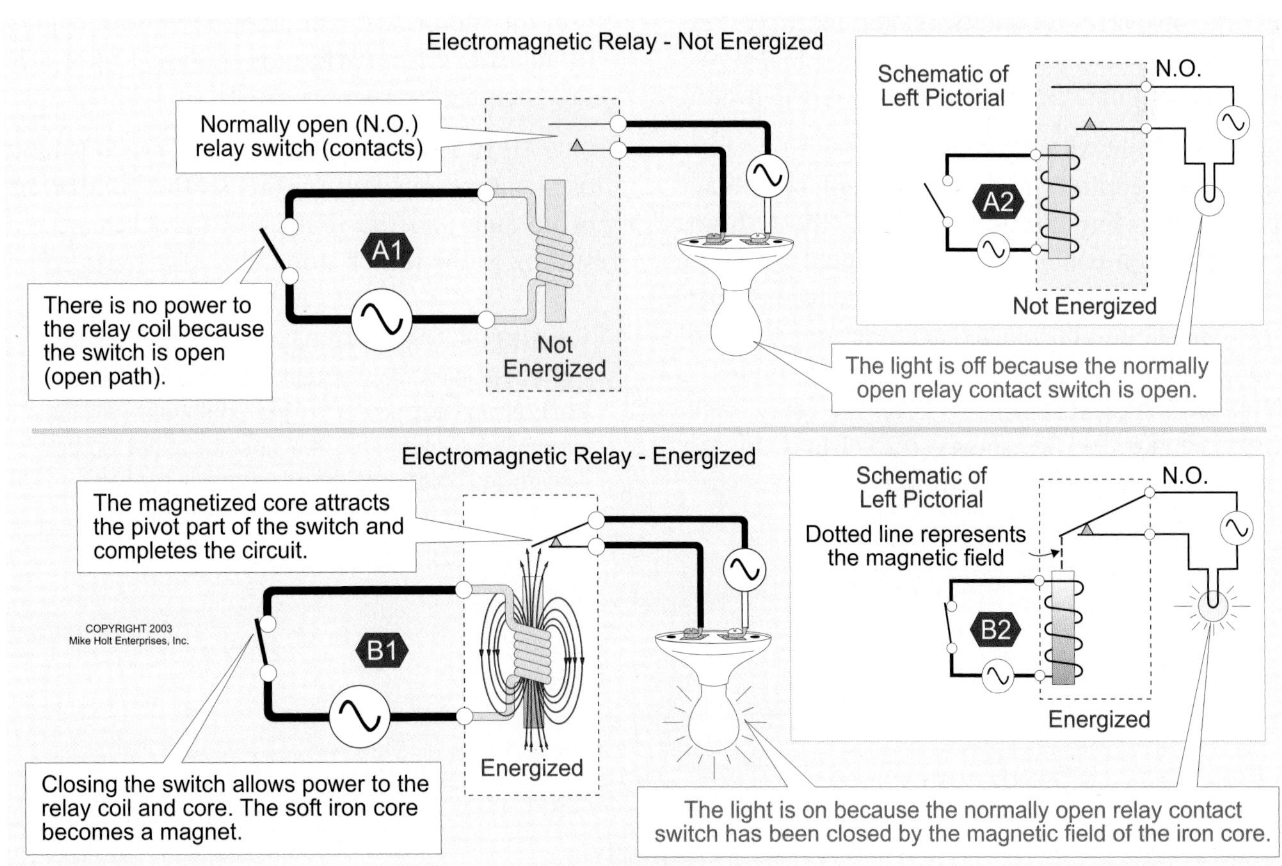

Figure 6–8

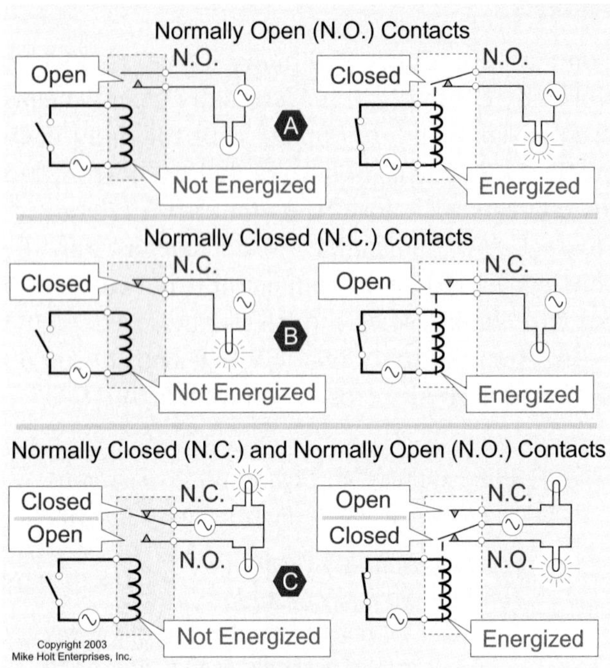

Figure 6–9

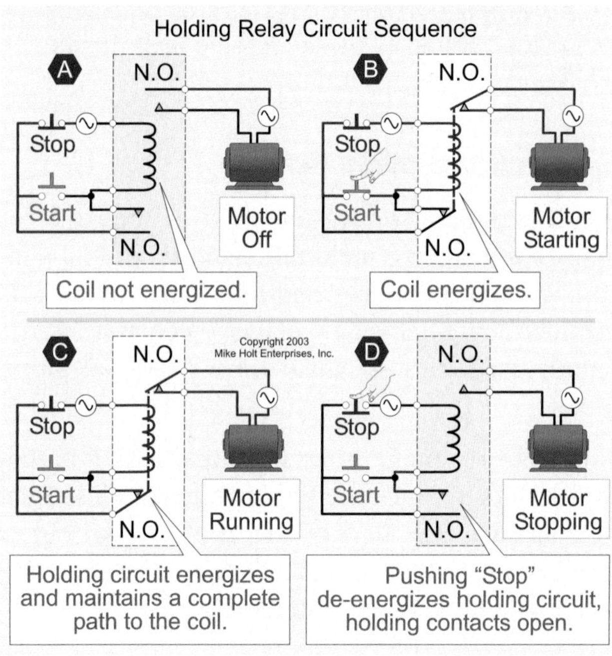

Figure 6–10

Holding Relay

A holding relay is used in many types of control circuits, primarily for safety. A holding relay contains at least two sets of contacts, one for the power circuit and the other for the control circuit.

Figure 6–10 shows a holding relay with two normally open contacts and two momentary contact pushbuttons. The auxiliary contact (the bottom, normally open contact) shown in **Figure 6–10A** of the relay is wired so that once the normally open "start" pushbutton is pushed and released, the auxiliary contact is held closed. This provides a "bypass" for current flow to keep the relay energized. **Figure 6–10A** shows the circuit in the "normal" nonenergized condition.

Figure 6–10B shows that pressing the "start" pushbutton energizes the coil. **Figure 6–10C** shows that when the coil is energized, the top contact will close, the motor will run, and the bottom contact will also close to provide the voltage to keep the relay energized.

Figure 6–10D shows that pressing the normally closed "stop" pushbutton breaks the control circuit voltage and the relay will be de-energized, resulting in the motor stopping.

> **AUTHOR'S COMMENT:** One of the safety features of the holding relay is that once the relay is de-energized, the power to the equipment will be removed. In addition, the circuit cannot be re-energized unless the "start" button is pushed.

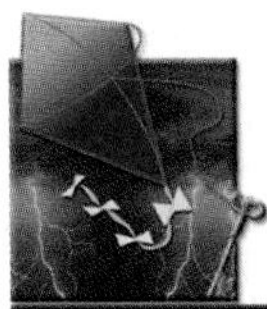

Unit 6 Summary

6.1 Basic Electric Meters

Voltmeter

Voltmeters are used to measure both dc and ac voltage. As current flows through the meter coil, the electromagnetic field of the coil exerts force on a soft iron bar that is in the center of the coil, causing it to move against spring tension and, in turn, causing the pointer attached to the bar to move.

The greater the voltage, the greater the current flow through the meter; the greater the magnetic field produced, the farther the iron bar is drawn into the coil and the greater the movement of the pointer.

DC Voltmeter

Voltmeters are connected in parallel with the circuit and measure the difference of potential between the two test leads. If it is unknown which is more positive or negative, momentarily touch the leads to the circuit in the locations to measure the dc voltage; if the meter pegs to the left, simply reverse the leads so that deflection is in the correct direction.

DC Ammeter

DC ammeters are used to measure dc current. In meters that are built for direct connection, actual circuit current is connected in series with the meter coil.

As the full current of the circuit flows through the meter coil, the magnetic field causes the meter needle to deflect. The greater the current flow through the coil, the greater the magnetic field produced by the coil, and the greater the deflection of the needle.

Measuring currents larger than 10mA with a directly connected meter often requires the use of a resistor, called a shunt, in parallel with the meter movement's coil. The resistance of the shunt is a known value, in relation to the internal resistance of the meter, and so the current that travels through the shunt is a known multiple of the current that travels through the meter.

If a dc ammeter is accidentally connected in parallel with the load, the meter will operate at the source voltage and the current flowing through the meter will be extremely high. This will likely destroy the meter if it is not internally protected against this condition.

When dc ammeters are connected in series with the circuit, dc current polarity (+ or –) must be observed. If the meter is connected in reverse polarity, the meter coil will move in the opposite direction.

To prevent damaging the meter from excessive current, start with the highest possible ampere setting.

Clamp-on AC Ammeter

Clamp-on ac ammeters are used to measure ac currents. A clamp-on ammeter has a coil that is clamped around the conductor and detects the rising and falling magnetic field around the conductor. The expanding and collapsing magnetic field around the conductor being tested induces a voltage in the sensing coil, which sends induced current to the meter coil.

Ohmmeters

Ohmmeters are used to measure the resistance or opposition to current flow of a circuit or component. An ohmmeter has a moving coil and a dc power supply (battery) and it is connected in series with the resistor being measured.

As current flows through the coil of the ohmmeter, the magnetic field around the coil draws in the soft iron bar. The greater the current flow through the circuit, the greater the magnetic field produced inside the coil, and the farther the iron bar is drawn into the coil, moving the pointer further.

Wheatstone Bridge

The Wheatstone Bridge is used for extremely accurate resistance measurements. It consists of two known-value precision resistors, a precision variable resistor, a galvanometer (an ammeter that has its pointer in the center with no current flow through it), and an unknown resistor. When the bridge is "balanced," the galvanometer pointer is aimed straight up, indicating no current flow. To determine the value of the unknown resistor, the variable resistor is adjusted until the bridge is balanced.

Megohmmeter

The Megohmmeter, or Megger, is used to measure very high-resistance values, such as those found in cable insulation or between motor or transformer windings. Meggers use a relatively high voltage (500 to 1,000V) in order to determine the resistance in megohms (one million ohms).

6.2 Electric Motor

The electric motor works on the principle of the attracting and repelling forces of a magnetic field. The electromagnetic field around the conductor, created by the current flow through the conductor interacting with the stationary magnetic field of a dc motor, causes the free moving conductor to move.

Motor Components

The stationary magnetic field of a dc motor will be either a permanent magnet or an electromagnet. This stationary component is called the "Stator." The conductor that rotates between the stationary magnetic field poles of the stator is called the "Rotor" or "Armature."

Understanding Motor Motion

The repelling force of similar magnetic polarities and the attracting force of opposite polarities cause the armature of the motor to rotate.

For a dc motor to function properly so that current will flow in the same direction through the magnetic field, a device called a commutator is placed on the end of the conductor loop.

6.3 Electrical Generator

In a generator, the rotor is forced to rotate by a "prime mover," while it is being subjected to the magnetic field of the stator. The movement of the magnetic field through the conductor (rotor) forces the electrons in the conductor to move, thereby producing electrical potential or voltage.

DC Generator

A dc generator requires the magnetic field of the stationary field (stator) to be produced from a permanent magnetic or electromagnetic field that is always in the same direction. The dc output is taken from the rotating conductors of the rotor through a commutator.

The current that flows through the stationary field winding to produce the electromagnetic field is called the excitation current.

AC Generator

The electromagnetic field of an ac generator is usually supplied by a dc or rectified (changed from ac to dc) power source. In actual practice, the magnetic field is placed on the revolving part of the generator and the ac windings are stationary.

6.4 Electromagnetic Relay

An electromagnetic relay is simply a switch that uses an electromagnetic field to open or close a set of contacts. One part of the contact (switch) is fixed and the other part is moved by the attraction of the magnetic field.

Contacts

"Normally Open" means that the contacts are "open" (not touching each other) when power is not applied to the coil, but the contacts will close when power is applied to the coil.

"Normally Closed" means that the contacts are closed when the relay is not energized, but will "open" when the relay is energized. A single relay may contain both normally open and normally closed contacts.

Holding Relay

A holding relay is used primarily for safety. A holding relay contains at least two sets of contacts, one for the power circuit and the other for the control circuit.

One of the safety features of the holding relay is that once the relay is de-energized, the power to the equipment will be removed. In addition, the circuit cannot be re-energized unless the "start" button is pushed.

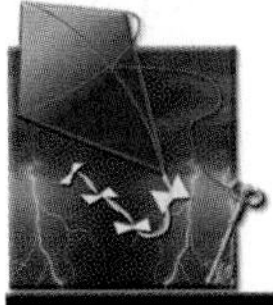

Unit 6 Conclusion

You can now see that magnetism plays a big role in electrical work. The principles of magnetism allow us to measure voltage, current, and resistance. They allow us to do that with input devices that don't even directly contact the circuit under test.

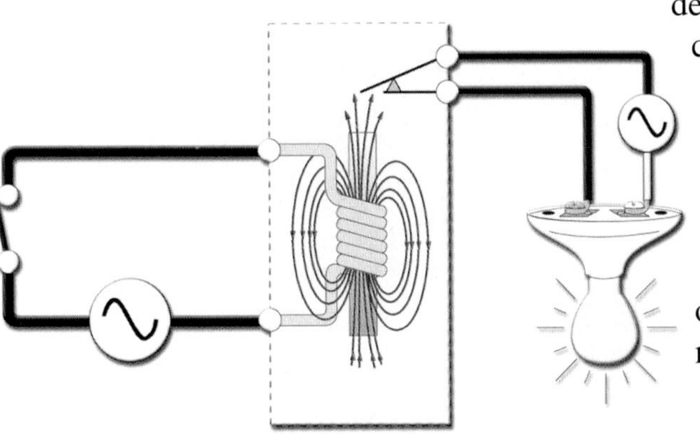

These principles also allow us to generate electricity in the first place. Using these same principles in a motor, we can convert electricity to motion, and we can control the actions of electrical circuits with coil-operated contacts, such as those in electromechanical relays.

Words to Live By: *The bridge you burn now may be the one you have to cross later.*

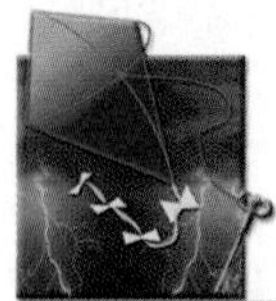

Unit 6 Practice Questions

6.1 Basic Electric Meters

1. Voltmeters are connected in _____ with the circuit and measure the difference of potential between the two test leads.

   (a) series (b) parallel (c) series-parallel (d) none of these

2. DC ammeters of the direct connection type must be connected in _____ with the power source and the load. If connected in reverse polarity, the coil will move in the opposite direction.

   (a) series (b) parallel (c) series-parallel (d) none of these

3. A clamp-on ac ammeter has a coil that is clamped around the conductor and detects the rising and falling _____ field being produced due to the ac flow through the conductor.

   (a) static (b) current (c) power (d) magnetic

4. Ohmmeters measure the _____ or opposition to current flow of a circuit or component.

   (a) voltage (b) current (c) power (d) resistance

5. The Wheatstone Bridge meter is used for extremely accurate _____ measurements.

   (a) voltage (b) current (c) power (d) resistance

6. The megger is used to measure very high-_____ values, such as those found in cable insulation, or motor and transformer windings.

   (a) voltage (b) current (c) power (d) resistance

6.2 Electric Motor

7. The electric motor works on the principle of the attracting and repelling forces of _____ fields.

   (a) voltage (b) current (c) power (d) magnetic

8. The stationary magnetic field of a dc motor, called a _____, will be a permanent magnet or an electromagnet.

   (a) winding (b) rotor (c) stator (d) none of these

9. The conductor that rotates between the stationary magnetic field poles of the stator is called the _____.

(a) winding (b) rotor (c) armature (d) b or c

6.3 Electrical Generator

10. The _____ of a generator is forced to rotate while it is being subjected to the magnetic field of the stator.

(a) winding (b) rotor (c) stator (d) b or c

6.4 Electromagnetic Relay

11. An electromagnetic relay is a switch that uses an electromagnetic field to open or close its contacts. One part of the contact is fixed and the other moves by the attraction of the electromagnetic field.

(a) True (b) False

12. "Normally Open" means that the contacts are open when power is applied to the coil, but will close when the coil is energized.

(a) True (b) False

13. "Normally Closed" means the contacts are closed when the coil is energized, but will open when the coil is energized.

(a) True (b) False

14. A holding relay is primarily used for worker convenience. A holding relay contains at least two sets of contacts, one for the power circuit and the other for the control circuit.

(a) True (b) False

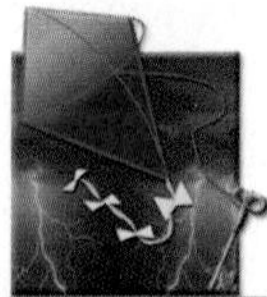

Chapter 1 Final Exam

Unit 1—Matter

1.2 Atomic Theory

1. Because of their light weight, _____ actively participate in the transfer of energy.

   (a) electrons (b) protons (c) neutrons (d) nuclei

1.5 Charged Material (Static Charge)

2. Electrostatic charge is due to an excess of, or a deficiency of, electrons between objects that have been separated.

   (a) True (b) False

3. Providing a path to the earth often helps reduce electrostatic charge.

   (a) True (b) False

1.6 Neutralizing a Charge

4. The discharge of electrons from a negatively charged object is sometimes seen as an arc, and the arc distance is a function of the _____ between the bodies.

   (a) static voltage (b) dielectric (c) a and b (d) a or b

1.7 Lightning

5. Lightning frequently terminates to a point of elevation and it strikes nonmetallic as well as metallic objects with the same frequency.

   (a) True (b) False

6. The termination of the lighting stroke is unlikely to ignite combustible materials.

   (a) True (b) False

1.8 Lightning Protection

7. Lightning protection is intended to protect the building structure itself, as well as the electrical equipment on or inside the building structure.

   (a) True (b) False

Unit 2—Electron Theory

2.4 Conductors

8. Conductive materials have one, two, or three valence electrons. Elements with one valence electron, such as silver, copper, and gold, make the best electrical conductors.

(a) True (b) False

2.8 Compounds

9. Compounds can change the electrical characteristics of an individual atom. For example, the insulating aluminum-oxide compound is very difficult to break and it often results in the overheating of aluminum conductors at their terminals.

(a) True (b) False

Unit 3—Magnetism

3.3 Magnetic Compass

10. The north end of the compass needle is actually the south pole of the compass needle seeking the earth's magnetic north pole.

(a) True (b) False

3.5 Magnetic Properties

11. Nonmagnetic metals are ferrous, meaning they do not contain any iron, and cannot be magnetized.

(a) True (b) False

12. Soft iron is used for temporary magnets.

(a) True (b) False

3.8 Demagnetizing Magnets

13. If a permanent magnet is struck with a hammer, it will lose some of its magnetism; each subsequent blow helps the molecules return to their original random positions.

(a) True (b) False

3.9 Magnetic Lines of Force

14. Magnetic lines of force can cross each other and they are called flux lines.

(a) True (b) False

3.10 Magnetic Materials

15. The law of attraction and repulsion of magnets states that like poles attract and unlike poles oppose each other.

    (a) True (b) False

3.12 Retentivity

16. Soft iron can be used to make a stronger magnet than hard steel, but the instant the magnetizing force is removed, the soft iron loses all of its magnetism.

    (a) True (b) False

Unit 4—Electricity

4.1 Electrical Current Flow (Electricity)

17. The movement of electrons to perform a useful function is called static electricity.

    (a) True (b) False

4.2 Electricity

18. It is not the force of the magnetic field through a conductor that produces electricity; it is the relative motion of the field to the electrons within the conductor that produces the movement of electrons.

    (a) True (b) False

4.3 Useful Purposes of Electricity

19. Electroplating is a process where metal from one surface is removed to another surface because of a chemical action caused by electrical current.

    (a) True (b) False

4.4 Danger of Electricity

20. People become injured and death occurs when voltage pushes electrons through the human body, causing it to go into ventricular fibrillation.

    (a) True (b) False

21. The severity of an electric shock is dependent on the current flowing through the body, which is impacted by circuit voltage and contact resistance.

    (a) True (b) False

22. An electrical arc blast can approach ______, which vaporizes metal parts and produces an explosive, and deadly pressure wave.

(a) 10,000°F (b) 15,000°F (c) 25,000°F (d) 30,000°F

4.5 National Electrical Code

23. To ensure the minimum practical safeguarding of persons and property from the use of electricity, all premises wiring must be installed in accordance with the *National Electrical Code (NEC).*

(a) True (b) False

Unit 5—Electromagnetism

5.1 Electromagnetism in a Wire

24. The direction of the electromagnetic field around a conductor because of current flow is determined by the right-hand rule as it relates to electron theory.

(a) True (b) False

5.3 Field Interaction

25. If a conductor carrying current is next to another conductor carrying current in the opposite direction, the electromagnetic field attempts to pull the conductors apart.

(a) True (b) False

Unit 6—Uses of Electromagnetism

6.1 Basic Electric Meters

26. Voltmeters are connected in _____ with the circuit and measure the difference of potential between the two test leads.

(a) series (b) parallel (c) series-parallel (d) none of these

27. A clamp-on ac ammeter has a coil that is clamped around the conductor and detects the rising and falling _____ field being produced due to the ac flow through the conductor.

(a) static (b) current (c) power (d) magnetic

28. Ohmmeters measure the _____ or opposition to current flow of a circuit or component.

(a) voltage (b) current (c) power (d) resistance

29. The megger is used to measure very high-_____ values, such as those found in cable insulation, or motor and transformer windings.

(a) voltage (b) current (c) power (d) resistance

6.2 Electric Motor

30. The electric motor works on the principle of the attracting and repelling forces of _____ fields.

(a) voltage (b) current (c) power (d) magnetic

31. The stationary magnetic field of a dc motor, called a __________, will be a permanent magnet or an electromagnet.

(a) winding (b) rotor (c) stator (d) none of these

32. The conductor that rotates between the stationary magnetic field poles of the stator is called the _____.

(a) winding (b) rotor (c) armature (d) b or c

6.3 Electrical Generator

33. The _____ of a generator is forced to rotate while it is being subjected to the magnetic field of the stator.

(a) winding (b) rotor (c) stator (d) b or c

6.4 Electromagnetic Relay

34. An electromagnetic relay is a switch that uses an electromagnetic field to open or close its contacts. One part of the contact is fixed and the other moves by the attraction of the electromagnetic field.

(a) True (b) False

35. A holding relay is primarily used for worker convenience.

(a) True (b) False

Chapter 2
Basic Electricity

Unit 7 – The Electrical Circuit

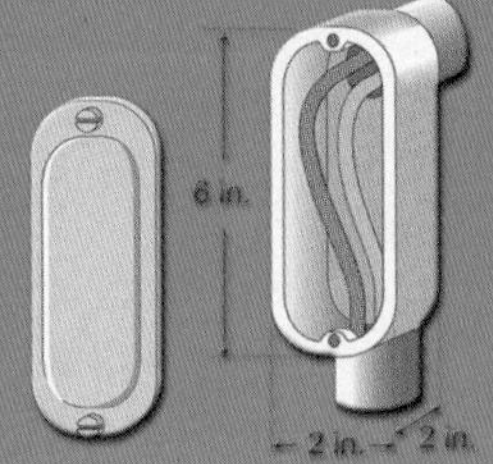

Unit 8 – Math

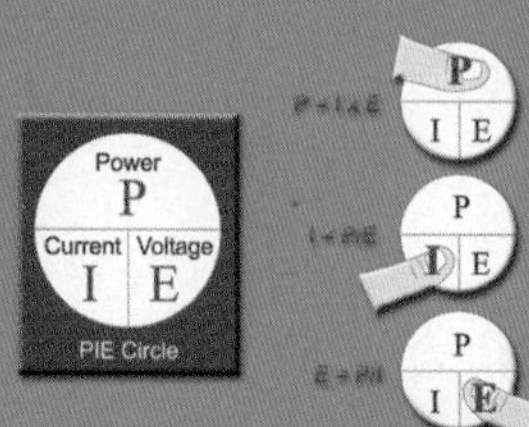

Unit 9 – Electrical Formulas

Notes

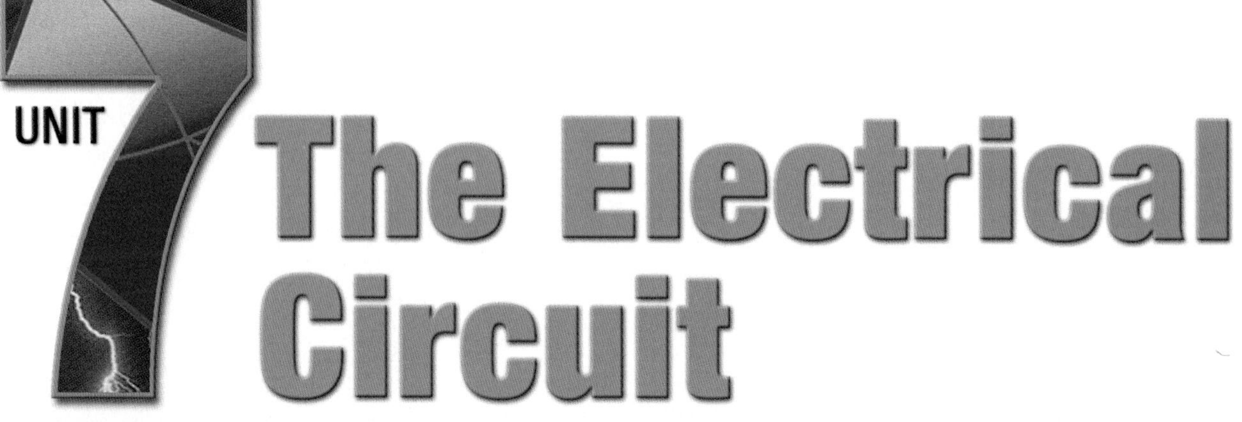

UNIT 7 The Electrical Circuit

Introduction

Once you know the basic terminology of electrical circuits, you can understand how they work. For example, can you define volt, ampere, or ohm? What does impedance do in a circuit, and how does it relate to the voltage or the current?

If you know the answers to the questions just posed, you will have no problem understanding how to work with Ohm's Law or the basic power equation. That means you'll be able to use electrical theory to solve real electrical problems.

7.1 The Electrical Circuit

The movement of electrons for the production of work can be compared to the movement of water. A pump driven by any independent force (water, wind, etc.) circulates the water in the closed-loop system. The water rotates the turbine and the turbine can be used to produce work. Figure 7–1

Electrical current is the movement of electrons that flow from the power source through the electrical circuit of the appliance or equipment and then return to the power source. The complete path the electrons take is called an electrical circuit. Figure 7–2

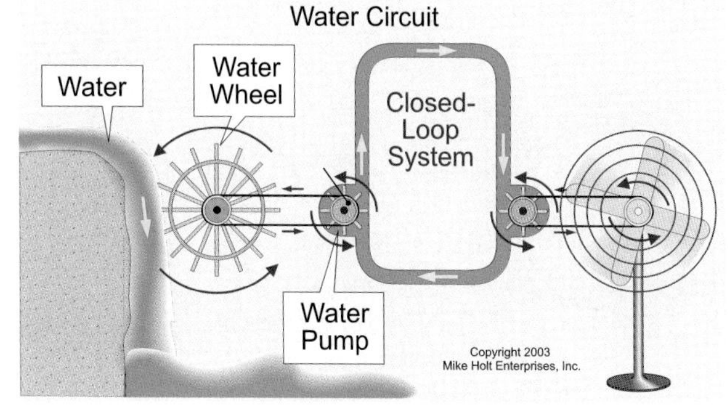

Figure 7–1

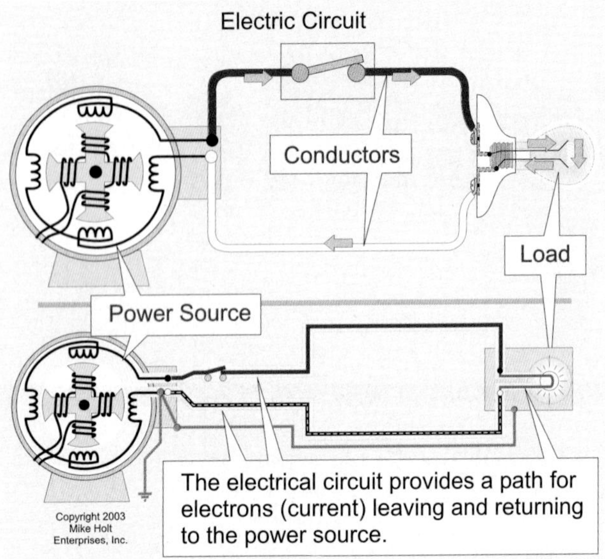

Figure 7-2

Electric current is produced by forcing electrons to move through an electrical circuit. For current to flow from the power source through the load and then back to the power source, the current flow path must be conductive.

The amount of electrical work (watts) that can be performed by the moving electrons, and the quantity of electrons that are forced to move (amperes), is dependent on the circuit pressure (voltage) and the circuit's opposition to the flow of electrons (resistance). **Figure 7–3**

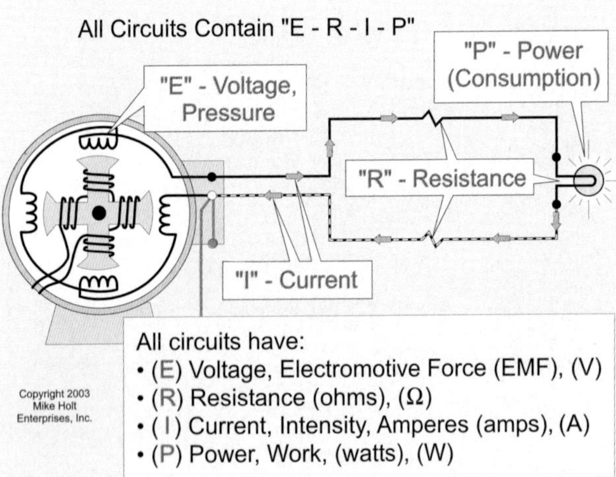

Figure 7–3

7.2 Electron Current Flow Theory

According to the "electron current flow theory," electrons flow away from the negative terminal of the source (where there is an excess of electrons), through the circuit and load, toward the positive terminal of the source (where there is a deficiency of electrons). **Figure 7–4**

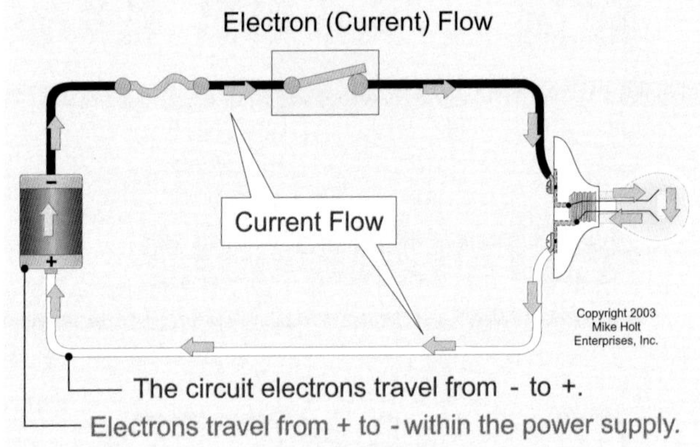

Figure 7–4

7.3 Conventional Current Flow Theory

Hundreds of years ago, it was thought that electrons traveled from positive to negative, but today we know that electrons travel from negative to positive. Even though we know that the conventional current flow theory was wrong, many textbooks, references and electrical semantics still continue to use this theory.

7.4 Voltage (Pressure)

The water pump is used to produce the pressure necessary to move the water. The greater the force used to rotate the impeller blades of the water pump, the greater the output water pressure. The greater the output water pressure, the greater the work that can be performed by the circulating water.

In electrical terms, the water pump would be equivalent to the electrical generator. The generator's rotating magnetic field through the conductor forces the electrons in the conductor to move, thereby producing electrical pressure.

The electrical pressure (output voltage) created by the rotating magnetic field in a generator is dependent upon the intensity of the magnetic field and the speed at which the field rotates. For example, a generator turning at 1,800 rpm to produce 30 Hz will produce 60 Hz at 3,600 rpm. The voltage produced at 60 Hz will be greater than the voltage at 30 Hz, assuming the iron in the stator has not reached its saturation point.

Electrical pressure is called "Electromotive Force" (EMF), "Potential," and "Voltage," and it is measured by the unit called the "Volt," named in honor of Alessandro Volta who invented the first electric battery. The circuit pressure is often abbreviated by the letters "E" for electromotive force or "V" for voltage.

7.5 Resistance

The piping that contains the water would be considered the conductor of a circuit. If a person took a water hose that had water flowing through it and squeezed or kinked the hose, it would make the flow of water more difficult, and less water would flow.

Similarly, adding resistance to an electrical circuit makes it more difficult for the electrons in the circuit to flow, resulting in fewer electrons completing the circuit. Resistance can be thought of as "restricting" the flow of electrons in the circuit. Every component of an electrical circuit (load and conductors) contains resistance, including the power supply (batteries, generators, and transformers).

Resistance is abbreviated by the letter "R," and is measured by the unit called "Ohm" in honor of the German physicist Georg Simon Ohm (1787-1854), who formulated the relationship between current, electromotive force, and resistance, known as "Ohm's Law."

Conductor Resistance

Smaller conductors have greater resistance and larger conductors have low resistance. For example, according to the *NEC*, the resistance of an 18 AWG conductor is 8Ω per 1,000 ft and the resistance of a 12 AWG conductor, with a cross-sectional area four times larger, is 2Ω. **Figure 7–5**

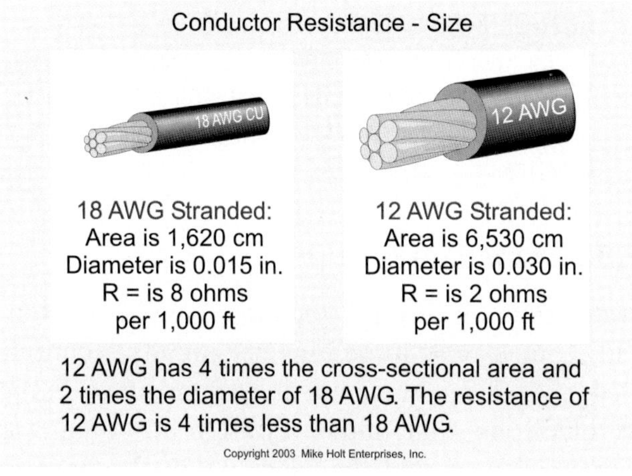

Conductor Resistance - Size
18 AWG CU
12 AWG
18 AWG Stranded:
Area is 1,620 cm
Diameter is 0.015 in.
R = is 8 ohms
per 1,000 ft
12 AWG Stranded:
Area is 6,530 cm
Diameter is 0.030 in.
R = is 2 ohms
per 1,000 ft
12 AWG has 4 times the cross-sectional area and 2 times the diameter of 18 AWG. The resistance of 12 AWG is 4 times less than 18 AWG.
Copyright 2003 Mike Holt Enterprises, Inc.

Figure 7–5

AUTHOR'S COMMENT: Unless identified otherwise, all conductors are considered copper.

The resistance also varies with the conductor material. For example, an aluminum conductor has a greater resistance to the flow of electrons than an equivalent size copper conductor. **Figure 7–6**

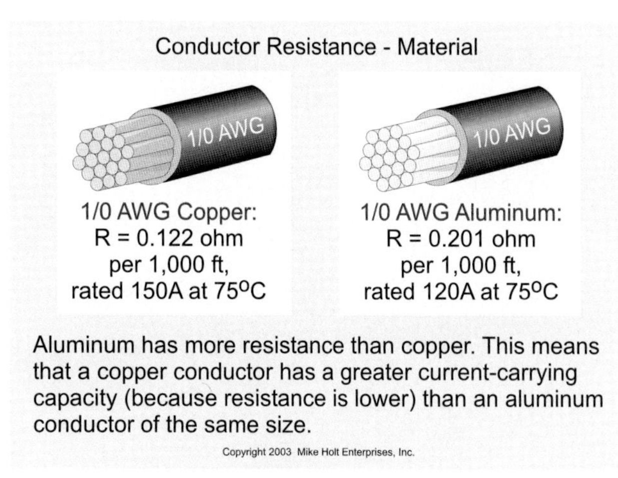

Conductor Resistance - Material
1/0 AWG
1/0 AWG
1/0 AWG Copper:
R = 0.122 ohm
per 1,000 ft,
rated 150A at 75°C
1/0 AWG Aluminum:
R = 0.201 ohm
per 1,000 ft,
rated 120A at 75°C
Aluminum has more resistance than copper. This means that a copper conductor has a greater current-carrying capacity (because resistance is lower) than an aluminum conductor of the same size.
Copyright 2003 Mike Holt Enterprises, Inc.

Figure 7–6

- The resistance of 1/0 AWG copper is 0.122Ω per 1,000 ft.
- The resistance of 1/0 AWG aluminum is 0.201Ω per 1,000 ft.

AUTHOR'S COMMENT: A 1/0 AWG copper conductor has a greater current-carrying capacity, 150A at 75°C, because its resistance is lower as compared to a 1/0 AWG aluminum conductor, which is only rated 120A.

7.6 Electric Current

Water flowing through the closed piping system can be measured in gallons per minute, abbreviated as "GPM." In electrical systems, the volume of electrons that move through a conductor (amperes) is called the intensity of the current flow and it is measured in amperes. The intensity of the circuit is abbreviated by the letters "I" or "A," in honor of Andre-Marie Ampere.

7.7 Power

Power is defined as the rate of work and it can be measured by the unit called the "Watt," which is abbreviated by the letter "W," in honor of James Watt.

AUTHOR'S COMMENT: The letter "P" is also used as the abbreviation for "Power" in electrical formulas.

Direct current (dc) power is determined by multiplying the voltage times the amperes, P = I x E. For ac power, consideration must be given to inductive reactance (the relationship between the voltage sine wave and the current sine wave). This means that ac power is not equal to E x I. But this will be discussed later in this textbook.

7.8 Electrical Formulas

Now that we have a basic understanding of the components that make up the electrical circuit, we can start applying this information when performing electrical calculations contained in Unit 9. But before we do that, we need to review basic math principles in Unit 8.

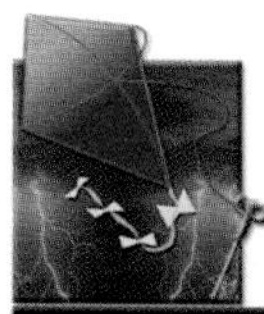

Unit 7 Summary

7.1 The Electrical Circuit

Electrical current is the movement of electrons that flow from the power source through the electrical circuit of the appliance or equipment and then return to the power source. The complete path the electrons take is called an electrical circuit.

Electric current is produced by forcing electrons to move through an electrical circuit. A power source accomplishes this by applying a negative charge at one end of the circuit (repels electrons from the source), and a positive charge to the other end (attracts the electrons to the source). For current to flow from the power source through the load and then back to the power source, the current flow path must be conductive.

The amount of electrical work that can be performed by an electrical circuit and the quantity of electrons that are forced to move (amperes) to produce work (watts) is dependent on the circuit pressure (voltage) and the circuit's opposition to the flow of electrons (resistance).

7.2 Electron Current Flow Theory

According to the "electron current flow theory," current always flows from the negative terminal of the source (where there is an excess of electrons), through the circuit and load, to the positive terminal of the source (where there is a deficiency of electrons).

7.3 Conventional Current Flow Theory

Hundreds of years ago, it was thought that electrons traveled from positive to negative. But, today we know that electrons travel from negative to positive. Even though we know that the conventional current flow theory was wrong, many textbooks, references and electrical semantics still continue to use this theory.

7.4 Voltage (Pressure)

The generator's rotating magnetic field through the conductor forces the electrons in the conductor to move, thereby producing electrical pressure.

Electrical pressure is called "Electromotive Force (EMF)," "Potential" or "Voltage," and it is measured by the unit called the "Volt," named in honor of Alessandro Volta who invented the first electric battery.

7.5 Resistance

Adding resistance to an electrical circuit makes it more difficult for the electrons in the circuit to flow back to the power supply, resulting in fewer electrons completing the circuit. The opposition can be thought of as "restricting" the flow of electrons in the circuit. Every component of an electrical circuit contains resistance, including the power supply.

Resistance is abbreviated by the letter "R," and is measured by the unit called "Ohm" in honor of the German physicist Georg Simon Ohm (1787-1854), who formulated the relationship between current, electromotive force, and resistance, known as Ohm's law.

Conductor Resistance

Smaller conductors have greater resistance and larger conductors have low resistance. The resistance also varies with the conductor material. For example, an aluminum conductor has a greater resistance to the flow of electrons than an equivalent size copper conductor.

7.6 Electric Current

In electrical systems, the volume of electrons that move through a conductor is called the intensity of the current flow and it is measured in amperes. The intensity of the circuit is abbreviated by the letters "I" or "A," in honor of Andre-Marie Ampere.

7.7 Power

Power is defined as the rate of work and it can be measured by the unit called the "Watt," which is abbreviated by the letter "W," in honor of James Watt. The letter "P" is also used as the abbreviation for "Power" in electrical formulas.

Unit 7 Conclusion

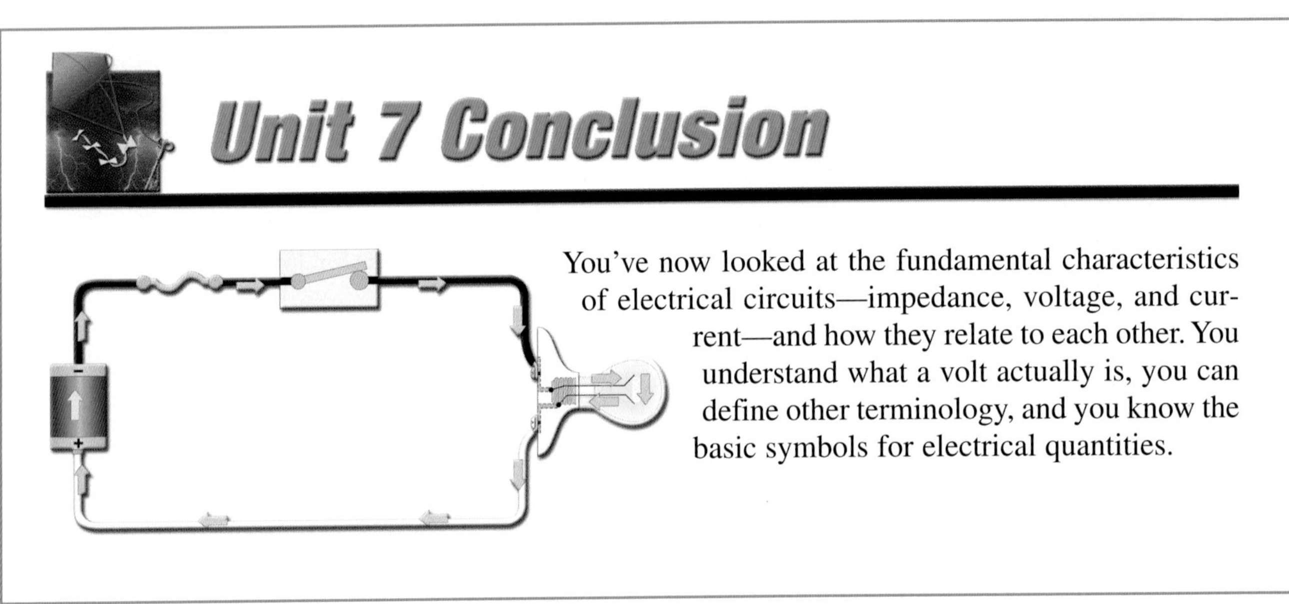

You've now looked at the fundamental characteristics of electrical circuits—impedance, voltage, and current—and how they relate to each other. You understand what a volt actually is, you can define other terminology, and you know the basic symbols for electrical quantities.

Words to Live By: *Falling down doesn't make you a failure. Staying down does.*

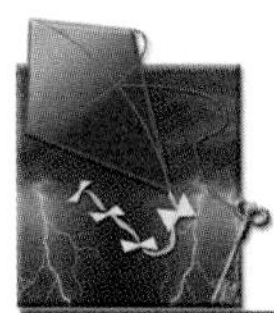

Unit 7 Practice Questions

7.1 The Electrical Circuit

1. The work that can be performed by the moving electrons is dependent on the circuit pressure and the circuit's opposition to the flow of electrons.

   (a) True (b) False

7.2 Electron Current Flow Theory

2. According to the electron current flow theory, electrons flow away from the negative terminal of the source, through the circuit and load, toward the positive terminal of the source.

   (a) True (b) False

7.3 Conventional Current Flow Theory

3. According to the conventional current flow theory, electrons travel from positive to negative.

   (a) True (b) False

7.4 Voltage (Pressure)

4. Electrical pressure is called _____, and it is measured in volts.

   (a) EMF (b) potential (c) a or b (d) none of these

7.5 Resistance

5. Every component of an electrical circuit contains resistance, except the power supply.

   (a) True (b) False

6. Smaller conductors have greater resistance and larger conductors have lower resistance.

   (a) True (b) False

7. Aluminum has a lower resistance to the flow of electrons than does copper.

   (a) True (b) False

7.6 Electric Current

8. In electrical systems, the volume of electrons that move through a conductor is called the circuit _____.

   (a) resistance (b) power (c) pressure (d) intensity

7.7 Power

9. _____ is defined as the rate of work measured by the unit called the watt.

   (a) Resistance (b) Power (c) Pressure (d) Intensity

10. DC power is determined by multiplying the electromotive force by the circuit intensity.

    (a) True (b) False

11. Power is not equal to E x I for ac circuits, because consideration must be given to inductive reactance.

    (a) True (b) False

Math

Introduction

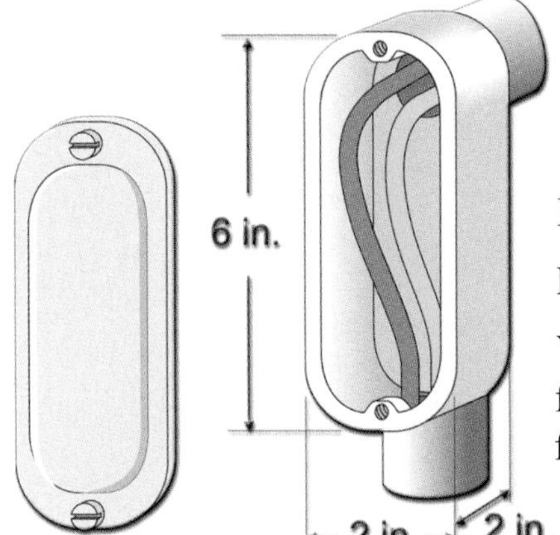

Numbers can take different forms:

Whole numbers: 1, 20, 300, 4,000, 5,000

Decimals: 0.8, 1.25, 0.75, 1.15

Fractions: $^1/_2$, $^1/_4$, $^5/_8$, $^4/_3$

Percentages: 80%, 125%, 250%, 500%

You'll need to be able to convert these numbers from one form to another and back again, because all of these number forms are part of electrical work and electrical calculations.

You'll also need to be able to do some basic algebra. Many people have a fear of algebra, but as you work through the material here you will see there is nothing to fear but fear itself.

8.1 Whole Numbers

Whole numbers are exactly what the term implies. These are numbers that do not contain any fractions, decimals, or a percentage.

8.2 Decimal

The decimal method is used to display numbers other than whole numbers, fractions or percentages; such as, 0.80, 1.25, 1.732, etc.

8.3 Fractions

A fraction represents part of a whole number. If you use a calculator for adding, dividing, subtracting, or multiplying, you need to convert the fraction to a decimal or whole number. To change a fraction to a decimal or whole number, divide the numerator (top number) by the denominator (bottom number).

Examples:

$^1/_6$ = one divided by six = 0.166
$^2/_5$ = two divided by five = 0.40
$^3/_6$ = three divided by six = 0.50
$^5/_4$ = five divided by four = 1.25
$^7/_2$ = seven divided by two = 3.5

8.4 Percentages

Use of a percentage is another method used to display a value. One hundred percent (100%) means all of the value; fifty percent (50%) means one-half of a value, and twenty-five percent (25%) means one-fourth of a value.

For convenience in multiplying or dividing by a percentage, convert the percentage value to a whole number or decimal, and then use this value for the calculation. When changing a percent value to a decimal or whole number, move the decimal point two places to the left. Figure 8–1

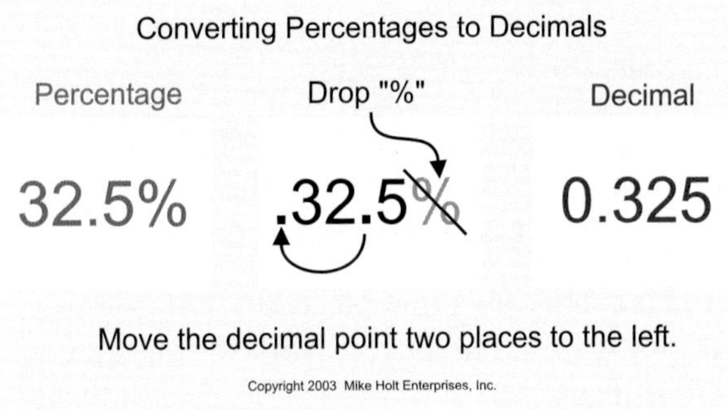

Figure 8–1

Example

Percentage	Number
32.5%	0.325
80%	0.80
125%	1.25
250%	2.50

8.5 Multiplier

When a number needs to be changed by multiplying it by a percentage, we can call this number a multiplier. The first step is to convert the percentage to a decimal, then multiply the original number by the decimal value.

Example A

An overcurrent protection device (breaker or fuse) must be sized no less than 125 percent of the continuous load. If the load were 80A, the overcurrent protection device would have to be sized no smaller than _____. Figure 8–2

(a) 80A (b) 100A
(c) 125A (d) none of these

• Answer: (b) 100A

Step 1 Convert 125 percent to a decimal: 1.25

Step 2 Multiply the value 80 by 1.25 = 100A

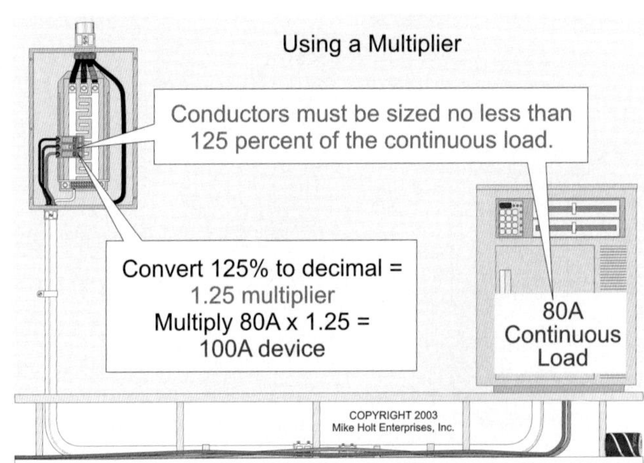

Using a Multiplier
Conductors must be sized no less than 125 percent of the continuous load.
Convert 125% to decimal = 1.25 multiplier
Multiply 80A x 1.25 = 100A device
80A Continuous Load
COPYRIGHT 2003 Mike Holt Enterprises, Inc.

Figure 8–2

Example B

The maximum continuous load on an overcurrent protection device is limited to 80 percent of the device rating. If the protective device is rated 50A, what is the maximum continuous load permitted on the protective device? Figure 8–3

(a) 80A (b) 125A
(c) 50A (d) none of these

• Answer: (d) none of these

Step 1 Convert 80 percent to a decimal: 0.80

Step 2 Multiply the value 50A by 0.80 = 40A

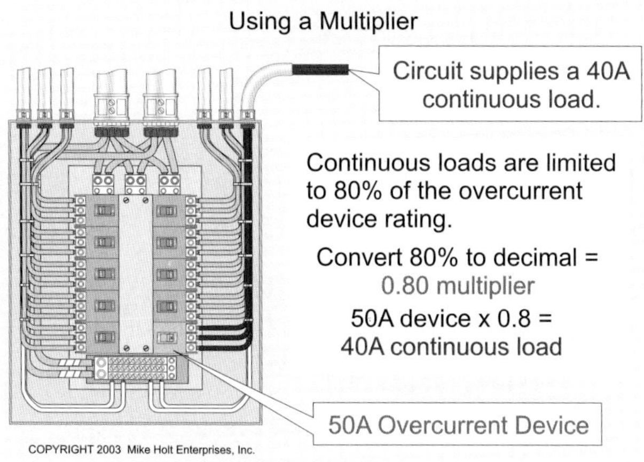

Using a Multiplier
Circuit supplies a 40A continuous load.
Continuous loads are limited to 80% of the overcurrent device rating.
Convert 80% to decimal = 0.80 multiplier
50A device x 0.8 = 40A continuous load
50A Overcurrent Device
COPYRIGHT 2003 Mike Holt Enterprises, Inc.

Figure 8–3

8.6 Percent Increase

The following steps accomplish increasing a number by a specific percentage:

Step 1 Convert the percent to a decimal value.

Step 2 Add one to the decimal value to create the multiplier.

Step 3 Multiply the original number by the multiplier (Step 2).

Example A

Increase the whole number 45 by 35 percent.

Step 1 Convert 35 percent to decimal form: 0.35

Step 2 Add one to the decimal value:
1 + 0.35 = 1.35

Step 3 Multiply 45 by the multiplier 1.35:
45 x 1.35 = 60.75

Example B

If the feeder demand load for a range is 8 kW and it is required to be increased by 15 percent, the total demand load will be _____ . Figure 8–4

(a) 8 kW (b) 15 kW
(c) 6.8 kW (d) 9.2 kW

• Answer: (d) 9.2 kW

Step 1 Convert to decimal form:
15 percent = 0.15

Step 2 Add one to the decimal:
1 + 0.15 = 1.15

Step 3 Multiply 8 by the multiplier 1.15:
8 kW x 1.15 = 9.2 kW

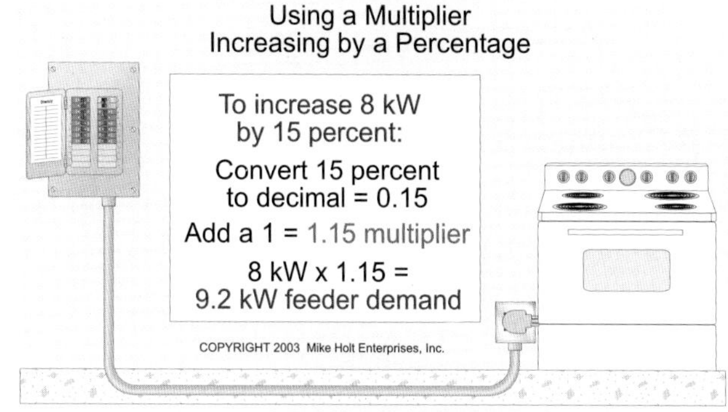

Using a Multiplier
Increasing by a Percentage
To increase 8 kW by 15 percent:
Convert 15 percent to decimal = 0.15
Add a 1 = 1.15 multiplier
8 kW x 1.15 = 9.2 kW feeder demand
COPYRIGHT 2003 Mike Holt Enterprises, Inc.

Figure 8–4

8.7 Reciprocals

The reciprocal of a number is obtained when a number is converted into a fraction with the number one as the numerator (top number). The reciprocal of a number can be determined by following these steps:

Step 1 Convert the number to a decimal value.

Step 2 Divide the value into the number one.

Example A

What is the reciprocal of 80 percent?

(a) 0.8 (b) 100%
(c) 125% (d) none of these

• Answer: (c) 125%

Step 1 Convert the 80 percent into a decimal (move the decimal two places to the left):
80 percent = 0.8

Step 2 Divide 0.8 into the number one:

$$\frac{1}{0.8} = 1.25 \text{ or } 125 \text{ percent}$$

Example B

What is the reciprocal of 125 percent?

(a) 0.8 (b) 100%
(c) 125% (d) none of these

• Answer: (a) 0.8

Step 1 Convert the 125 percent into a decimal: 125 percent = 1.25

Step 2 Divide 1.25 into the number one:

$$\frac{1}{1.25} = 0.8 \text{ or } 80 \text{ percent}$$

8.8 Squaring a Number

Squaring a number is accomplished by multiplying the number by itself.

$10^2 = 10 \times 10 = 100$

$23^2 = 23 \times 23 = 529$

Example A

What is the power consumed in watts by a 12 AWG conductor that is 200 ft long, and has a total resistance of 0.4Ω, if the current (I) in the circuit conductors is 16A?

Formula: Power = $I^2 \times R$
(Answers are rounded to the nearest 50).

(a) 50 (b) 150
(c) 100 (d) none of these

• Answer: (c) 100

$P = I^2 \times R$
$I = 16A$
$R = 0.4\Omega$
$P = 16A^2 \times 0.4\Omega$
$P = 16A \times 16A \times 0.4\Omega$
$P = 102.4W$

Example B

What is the area in square inches (sq in.) of a 1 in. raceway whose diameter is 1.049 in.?

Formula: Area = $\pi \times r^2$
$\pi = 3.14$
r = radius (is equal to 0.5 of the diameter).

(a) 1 (b) 0.86
(c) 0.34 (d) 0.5

• Answer: (b) 0.86

Area = $\pi \times r^2$
Area = $3.14 \times (0.5 \times 1.049)^2$
Area = 3.14×0.5245^2
Area = $3.14 \times (0.5245 \times 0.5245)$
Area = 3.14×0.2751
Area = 0.86 sq in.

Example C

What is the sq in. area of an 8 in. pizza? **Figure 8–5A**

(a) 50 (b) 75
(c) 25 (d) none of these

• Answer: (a) 50

Area = $\pi \times r^2$
Area = $3.14 \times (0.5 \times 8)^2$
Area = 3.14×4^2
Area = $3.14 \times 4 \times 4$
Area = 3.14×16
Area = 50 sq in.

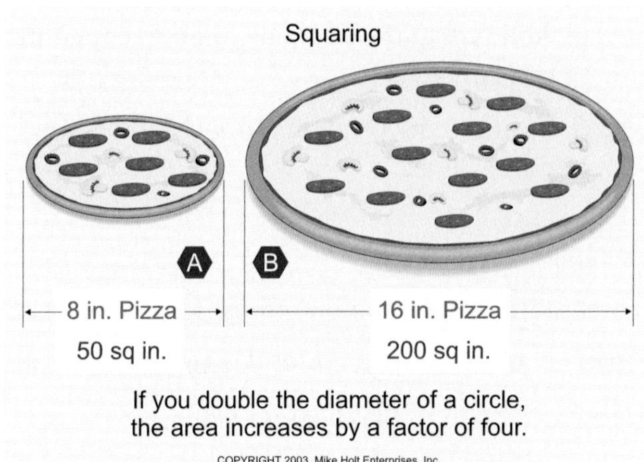

Figure 8–5

Example D

What is the sq in. area of a 16 in. pizza? **Figure 8–5B**

(a) 100 (b) 200
(c) 150 (d) none of these

• Answer: (b) 200

Area = $\pi \times r^2$
Area = $3.14 \times (0.5 \times 16)^2$
Area = 3.14×8^2
Area = $3.14 \times 8 \times 8$
Area = 3.14×64
Area = 200 sq in.

AUTHOR'S COMMENT: As you see in examples C and D, if you double the diameter of the circle, the area contained in the circle is increased by a factor of four! By the way, a large pizza is always cheaper per sq in. than a small pizza.

8.9 Square Root

Deriving the square root ($\sqrt{n}$) of a number is the opposite of squaring a number.

The square root of 36 is a number that, when multiplied by itself, gives the product 36. The $\sqrt{36}$ is equal to six (6), because six, multiplied by itself (6^2) equals the number 36.

Because it's difficult to do this manually, we'll just use the square root key of the calculator.

Example

$\sqrt{3}$: Depending on your calculator's instructions, enter the number 3 in the calculator, then press the square root key = 1.732

$\sqrt{1,000}$: enter the number 1,000, then press the square root key = 31.62

If your calculator does not have a square root key, don't worry about it. For all practical purposes of this textbook, the only number you need to know the square root of is the $\sqrt{3}$, which equals approximately 1.732.

To multiply, divide, add, or subtract a number by a square root value, determine the decimal value, then perform the math function.

Example A

$\frac{36,000W}{(208V \times \sqrt{3})}$ is equal to _____.

(a) 120A (b) 208A
(c) 360A (d) 100A

• Answer: (d) 100A

Step 1 Determine the decimal value for the $\sqrt{3} = 1.732$

Step 2 Divide 36,000W by (208V × 1.732) = 100A

Example B

The phase voltage, $\frac{208V}{\sqrt{3}}$, is equal to _____.

(a) 120V (b) 208V
(c) 360V (d) none of these

• Answer: (a) 120V

Step 1 Determine the decimal value for the $\sqrt{3} = 1.732$

Step 2 Divide 208V by 1.732 = 120V

8.10 Volume

The volume of an enclosure is expressed in cubic inches (cu in.), which is determined by multiplying the length, by the width, by the depth of the enclosure.

Example

What is the volume of a conduit body that has the dimensions 2 x 2 x 6 in.? **Figure 8–6**

(a) 20 cu in. (b) 24 cu in.
(c) 30 cu in. (d) none of these

• Answer: (b) 24 cu in.
2 x 2 x 6 = 24 cu in.

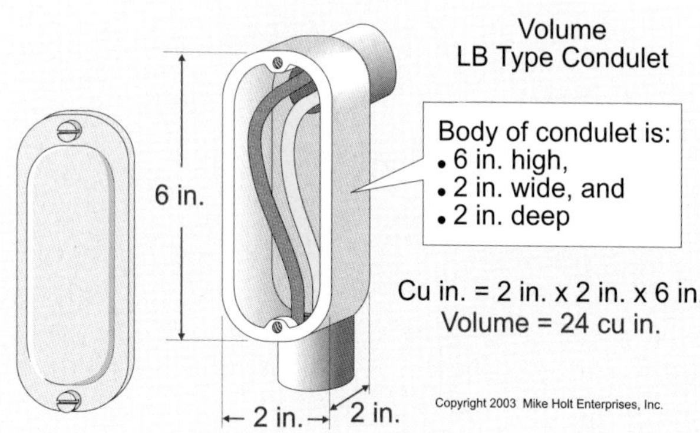

Figure 8–6

8.11 Kilo

The letter "k" in the electrical trade is used for the abbreviation of the metric prefix "kilo," which represents a value of 1,000.

Example A

What is the wattage of an 8 kW rated range?

(a) 8W (b) 8,000W
(c) 4,000W (d) none of these

• Answer: (b) 8,000W

Wattage equals kW x 1,000. In this case:
8 kW x 1,000 = 8,000W

Example B

A 300W load would have a _____ kW rating. Figure 8–7

(a) 300 kW (b) 3,000 kW
(c) 30 kW (d) 0.3 kW

• Answer: (d) 0.3 kW

$$\text{kW} = \frac{\text{Watts}}{1.000}$$

$$\text{kW} = \frac{300\text{W}}{1.000} = 0.3\text{ kW}$$

AUTHOR'S COMMENT: The use of the letter "k" is not limited to "kW." It is often used for kVA (1,000 volt-amps), and kcmil (1,000 circular mils).

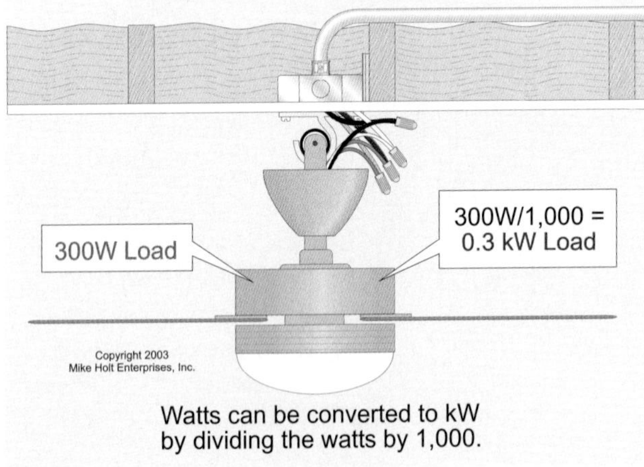
Kilo (1,000) - Converting Watts to kW
300W Load
300W/1,000 = 0.3 kW Load
Copyright 2003 Mike Holt Enterprises, Inc.
Watts can be converted to kW by dividing the watts by 1,000.

Figure 8–7

8.12 Rounding Off

There is no specific rule for rounding off, but rounding to two or three "significant figures" should be sufficient for most electrical calculations. Numbers below five are rounded down, while numbers five and above are rounded up.

Example

0.1245—fourth number is five or above = 0.125 rounded up

1.674—fourth number is below five = 1.67 rounded down

21.99—fourth number is five or above = 22 rounded up

367.2—fourth number is below five = 367 rounded down

Rounding Answers for Multiple Choice Questions

You should round your answers in the same manner as the multiple choice selections given in the question.

Example

The sum* of 12, 17, 28, and 40 is equal to _____.

(a) 70 (b) 80
(c) 90 (d) 100

• Answer: (d) 100

The sum of these values equals 97, but this is not listed as one of the choices. The multiple choice selections in this case are rounded off to the closest "tens."

*A sum is the result of adding numbers.

8.13 Parentheses

Whenever numbers are in parentheses, complete the mathematical function within the parentheses before proceeding with the rest of the problem.

What is the current of a 36,000W, 208V, 3Ø load? Figure 8–8

Formula: $\text{Ampere (I)} = \frac{\text{Watts}}{(\text{E} \times \sqrt{3})}$

(a) 50A (b) 100A
(c) 150A (d) none of these

• Answer: (b) 100A

Step 1 Perform the operation inside the parentheses first—determine the product of: 208V × 1.732 = 360

Step 2 Divide 36,000W by 360 = 100A

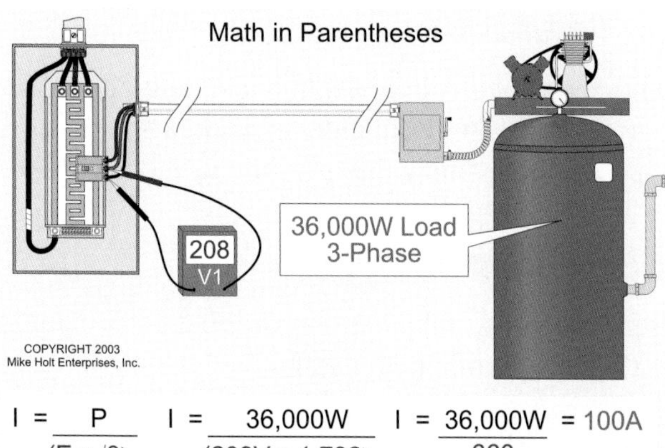

$I = \frac{P}{(E \times \sqrt{3})}$ $I = \frac{36{,}000W}{(208V \times 1.732)}$ $I = \frac{36{,}000W}{360} = 100A$

Whenever numbers are in parentheses, we must complete the mathematical function within the parentheses before proceeding with the rest of the problem.

Figure 8–8

8.14 Testing Your Answer for Reasonableness

When working with any mathematical calculation, don't just blindly do a calculation. When you perform the mathematical calculation, you need to know if the answer is greater than or less than the values given in the problem. Always do a "reality check" to be certain that your answer is not nonsense. Even the best of us make mistakes at times, so always examine your answer to make sure it makes sense!

Example

The input of a transformer is 300W; the transformer efficiency is 90 percent. Since output is always less than input because of efficiency, what is the transformer output? Figure 8–9

(a) 300W (b) 270W
(c) 333W (d) 500W

• Answer: (b) 270W

Since the output has to be less than the input (300W), you would not have to perform any mathematical calculation; the only multiple choice selection that is less than 300W is (b) 270W.

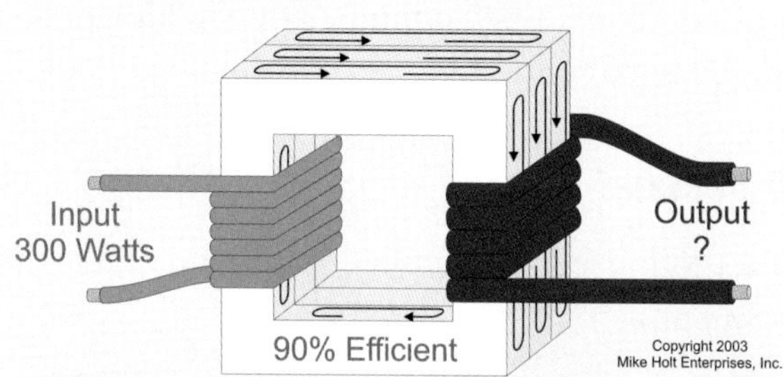

If you know the output must be less than the input where efficiency is involved, you will know the answer must be less than 300. The only multiple choice selection less than 300 is (b) 270. No calculation is necessary.

Figure 8–9

Example A

The math to get the answer was:

300W x 0.9 = 270W.

To check your answer:

$$\frac{270W}{0.9} = 300W$$

Example B

If the math was:

$$\frac{36{,}000W}{360} = 100A$$

To check your answer:

100A x 360 = 36,000W

AUTHOR'S COMMENT: One of the nice things about mathematical equations is that you can usually test to see if your answer is correct. To do this test, substitute the answer you arrived at back into the equation you are working with, and verify that it is indeed an equality. This method of checking your math will become easier once you know more of the formulas and how they relate to each other.

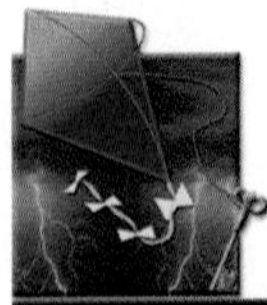

Unit 8 Summary

8.1 Whole Numbers

Numbers that do not contain any fractions, decimals, or a percentage.

8.2 Decimal

A method used to display numbers other than whole numbers.

8.3 Fractions

A fraction represents part of a whole number. To change a fraction to a decimal or whole number, divide the numerator (top number) by the denominator (bottom number).

8.4 Percentages

Percentage is another method used to display a value. To change a percent value to a decimal or whole number, move the decimal point two places to the left.

8.5 Multiplier

When a number needs to be changed by multiplying it by a percentage, the first step is to convert the percentage to a decimal, then multiply the original number by the decimal.

8.6 Percent Increase

Increasing a number by a specific percentage is accomplished by converting the percent to a decimal value, adding one to the decimal value to create the multiplier, and then multiplying the original number by the multiplier.

8.7 Reciprocals

The reciprocal of a number is obtained by converting the number to a decimal or whole number, then dividing this value into the number one.

8.8 Squaring a Number

Squaring a number is accomplished by multiplying the number by itself.

8.9 Square Root

Deriving the square root of a number is the opposite of squaring a number. Because it is difficult to do this manually, we'll just use the square root key of the calculator.

8.10 Volume

The volume of an enclosure is expressed in cubic inches (cu in.), which is determined by multiplying the length, by the width, by the depth of the enclosure.

8.11 Kilo

The letter "k" in the electrical trade is used for the abbreviation of the metric prefix "kilo," which represents a value of 1,000.

8.12 Rounding Off

There is no specific rule for rounding off, but rounding to two or three "significant figures" should be sufficient for most electrical calculations. Numbers below five are rounded down, while numbers five and above are rounded up.

Rounding Answers for Multiple Choice Questions

You should round your answer in the same manner as the answers given in the question.

8.13 Parentheses

Whenever numbers are in parentheses, complete the mathematical function within the parentheses before proceeding with the rest of the problem.

8.14 Testing Your Answer for Reasonableness

When you perform the mathematical calculation, you need to know if the answer is greater than or less than the values given in the problem. Always do a "reality check" to be certain that your answer is not nonsense. Even the best of us make mistakes at times, so always examine your answer to make sure it makes sense!

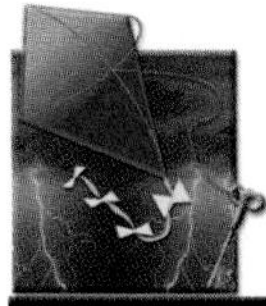

Unit 8 Conclusion

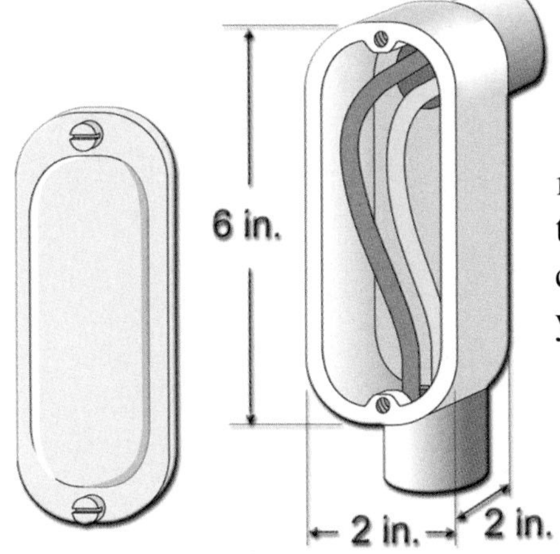

You've now worked through converting numbers from one form to another. If you had a fear of algebra when you started, that fear should be gone by now. As you work through the practice questions, you'll see you have mastered the mathematical concepts and are ready to put them to use in electrical formulas. Always remember to check your answer when you are done—then you'll know you have a right answer every time.

Words to Live By: *The measure of a man's character is not what he gets from his ancestors, but what he leaves his descendants.*

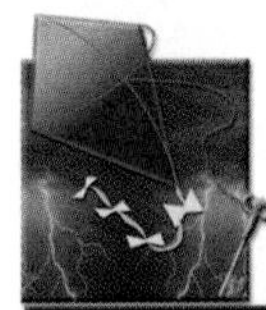

Unit 8 Practice Questions

8.3 Fractions

1. The decimal equivalent for the fraction "$^1/_2$" is _____.

(a) 0.5 (b) 5 (c) 2 (d) 0.2

2. The decimal equivalent for the fraction "$^4/_{18}$" is _____.

(a) 4.5 (b) 3.5 (c) 2.5 (d) 0.2

8.4 Percentages

3. To change a percent value to a decimal or whole number, move the decimal point two places to the _____.

(a) right (b) left (c) depends (d) none of these

4. The decimal equivalent for "75 percent" is _____.

(a) 0.075 (b) 0.75 (c) 7.5 (d) 75

5. The decimal equivalent for "225 percent" is _____.

(a) 225 (b) 22.5 (c) 2.25 (d) 0.225

6. The decimal equivalent for "300 percent" is _____.

(a) 0.03 (b) 0.3 (c) 3 (d) 30.0

8.5 Multiplier

7. The method of increasing a number by another number is called the _____ method.

(a) percentage (b) decimal (c) fraction (d) multiplier

8. An overcurrent protection device (breaker or fuse) must be sized no less than 125 percent of the continuous load. If the load were 16A, the overcurrent protection device would have to be sized at no less than _____.

(a) 20A (b) 23A (c) 17A (d) 30A

9. The maximum continuous load on an overcurrent protection device is limited to 80 percent of the device rating. If the overcurrent device is rated 100A, the maximum continuous load is _____.

(a) 72A (b) 80A (c) 90A (d) 125A

8.6 Percent Increase

10. The feeder demand load for an 8 kW load, increased by 20 percent is _____.

(a) 8 kW (b) 9.6 kW (c) 6.4 kW (d) 10 kW

8.7 Reciprocals

11. What is the reciprocal of 1.25?

(a) 0.8 (b) 1.10 (c) 1.25 (d) 1.5

12. A continuous load requires an overcurrent protection device sized no smaller than 125 percent of the load. What is the maximum continuous load permitted on a 100A overcurrent protection device?

(a) 100A (b) 125A (c) 80A (d) none of these

8.8 Squaring a Number

13. Squaring a number is accomplished by multiplying the number by itself.

(a) True (b) False

14. What is the power consumed in watts by a 12 AWG conductor that is 100 ft long and has a resistance (R) of 0.2Ω, when the current (I) in the circuit is 16A? Formula: Power = $I^2 \times R$.

(a) 75 (b) 50 (c) 100 (d) 200

15. What is the area in sq in. of a 2 in. raceway? Formula: Area = $\pi \times r^2$, $\pi = 3.14$, r = radius, which equals $^1/_2$ of the diameter

(a) 1 sq. in. (b) 2 sq. in. (c) 3 sq. in. (d) 4 sq. in.

16. The numeric equivalent of 4^2 is _____.

(a) 2 (b) 8 (c) 16 (d) 32

17. The numeric equivalent of 12^2 is _____.

(a) 3.46 (b) 24 (c) 144 (d) 1728

8.9 Square Root

18. Deriving the square root of a number is almost the same as squaring a number.

(a) True (b) False

19. What is square root of 1,000 ($\sqrt{1,000}$)?

(a) 3 (b) 32 (c) 100 (d) 500

20. The square root of 3 ($\sqrt{3}$) is _____.

(a) 1.732 (b) 9 (c) 729 (d) 1.5

8.10 Volume

21. The volume of an enclosure is expressed in _____, and it is calculated by multiplying the length, by the width, by the depth of the enclosure.

(a) cubic inches (b) weight (c) inch-pounds (d) none of these

22 What is the volume (in inches) of a 4 x 4 x 1.5 in. box?

(a) 20 sq. in. (b) 24 sq. in. (c) 30 sq. in. (d) 33 sq. in.

8.11 Kilo

23. What is the kW of a 75W load?

(a) 75 kW (b) 7.5 kW (c) 0.75 kW (d) 0.075 kW

8.12 Rounding Off

24. The sum of 2, 7, 8 and 9 is equal to _____.

(a) 20 (b) 25 (c) 30 (d) 35

8.13 Parentheses

25. What is the maximum distance that two 14 AWG conductors can be run if they carry 16A and the maximum allowable voltage drop is 10V?

$$D = \frac{(CM \text{ x } VD)}{(2 \times K \text{ x } I)}$$

$$D = \frac{(4{,}160 \text{ cm x } 10V)}{(2 \text{ x } 12.9\Omega \text{ x } 16A)}$$

(a) 50 ft (b) 75 ft (c) 100 ft (d) 150 ft

26. What is the current in amperes of an 18kW, 208V, 3Ø load?

Formula: $I = \frac{P}{(E \times \sqrt{3})}$ $\frac{18{,}000 \text{ VA}}{(208\text{V} \times 1.732)}$

(a) 25A (b) 50A (c) 100A (d) 150A

8.14 Testing Your Answer for Reasonableness

27. The output power of a transformer is 100W and the transformer efficiency is 90 percent. What is the transformer input if the output is lower than the input?

(a) 90W (b) 110W (c) 100W (d) 125W

Notes

UNIT 9

Electrical Formulas

Introduction

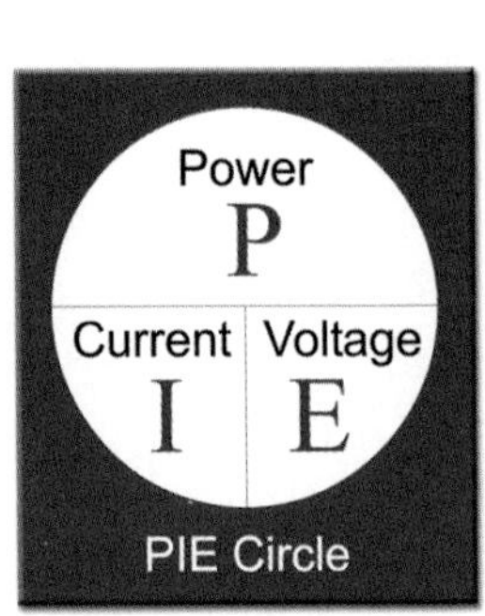

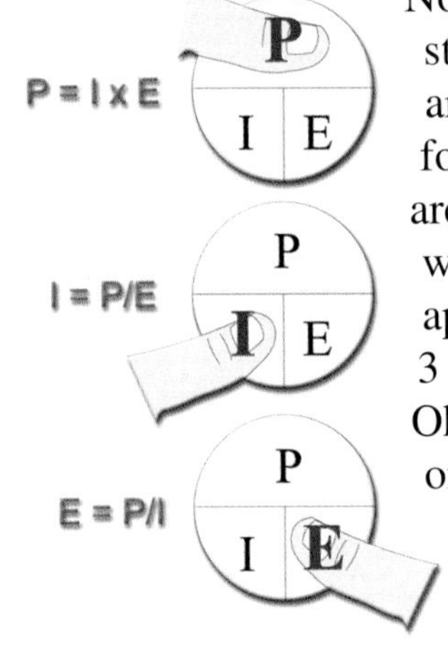

Now that you've mastered the math and understand some basics about electrical circuits, you are ready to take your knowledge of electrical formulas to the next level. One of the things we are going to do here is strengthen your proficiency with Ohm's Law. Many false notions about the application of *NEC* Article 250 and *NEC* Chapter 3 wiring methods arise when people can use Ohm's Law only when solving practice problems on paper but lack a real understanding of how it works and how to apply it. You will have that understanding, and you will not be subject to those false notions—or the unsafe conditions they lead to. But, we won't stop with Ohm's Law. You are also going to have a high level of proficiency with the power equation. One of the tools for handling the power equation—and Ohm's Law—with ease is the power wheel. You will be able to use that to solve all kinds of problems.

9.1 Electrical Circuit

An electrical circuit consists of the power source, the conductors, and the load. A switch can be placed in series with the circuit conductors to control the operation of the load (on or off). Figure 9–1

AUTHOR'S COMMENT: According to the "electron current flow theory," current always flows from the negative terminal of the source, through the circuit and load, to the positive terminal of the source.

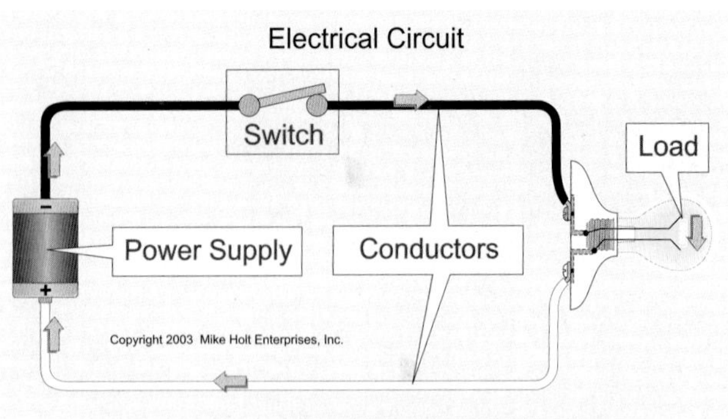

Figure 9–1

9.2 Power Source

Electrical pressure necessary to move the electrons out of their valence shell can be produced by chemical, magnetic, photovoltaic, and other means. The two categories of power sources are direct current (dc) and alternating current (ac).

Direct Current

The polarity and the output voltage from a dc power source never change direction. One terminal will be negative and the other will be positive, relative to each other. Direct-current power is often produced by batteries, dc generators, and electronic power supplies. Figure 9–2

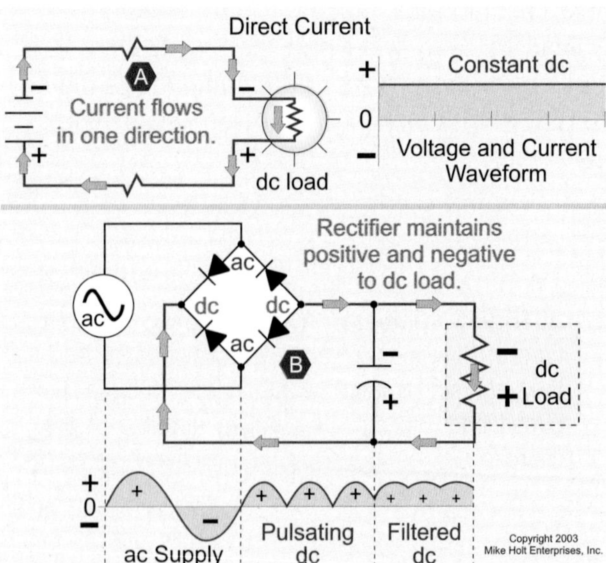

Figure 9–2

Direct current is used for electroplating, street trolley and railway systems, or where a smooth and wide range of speed control is required for a motor-driven application. Direct current is also used for control circuits and electronic instruments.

Alternating Current

Alternating-current power sources produce a voltage that changes polarity and magnitude. Alternating current is produced by an ac power source such as an ac generator. The major advantage of ac over dc is the ease at which voltage can be changed through the use of a transformer. Figure 9–3

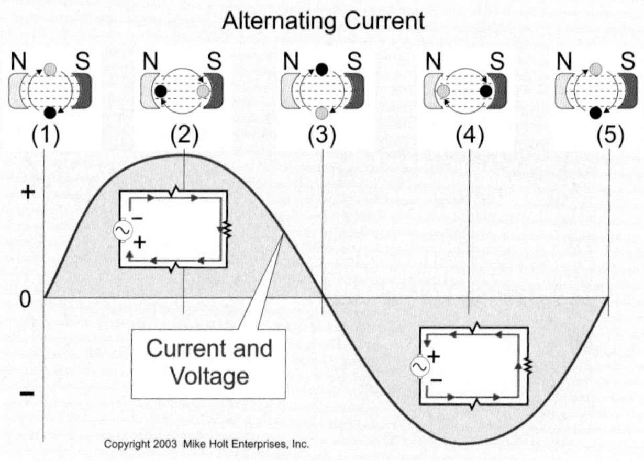

Figure 9–3

AUTHOR'S COMMENT: Alternating current accounts for more than 90 percent of all electric power used throughout the world.

9.3 Conductance

Conductance or conductivity is the property of a metal that permits current to flow. The best conductors in order of their conductivity are: silver, copper, gold, and aluminum. Many people think that gold is the best conductor, but that is not the case. Figure 9–4

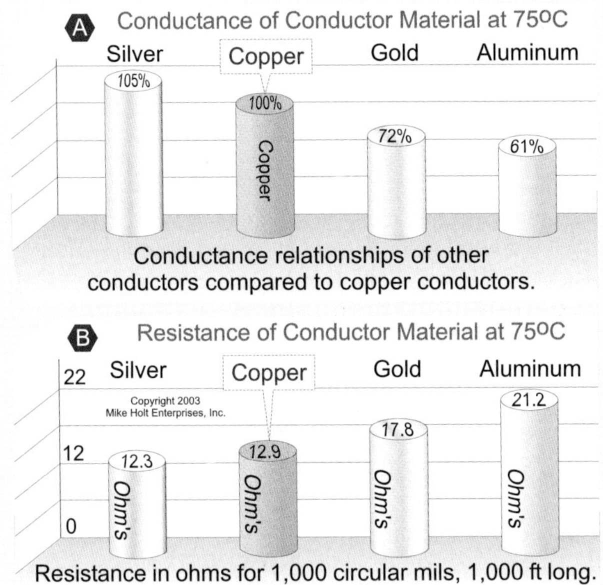

Figure 9–4

9.4 Circuit Resistance

The total resistance of a circuit includes the resistance of the power supply, the circuit wiring, and the load. Appliances such as heaters and toasters use high-resistance conductors to produce the heat needed for the application. Because the resistance of the power source and conductor is so much smaller than that of the load, they are generally ignored in circuit calculations. Figure 9–5

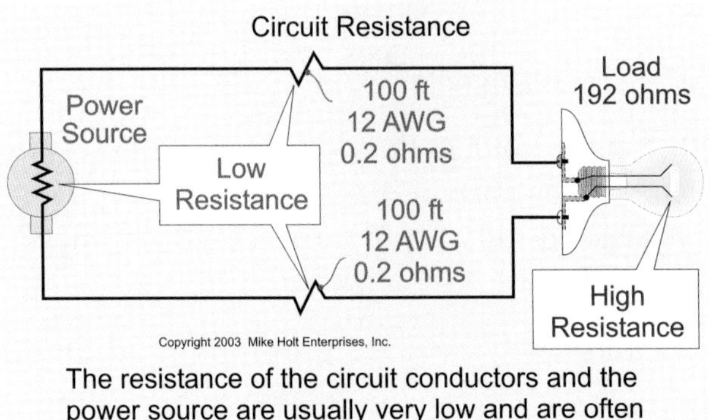

Figure 9–5

9.5 Ohm's Law

Ohm's Law is used to demonstrate the relationship between the dc circuit's current intensity (I), its electromotive force (E), and the resistance (R). It is expressed by the formula, I = E/R.

The German physicist Georg Simon Ohm (1787-1854) stated that current is directly proportional to voltage, and inversely proportional to resistance. Figure 9–6

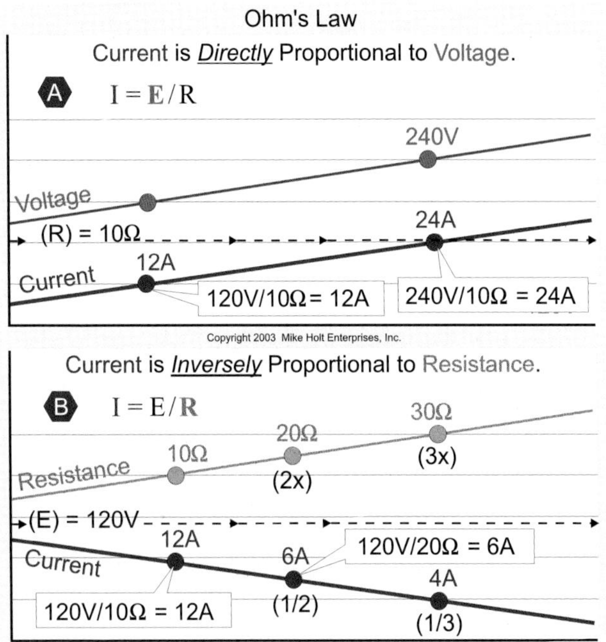

Figure 9–6

Direct proportion means that changing one factor results in a direct change to another factor in the same direction and by the same magnitude. Figure 9–6A

If the voltage increases 25 percent, the current will increase 25 percent—in direct proportion (for a given resistance). If the voltage decreases 25 percent, the current will decrease 25 percent—in direct proportion (for a given resistance).

Inverse proportion means that increasing one factor will result in a decrease in another factor by the same magnitude, or a decrease in one factor will result in an increase of the same magnitude in another factor. Figure 9–6B

If the resistance increases by 25 percent, the current will decrease by 25 percent—in inverse proportion (for a given voltage), or if the resistance decreases by 25 percent, the current will increase by 25 percent—in inverse proportion (for a given voltage).

9.6 Ohm's Law and Alternating Current

Direct Current

In a dc circuit, the only opposition to current flow is the physical resistance of the material that the current flows through. This opposition is measured in ohms and is called resistance.

Alternating Current

In an ac circuit, there are three factors that oppose current flow: the resistance of the material, the inductive reactance of the circuit, and the capacitive reactance of the circuit.

AUTHOR'S COMMENT: For now, we will assume that the effects of inductance and capacitance on the circuit are insignificant and they will be ignored.

9.7 Ohm's Law Formula Circle

Ohm's Law, the relationship between current, voltage, and resistance expressed in the formula, I = E/R, can be transposed to E = I x R or R = E/I. In order to use these formulas, two of the values must be known.

AUTHOR'S COMMENT: Place your thumb on the unknown value in **Figure 9–7**, and the two remaining variables will "show" you the correct formula.

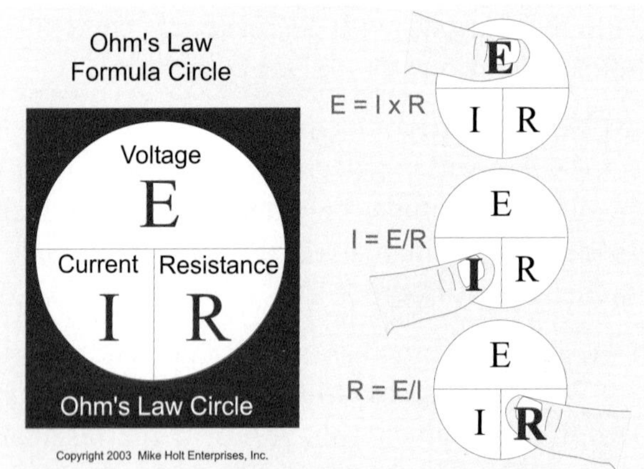

Figure 9–7

Current Example

120V supplies a lamp that has a resistance of 192Ω. What is the current flow in the circuit? **Figure 9–8**

(a) 0.6A (b) 0.5A
(c) 2.5A (d) 1.3A

• Answer: (a) 0.6A

Step 1 What is the question? What is "I?"

Step 2 What do you know?
E = 120V, R = 192Ω

Step 3 The formula is I = E/R

Step 4 The answer is $I = \frac{120V}{192 \text{ ohms}} = 0.625A$

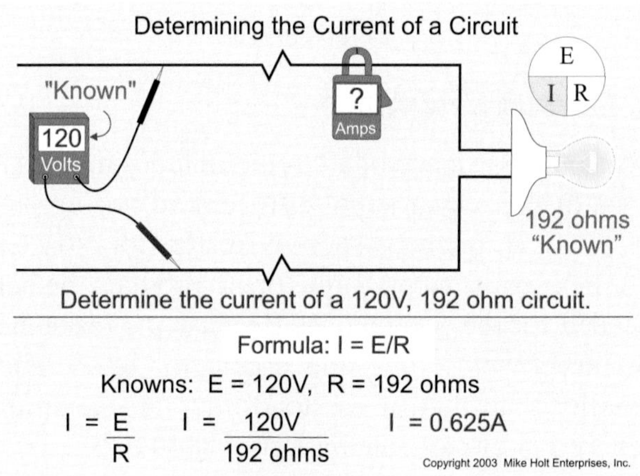

Figure 9–8

Voltage Drop Example

What is the voltage drop over two 12 AWG conductors (resistance of 0.2Ω for 100 ft) supplying a 16A load located 50 ft from the power supply? **Figure 9–9**

(a) 16V (b) 32V
(c) 1.6V (d) 3.2V

• Answer: (d) 3.2V

Step 1 What is the question? What is "E?"

Step 2 What do you know about the conductors?

I = 16A, R = 0.2Ω. The *NEC* lists the ac resistance of 1,000 ft of 12 AWG as 2Ω. The resistance of 100 ft is equal to 0.2Ω. **Figure 9–10**

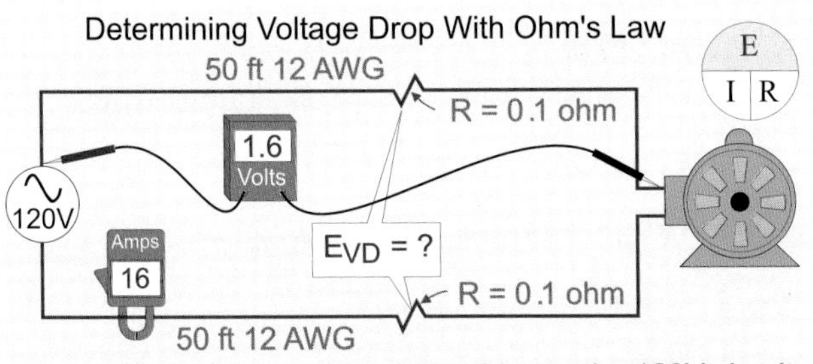

Determine the conductor voltage drop on the 120V circuit.

Formula: $E_{VD} = I \times R$

To determine the voltage drop of conductors, use the resistance of conductors.

Known: I = 16A (given), R of each conductor = 0.1 ohm

E_{VD} = I x R

E_{VD} = 16A x 0.1 ohm = 1.6V

E_{VD} = 1.6V per conductor

Voltage drop of both conductors = 16A x 0.2 ohms = 3.2V

Note: Load operates at 120V - 3.2 VD = 116.8V

Figure 9–9

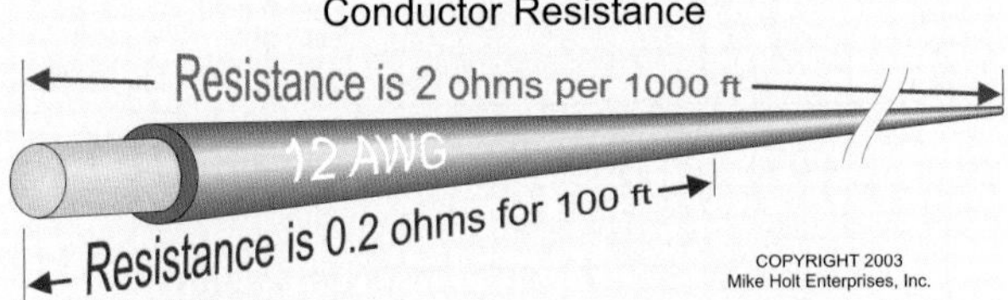

Each 12 AWG is 50 ft x 2 wires = 100 ft in circuit

To determine the resistance of 100 ft of 12 AWG
NEC Chapter 9, Table 9, 1,000 ft of 12 AWG = 2 ohms.
2 ohms/1,000 ft = 0.002 ohms per ft
0.002 ohms per ft x 100 ft = 0.2 ohms for 100 ft

Figure 9–10

Step 3 The formula is E = I x R

Step 4 The answer is E = 16A x 0.2Ω

Step 5 The answer is E = 3.2V

Resistance Example

What is the resistance of the circuit conductors when the conductor voltage drop is 3V and the current flowing in the circuit is 100A? **Figure 9–11**

(a) 0.03Ω (b) 2Ω
(c) 30Ω (d) 300Ω

• Answer: (a) 0.03Ω

Step 1 What is the question? What is "R?"

Step 2 What do you know about the conductors? E = 3V dropped, I = 100A

Step 3 The formula is $R = \frac{E}{I}$

Step 4 The answer is $R = \frac{3V}{100A}$

Step 5 The answer is R = 0.03Ω

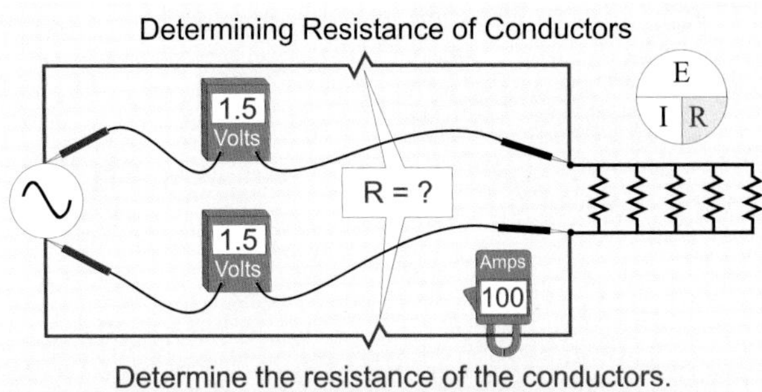

Determine the resistance of the conductors.

Formula: R = E/I

Known: E_{VD} = 1.5 VD per conductor, I = 100A

$R = \frac{E}{I}$ $R = \frac{1.5\ VD}{100A}$ R = 0.015 ohms per conductor

R = 0.015 ohm x 2 conductors = 0.03 ohm, both conductors

OR... $R = \frac{3\ VD}{100A}$ = 0.03 ohms for both conductors

Figure 9–11

9.8 PIE Formula Circle

The PIE formula circle demonstrates the relationship between power, current, and voltage, and it is expressed in the formula P = I x E. This formula can be transposed to I = P/E or E = P/I. In order to use these formulas, two of the values must be known.

AUTHOR'S COMMENT: Place your thumb on the unknown value in **Figure 9–12** and the two remaining variables will "show" you the correct formula.

Power Loss Example

What is the power loss in watts for two conductors that carry 12A and have a voltage drop of 3.6V? **Figure 9–13**

(a) 4.3W (b) 43.2W
(c) 432W (d) none of these

• Answer: (b) 43.2W

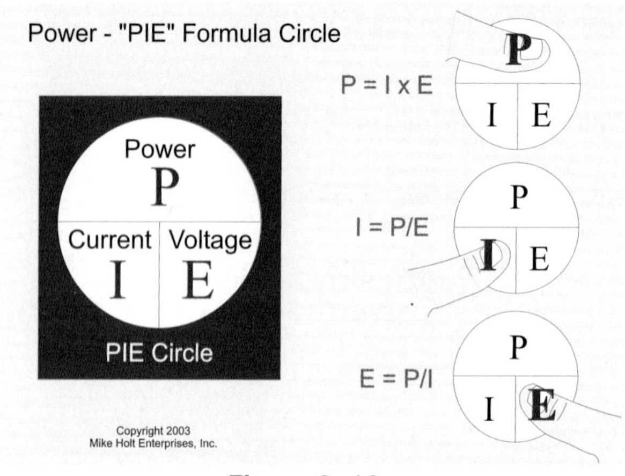

Figure 9–12

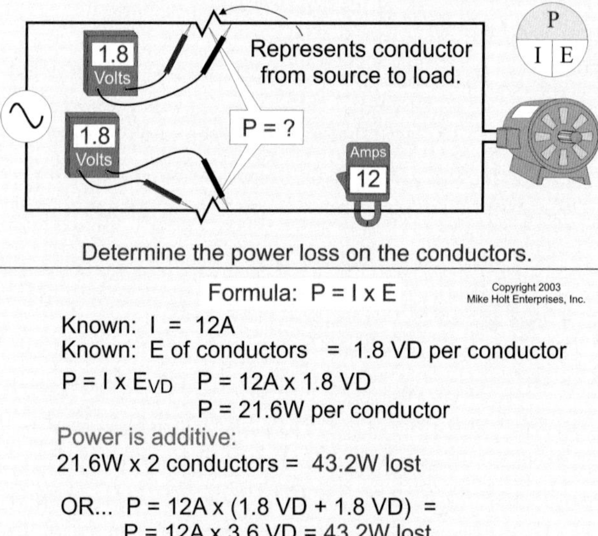

Determining Conductor Power Loss
1.8 Volts
Represents conductor from source to load.
1.8 Volts
P = ?
Amps 12
Determine the power loss on the conductors.
Formula: P = I x E
Copyright 2003
Mike Holt Enterprises, Inc.
Known: I = 12A
Known: E of conductors = 1.8 VD per conductor
P = I x EVD P = 12A x 1.8 VD
P = 21.6W per conductor
Power is additive:
21.6W x 2 conductors = 43.2W lost
OR... P = 12A x (1.8 VD + 1.8 VD) =
P = 12A x 3.6 VD = 43.2W lost

Figure 9–13

Step 1 What is the question? What is "P?"

Step 2 What do you know?
I = 12A, E = 3.6 VD

Step 3 The formula is P = I x E

Step 4 The answer is P = 12A x 3.6V

Step 5 The answer is 43.2W

Current Example

What is the current flow in amperes through a 7.5 kW heat strip rated 230V when connected to a 230V power supply? **Figure 9–14**

(a) 25A (b) 33A
(c) 39A (d) none of these

• Answer: (b) 33A

Step 1 What is the question? What is "I?"

Step 2 What do you know?
P = 7,500W, E = 230V

Step 3 The formula is $I = \frac{P}{E}$

Step 4 The answer is $I = \frac{7{,}500W}{230V} = 32.6A$

Step 5 The answer is 32.6A

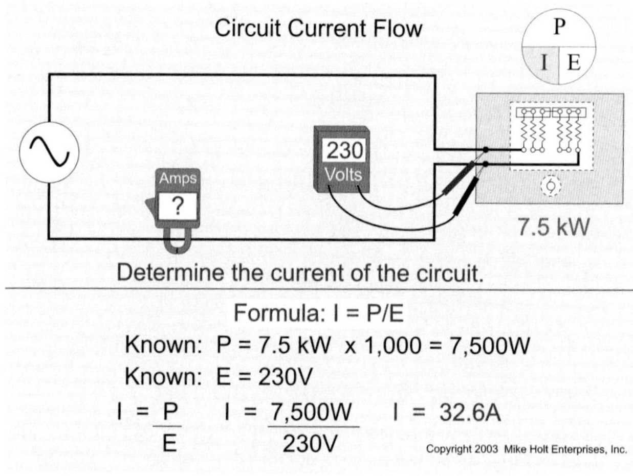

Circuit Current Flow
Amps ?
230 Volts
7.5 kW
Determine the current of the circuit.
Formula: I = P/E
Known: P = 7.5 kW x 1,000 = 7,500W
Known: E = 230V
I = P/E I = 7,500W/230V I = 32.6A
Copyright 2003 Mike Holt Enterprises, Inc.

Figure 9–14

9.9 Formula Wheel

The formula wheel is a combination of the Ohm's Law and the PIE formula wheels. The formulas in the formula wheel can be used for dc circuits or ac circuits with unity power factor. **Figure 9–15**

AUTHOR'S COMMENT: Unity power factor is explained in Unit 17. For the purpose of this Unit, we will assume a unity power factor for all ac circuits.

9.10 Using the Formula Wheel

The formula wheel is divided into four sections with three formulas in each section. **Figure 9–16**

When working the formula wheel, the key to getting the correct answer is to follow these steps:

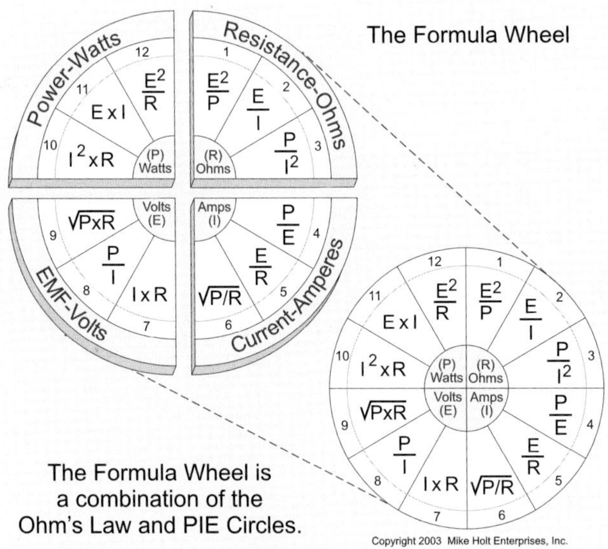

Figure 9–15

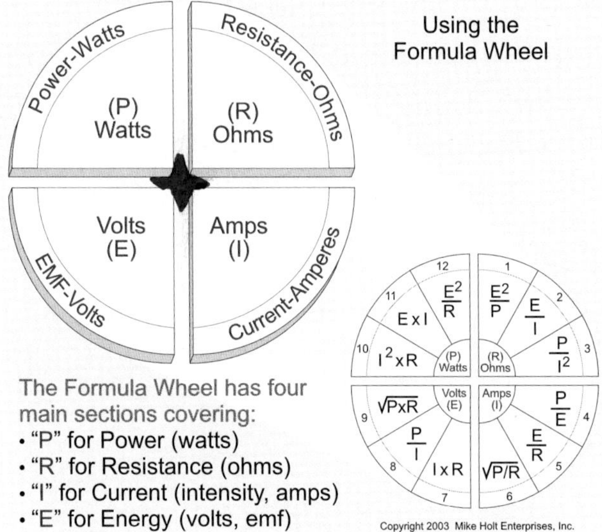

Figure 9–16

Step 1 Know what the question is asking for: I, E, R, or P.

Step 2 Determine the knowns: I, E, R, or P.

Step 3 Determine which section of the formula wheel applies: I, E, R, or P.

Step 4 Select the formula from that section, based on what you know.

Step 5 Work out the calculation.

Example

The total resistance of two 12 AWG conductors, 75 ft long is 0.3Ω, and the current through the circuit is 16A. What is the power loss of the conductors? **Figure 9–17**

(a) 20W (b) 75W
(c) 150W (d) 300W

• Answer: (b) 75W

Step 1 What is the question? What is the power loss of the conductors? "P."

Step 2 What do you know about the conductors? I = 16A, R = 0.3Ω

Step 3 What is the formula? $P = I^2 \times R$

Step 4 Calculate the answer: $P = 16A^2 \times 0.3\Omega = 76.8W$

Step 5 The answer is 76.8W

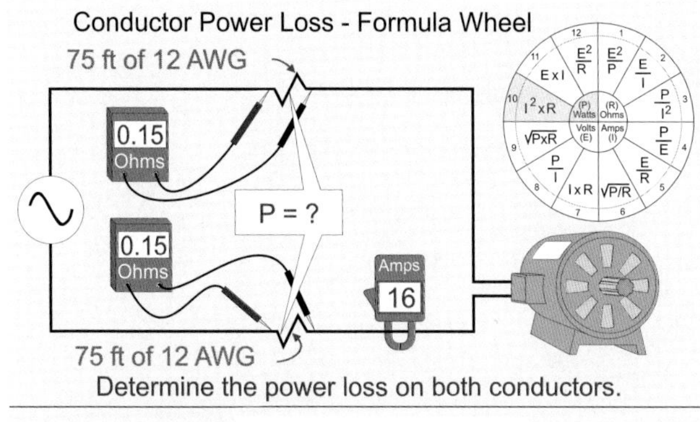

Formula 10: $P = I^2 \times R$
Known: I = 16A
Known: R of one conductor = *0.15 ohms
*0.15 ohms determined by *NEC* Ch 9, Tbl 9 (per ft method)

P = I² x R
P = (16A x 16A) x 0.15 ohms
P = 256A x 0.15 ohms
P = 38.4W on one conductor
P = 38.4W x 2 conductors
P = 76.8W on both conductors

Or

P = I² x R
P = (16A x 16A) x 0.3 ohms
P = 256A x 0.3 ohms
P = 76.8W on both conductors

Figure 9–17

9.11 Power Losses of Conductors

Power in a circuit can be either "useful" or "wasted." Most of the power used by loads such as fluorescent lighting, motors, or stove elements is consumed in useful work. However, the heating of conductors, transformers and motor windings is wasted work. Wasted work is still energy used; therefore it must be paid for, so we call these power losses.

Example

What is the conductor power loss in watts for a 10 AWG conductor that has a voltage drop of 7.2V and carries a current flow of 24A? Figure 9–18

(a) 17W (b) 173W
(c) 350W (d) none of these

• Answer: (b) 173W

Step 1 What is the problem asking you to find? What is wasted? "P."

Step 2 What do you know about the conductors?
I = 24A
E = 7.2 VD

Step 3 The formula is P = I x E

Step 4 Calculate the answer:
P = 24A x 7.2 VD

Step 5 The answer is 172.8W

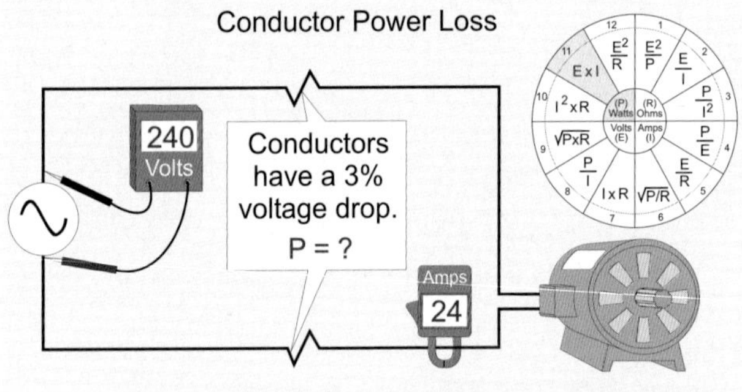
Conductor Power Loss
240 Volts
Conductors have a 3% voltage drop.
P = ?
Amps
24
Determine the power loss on both conductors.
Formula 11: $P = E_{VD} \times I$
Known: I = 24A, E_{VD} = 240V x 3% = 7.2 VD
$P = E_{VD} \times I$
P = 7.2 VD x 24A = 172.8W
Copyright 2003 Mike Holt Enterprises, Inc.

Figure 9–18

9.12 Cost of Power

Since we pay our electric bills on the basis of power consumed in watts, we should understand how to determine the cost of power.

Example

What does it cost per year (at 8.6 cents per kWh) for the power loss of two 10 AWG circuit conductors that have a total resistance of 0.3Ω with a current flow of 24A? Figure 9–19

(a) $1.30 (b) $13.00
(c) $130 (d) $1,300

• Answer: (c) $130

Step 1 Determine the power consumed:
$P = I^2 \times R$
$P = 24A^2 \times 0.3\Omega$
P = 172.8W

Step 2 Convert answer in Step 1 to kW:
$P = \frac{172.8W}{1{,}000W}$
P = 0.1728 kW

Step 3 Determine cost per hour:

(0.086 dollars per kWh) x 0.172.8 kW = 0.01486 dollars per hr

Step 4 Determine dollars per day:

0.01486 dollars per hr x (24 hrs per day) = 0.3567 dollars per day

Step 5 Determine dollars per year.

0.3567 dollars per day x (365 days per year) = $130.20 per year

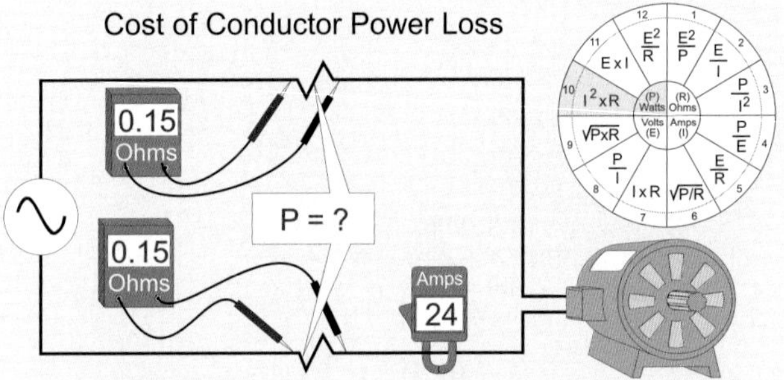
Cost of Conductor Power Loss
0.15 Ohms
0.15 Ohms
P = ?
Amps
24
Determine the cost of power loss on both conductors.

Formula 10: $P = I^2 \times R$	Cost at 8.6 cents per kW hour
Known: I = 24A Known: R = 0.3 ohms $P = I^2 \times R$ P = (24A x 24A) x 0.3 ohms P = 576A x 0.3 ohms P = 172.8W Copyright 2003 Mike Holt Enterprises, Inc.	172.8W/1,000 = 0.1728 kW 8.6 cents/1,000 = $0.086 $0.086 x 0.1728 kW = $0.01486 per hour $0.01486 x 24 hr = $0.3567 per day 0.3567 x 365 days = $130.20 per year

Figure 9–19

AUTHOR'S COMMENT: That's a lot of money just to heat up two 10 AWG conductors for one circuit. Imagine how much it costs to heat up the conductors for an entire building!

9.13 Power Changes with the Square of the Voltage

The voltage applied to the resistor dramatically affects the power consumed by a resistor. This is because power is determined by the square of the voltage. This means that if the voltage is doubled, the power will increase four times. If the voltage is decreased 50 percent, the power will decrease to 25 percent of its original value. Figure 9–20

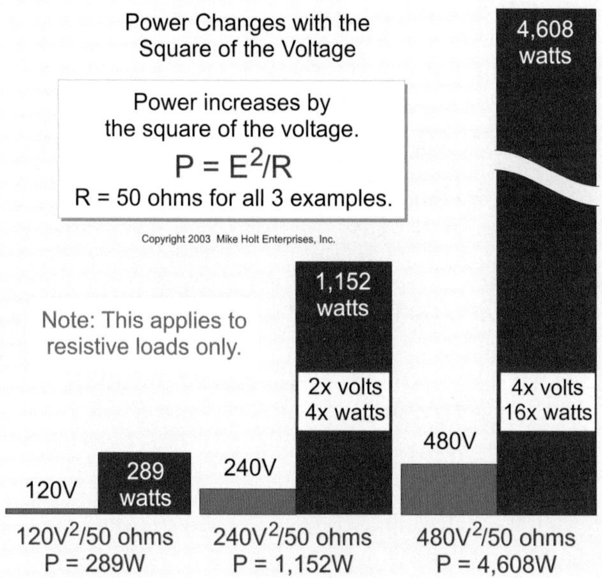
Power Changes with the Square of the Voltage
Power increases by the square of the voltage.
P = E2/R
R = 50 ohms for all 3 examples.
Copyright 2003 Mike Holt Enterprises, Inc.
Note: This applies to resistive loads only.
4,608 watts
1,152 watts
289 watts
120V
240V
480V
2x volts 4x watts
4x volts 16x watts
120V2/50 ohms P = 289W
240V2/50 ohms P = 1,152W
480V2/50 ohms P = 4,608W

Figure 9–20

Power Example at 230V

What is the power consumed by a 9.6 kW heat strip rated 230V connected to a 230V circuit? Figure 9–21

(a) 7.85 kW (b) 9.6 kW
(c) 11.57 kW (d) none of these

• Answer: (b) 9.6 kW

Step 1 What is the problem asking you to find? Power consumed by the resistance.

Step 2 What do you know about the heat strip?

You were given P = 9.6 kW in the statement of the problem.

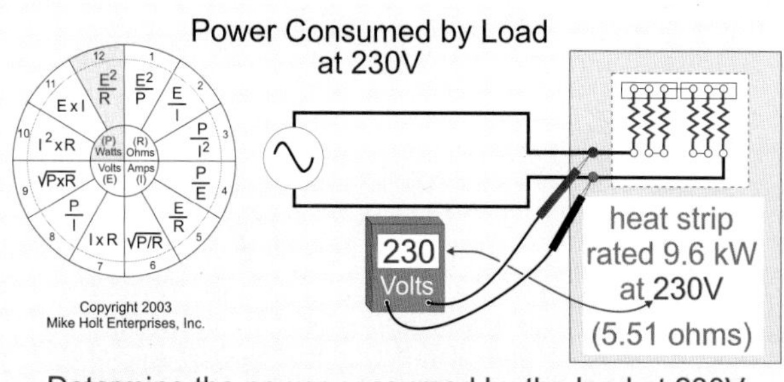
Power Consumed by Load at 230V
230 Volts
heat strip rated 9.6 kW at 230V (5.51 ohms)
Copyright 2003 Mike Holt Enterprises, Inc.
Determine the power consumed by the load at 230V.
Formula 12: P = E2/R
Knowns: E = 230V, R = 5.51 ohms
P = E2/R
P = (230V x 230V)/5.51 ohms = 9,600W
5.51 ohm resistor consumes 9.6 kW at 230V.

Figure 9–21

Power Example at 208V

What is the power consumed by a 9.6 kW heat strip rated 230V connected to a 208V circuit? Figure 9–22

(a) 7.85 kW (b) 9.6 kW
(c) 11.57 kW (d) none of these

• Answer: (a) 7.85 kW

Step 1 What is the problem asking you to find? Power consumed by the resistance.

Step 2 What do you know about the heat strip? $E = 208V$, $R = 5.51\Omega$

Step 3 The formula to determine power is: $P = E^2/R$

Step 4 The answer is:

$$P = \frac{208V^2}{5.51\Omega}$$

$P = 7{,}851W$ or $7.85\ kW$

AUTHOR'S COMMENT: It is important to realize that the resistance of the heater unit does not change—it is a property of the material that the current flows through and is not dependent on the voltage applied.

Thus, for a small change in voltage, there is a considerable change in power consumption by this heater.

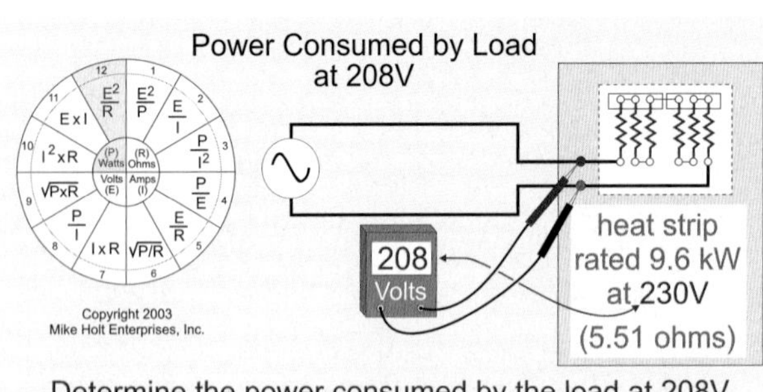
Power Consumed by Load
at 208V
208
Volts
heat strip
rated 9.6 kW
at 230V
(5.51 ohms)
Copyright 2003
Mike Holt Enterprises, Inc.
Determine the power consumed by the load at 208V.
Formula 12: P = E2/R
Knowns: E = 208V, R = 5.51 ohms
P = E2/R
P = (208V x 208V)/5.51 ohms = 7,852W
5.51 ohm resistor consumes 7.85 kW at 208V.

Figure 9–22

AUTHOR'S COMMENT: The current flow for this heat strip is I = P/E

$P = 7{,}851W$

$E = 208V$

$$I = \frac{7{,}851W}{208V}$$

$I = 38A$

Power Example at 240V

What is the power consumed by a 9.6 kW heat strip rated 230V connected to a 240V circuit? Figure 9–23

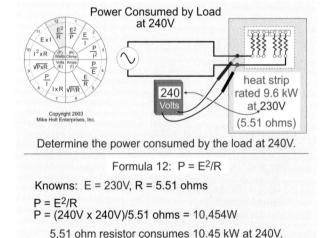

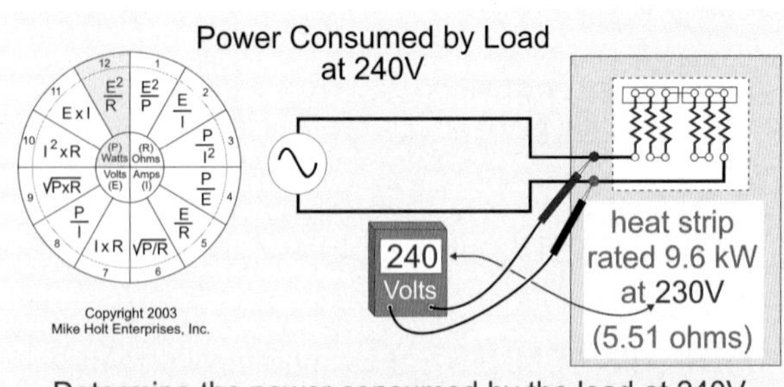
Power Consumed by Load
at 240V
240
Volts
heat strip
rated 9.6 kW
at 230V
(5.51 ohms)
Copyright 2003
Mike Holt Enterprises, Inc.
Determine the power consumed by the load at 240V.
Formula 12: P = E2/R
Knowns: E = 230V, R = 5.51 ohms
P = E2/R
P = (240V x 240V)/5.51 ohms = 10,454W
5.51 ohm resistor consumes 10.45 kW at 240V.

Figure 9–23

(a) 7.85 kW (b) 9.6 kW
(c) 10.45 kW (d) 11.57 kW

• Answer: (c) 10.45 kW

Step 1 What is the problem asking you to find? Power consumed by the resistance.

Step 2 What do you know about the resistance? E = 240V, R = 5.51Ω*

Step 3 The formula to determine power is:

$$P = \frac{E^2}{R}$$

Step 4 The answer is:

$$P = \frac{240V^2}{5.51\Omega}$$

$P = 10{,}454W$

$P = 10.45\ kW$

AUTHOR'S COMMENT: The current flow for this heat strip is, I = P/E.

$P = 10{,}454W$

$E = 240V$

$$I = \frac{10{,}454W}{240V}$$

$I = 44A$

As you can see, when the voltage changes, the power changes by the square of the change in the voltage, but the current changes in direct proportion.

*The resistance of the heat strip is determined by the formula $R = E^2/P$

E = Nameplate voltage rating of the resistance, 230V

P = Nameplate power rating of the resistance, 9,600W

$$R = \frac{E^2}{P} = \frac{230V^2}{9{,}600W}$$

$R = 5.51\Omega$

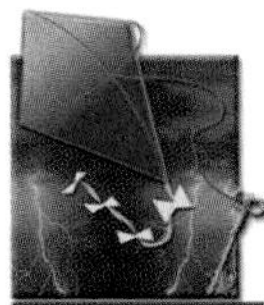

Unit 9 Summary

9.1 Electrical Circuit

An electrical circuit consists of the power source, the conductors, and the load.

> **AUTHOR'S COMMENT:** According to the "electron current flow theory," current always flows from the negative terminal of the source, through the circuit and load, to the positive terminal of the source.

9.2 Power Source

Direct Current

The polarity and the output voltage from a dc power source never change direction. One terminal will be negative and the other will be positive, relative to each other. Direct-current power is often produced by batteries, dc generators, and electronic power supplies.

Alternating Current

Alternating-current power sources produce voltage that changes polarity and magnitude. Alternating current is produced by an ac power source such as an ac generator. The major advantage of ac over dc is the ease at which voltage can be changed through the use of a transformer.

9.3 Conductance

Conductance or conductivity is the property of a metal that permits current to flow. The best conductors in order of their conductivity are: silver, copper, gold, and aluminum.

9.4 Circuit Resistance

The total resistance of a circuit includes the resistance of the power supply, the circuit wiring, and the load. Because the resistance of the power source and conductor is so much smaller than that of the load, they are generally ignored in circuit calculations.

9.5 Ohm's Law

Ohm's Law is used to demonstrate the relationship between the circuit's current intensity (I), its Electromotive Force (E), and the circuit Resistance (R) in a dc circuit. It is expressed by the formula, I = E/R.

9.6 Ohm's Law and Alternating Current

Direct Current

In a dc circuit, the only opposition to current flow is the physical resistance of the material that the current flows through.

Alternating Current

In an ac circuit, there are three factors that oppose current flow: the resistance of the material, the inductive reactance of the circuit, and the capacitive reactance of the circuit.

9.7 Ohm's Law Formula Circle

Ohm's Law, the relationship between current, voltage, and resistance expressed in the formula, I = E/R, can be transposed to E = I x R or R = E/I.

9.8 PIE Formula Circle

The PIE formula circle demonstrates the relationship between power, current, and voltage, and it is expressed in the formula P = I x E. This formula can be transposed to I = P/E or E = P/I.

9.9 Formula Wheel

The formula wheel is a combination of the Ohm's Law and the PIE formula wheels. The formulas in the wheel apply to dc circuits or to ac circuits with unity power factor.

9.10 Using the Formula Wheel

The formula wheel is divided into four sections with three formulas in each section. When working the formula wheel, the key to getting the correct answer is to follow these steps:

Step 1 Know what the question is asking for: I, E, R, or P.

Step 2 Determine the known: I, E, R, or P.

Step 3 Determine which section of the formula wheel applies: I, E, R, or P.

Step 4 Select the formula from that section, based on what you know.

Step 5 Work out the calculation.

9.11 Power Losses of Conductors

Power in a circuit can be either "useful" or "wasted." The heating of conductors, transformers and motor windings is wasted work. Wasted work is still energy used, therefore it must be paid for.

9.12 Cost of Power

Since we pay our electric bills on the basis of power consumed in watts, we should understand how to determine the cost of power.

9.13 Power Changes with the Square of the Voltage

The voltage applied to the resistor dramatically affects the power consumed by a resistor. If the voltage is doubled, the power will increase four times. If the voltage is decreased 50 percent, the power will decrease to 25 percent of its original value.

Thus, for a small change in voltage, there is a considerable change in power consumption.

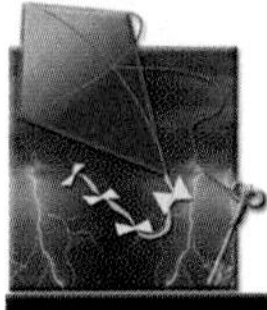

Unit 9 Conclusion

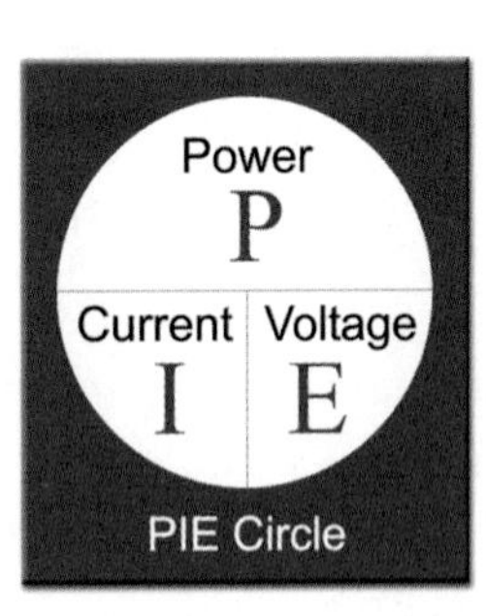

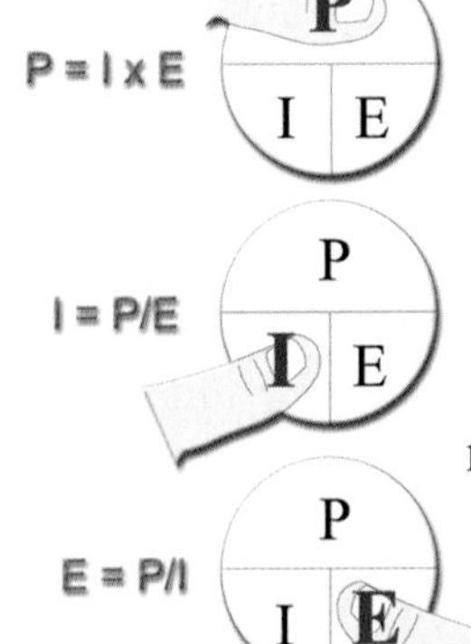

You've gained skill in working with Ohm's Law and the power equation, and you can use the power wheel to solve a wide variety of electrical problems. You also know how to calculate voltage drop and power loss, and you can relate the costs in real dollars.

As useful as these skills are, there is still more to learn. But, your mastery of the basic electrical formulas means you are well-prepared. Work through the questions that follow, and go back over the instructional material if you have any difficulty. When you feel you know the material in Units 7, 8, and 9, you are ready to tackle series, parallel, series-parallel, and multiwire circuits.

Words to Live By: ***He who wants milk should not sit on a stool in the middle of the pasture expecting the cow to back up to him.***

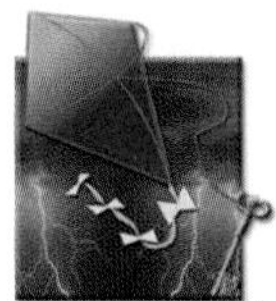

Unit 9 Practice Questions

9.1 Electrical Circuit

1. An electrical circuit consists of the _____.

   (a) power source (b) conductors (c) load (d) all of these

9.2 Power Source

2. The polarity and the output voltage from a dc power source changes direction. One terminal will be negative and the other will be positive.

   (a) True (b) False

3. According to electron flow theory, electrons leave the _____ terminal of the source, flow through the conductors and load(s), and return to the _____ terminal of the source.

   (a) positive, negative (b) negative, positive
   (c) negative, negative (d) positive, positive

4. Direct current is used for electroplating, street trolley and railway systems, or where a smooth and wide range of speed control is required for a motor-driven application.

   (a) True (b) False

5. The polarity and the output voltage from an ac power source never change direction.

   (a) True (b) False

6. The major advantage of ac over dc is the ease of voltage regulation by the use of a transformer.

   (a) True (b) False

9.3 Conductance

7. Conductance is the property that permits current to flow.

   (a) True (b) False

8. The best conductors, in order of their conductivity, are: gold, silver, copper, and aluminum.

   (a) True (b) False

9. Conductance or conductivity is the property of metal that permits current to flow. The best conductors in order of their conductivity are: _____.

(a) gold, silver, copper, aluminum
(b) gold, copper, silver, aluminum
(c) silver, gold, copper, aluminum
(d) silver, copper, gold, aluminum

9.4 Circuit Resistance

10. The circuit resistance includes the resistance of the _____.

(a) power source (b) conductors (c) load (d) all of these

11. Often the resistance of the power source and conductor are ignored in circuit calculations.

(a) True (b) False

9.5 Ohm's Law

12. The Ohm's Law formula, I = E/R, states that current is _____ proportional to the voltage, and _____ proportional to the resistance.

(a) indirectly, inversely (b) inversely, directly (c) inversely, indirectly (d) directly, inversely

13. Ohm's Law demonstrates the relationship between circuit _____.

(a) intensity (b) EMF (c) resistance (d) all of these

9.6 Ohm's Law and Alternating Current

14. In a dc circuit, the only opposition to current flow is the physical resistance of the material. This opposition is called reactance and it is measured in ohms.

(a) True (b) False

15. In an ac circuit, the factors that oppose current flow are _____.

(a) resistance (b) inductive reactance (c) capacitive reactance (d) all of these

9.7 Ohm's Law Formula Circle

16. What is the voltage drop of two 12 AWG conductors supplying a 16A load, located 100 ft from the power supply? Formula:

$E_{VD} = I \times R$
$E_{VD} = 16A \times 0.4\Omega$

(a) 6.4V (b) 12.8V (c) 1.6V (d) 3.2V

17. What is the resistance of the circuit conductors when the conductor voltage drop is 7.2V and the current flow is 50A?

(a) 0.14Ω (b) 0.3Ω (c) 3Ω (d) 14Ω

9.8 PIE Formula Circle

18. What is the power loss in watts of a conductor that carries 24A and has a voltage drop of 7.2V?

(a) 175W (b) 350W (c) 700W (d) 2,400W

19. What is the approximate power consumed by a 10 kW heat strip rated 230V, when connected to a 208V circuit?

(a) 8 kW (b) 9 kW (c) 11 kW (d) 12 kW

9.9 Formula Wheel

20. The formulas in the power wheel apply to _____.

(a) dc
(b) ac with unity power factor
(c) dc or ac circuits
(d) a and b

9.10 Using the Formula Wheel

21. When working any formula, the key to getting the correct answer is following these four steps:

Step 1 Know what the question is asking you to find.

Step 2 Determine the knowns of the circuit or resistance.

Step 3 Select the formula.

Step 4 Work out the formula calculation.

(a) True (b) False

9.11 Power Losses of Conductors

22. Power in a circuit can be either "useful" or "wasted." Wasted work is still energy used; therefore it must be paid for, so we call this _____.

(a) resistance
(b) inductive reactance
(c) capacitive reactance
(d) power losses

23. The total circuit resistance of two 12 AWG conductors (each 100 ft long) is 0.4Ω. If the current of the circuit is 16A, what is the power loss of the conductors in watts?

(a) 75W (b) 100W (c) 300W (d) 600W

24. What is the conductor power loss in watts for a 120V circuit that has a 3 percent voltage drop and carries a current flow of 12A?

(a) 43W (b) 86W (c) 172W (d) 1,440W

9.12 Cost of Power

25. What does it cost per year (at 8 cents per kWh) for the power loss of a 12 AWG circuit conductor (100 ft long) that has a total resistance of 0.4Ω and current flow of 16A?

(a) $30 (b) $50 (c) $70 (d) $90

9.13 Power Changes with the Square of the Voltage

26. The voltage applied to the resistor dramatically affects the power consumed by a resistor, because power is affected in direct proportion to the voltage.

(a) True (b) False

27. What is the power consumed by a 10 kW heat strip rated 230V connected to a 115V circuit?

(a) 2.5 kW (b) 5 kW (c) 7.5 kW (d) 15 kW

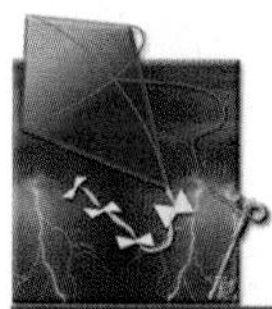

Chapter 2 Final Exam

Unit 7—The Electrical Circuit

7.2 Electron Current Flow Theory

1. According to the electron current flow theory, electrons flow away from the negative terminal of the source, through the circuit and load, toward the positive terminal of the source.

   (a) True (b) False

7.3 Conventional Current Flow Theory

2. According to the conventional current flow theory, electrons travel from positive to negative.

   (a) True (b) False

7.4 Voltage (Pressure)

3. Electrical pressure is called _____, and it is measured in volts.

   (a) EMF (b) potential (c) a or b (d) none of these

7.6 Electric Current

4. In electrical systems, the volume of electrons that move through a conductor is called the circuit _____.

   (a) resistance (b) power (c) pressure (d) intensity

7.7 Power

5. DC power is determined by multiplying the electromotive force by the circuit intensity.

   (a) True (b) False

6. Power is not equal to E x I for ac circuits, because consideration must be given to inductive reactance.

   (a) True (b) False

Unit 8—Math

8.5 Multiplier

7. An overcurrent protection device (breaker or fuse) must be sized no less than 125 percent of the continuous load. If the load were 16A, the overcurrent protection device would have to be sized at no less than _____.

   (a) 20A (b) 23A (c) 17A (d) 30A

8. The maximum continuous load on an overcurrent protection device is limited to 80 percent of the device rating. If the overcurrent device is rated 100A, the maximum continuous load is _____.

   (a) 72A (b) 80A (c) 90A (d) 125A

8.6 Percent Increase

9. The feeder demand load for an 8 kW load, increased by 20 percent is _____.

   (a) 8 kW (b) 9.6 kW (c) 6.4 kW (d) 10 kW

8.8 Squaring a Number

10. What is the power consumed in watts by a 12 AWG conductor that is 100 ft long and has a resistance (R) of 0.2Ω, when the current (I) in the circuit is 16A?

    Formula: Power = $I^2 \times R$.

    (a) 75 (b) 50 (c) 100 (d) 200

11. What is the area in sq in. of a 2 in. raceway?
    Formula: Area = $\pi \times r^2$, $\pi = 3.14$, r = radius, which equals $^1/_2$ of the diameter.

    (a) 1 (b) 2 (c) 3 (d) 4

8.9 Square Root

12. The square root of three is _____.

    (a) 1.732 (b) 9 (c) 729 (d) 1.5

8.12 Rounding Off

13. The sum of 2, 7, 8 and 9 is equal to _____.

    (a) 20 (b) 25 (c) 30 (d) 35

8.13 Parentheses

14. What is the maximum distance that two 14 AWG conductors can be run if they carry 16A and the maximum allowable voltage drop is 10V?

$$D = \frac{(CM \times VD)}{(2 \times K \times I)}$$

$$D = \frac{(4{,}160\ CM \times 10V)}{(2 \times 12.9\Omega \times 16A)}$$

(a) 50 (b) 75 (c) 100 (d) 150

15. What is the current in amperes of an 18kW, 208V, 3Ø load?

Formula: $I = \frac{P}{(E \times \sqrt{3})} \quad \frac{18{,}000VA}{(208V \times 1.732)}$

(a) 25 (b) 50 (c) 100 (d) 150

8.14 Testing Your Answer for Reasonableness

16. The output power of a transformer is 100W and the transformer efficiency is 90 percent. What is the transformer input if the output is lower than the input?

(a) 90W (b) 110W (c) 100W (d) 125W

Unit 9—Electrical Formulas

9.2 Power Source

17. Direct current is used for electroplating, street trolley and railway systems, or where a smooth and wide range of speed control is required for a motor-driven application.

(a) True (b) False

18. The major advantage of ac over dc is the ease of voltage regulation by the use of a transformer.

(a) True (b) False

9.3 Conductance

19. The best conductors, in order of their conductivity, are: gold, silver, copper, and aluminum.

(a) True (b) False

9.5 Ohm's Law

20. The Ohm's Law formula, I = E/R, states that current is _____ proportional to the voltage, and _____ proportional to the resistance.

    (a) indirectly, inversely (b) inversely, directly (c) inversely, indirectly (d) directly, inversely

21. Ohm's Law demonstrates the relationship between circuit _____.

    (a) intensity (b) EMF (c) resistance (d) all of these

9.6 Ohm's Law and Alternating Current

22. In a dc circuit, the only opposition to current flow is the physical resistance of the material. This opposition is called reactance and it is measured in ohms.

    (a) True (b) False

23. In an ac circuit, the factors that oppose current flow are _____.

    (a) resistance (b) inductive reactance
    (c) capacitive reactance (d) all of these

9.7 Ohm's Law Formula Circle

24. What is the voltage drop of two 12 AWG conductors supplying a 16A load, located 100 ft from the power supply? Formula:

    E_{VD} = I x R

    E_{VD} = 16A x 0.4Ω

    (a) 6.4V (b) 12.8V (c) 1.6V (d) 3.2V

25. What is the resistance of the circuit conductors when the conductor voltage drop is 7.2V and the current flow is 50A?

    (a) 0.14Ω (b) 0.3Ω (c) 3Ω (d) 14Ω

9.8 PIE Formula Circle

26. What is the power loss in watts of a conductor that carries 24A and has a voltage drop of 7.2V?

    (a) 175W (b) 350W (c) 700W (d) 2,400W

27. What is the approximate power consumed by a 10 kW heat strip rated 230V, when connected to a 208V circuit?

    (a) 8 kW (b) 9 kW (c) 11 kW (d) 12 kW

9.9 Formula Wheel

28. The formulas in the power wheel apply to _____.

(a) dc
(b) ac with unity power factor
(c) dc or ac circuits
(d) a and b

9.11 Power Losses of Conductors

29. Power in a circuit can be either "useful" or "wasted." Wasted work is still energy used; therefore it must be paid for, so we call this _____.

(a) resistance
(b) inductive reactance
(c) capacitive reactance
(d) power losses

30. The total circuit resistance of two 12 AWG conductors (each 100 ft long) is 0.4Ω. If the current of the circuit is 16A, what is the power loss of the conductors in watts?

(a) 75W (b) 100W (c) 300W (d) 600W

31. What is the conductor power loss in watts for a 120V circuit that has a 3 percent voltage drop and carries a current flow of 12A?

(a) 43W (b) 86W (c) 172W (d) 1,440W

9.12 Cost of Power

32. What does it cost per year (at 8 cents per kWh) for the power loss of a 12 AWG circuit conductor (100 ft long) that has a total resistance of 0.4Ω and current flow of 16A?

(a) $30 (b) $50 (c) $70 (d) $90

9.13 Power Changes with the Square of the Voltage

33. The voltage applied to the resistor dramatically affects the power consumed by a resistor, because power is affected in direct proportion to the voltage.

(a) True (b) False

34. What is the power consumed by a 10 kW heat strip rated 230V connected to a 115V circuit?

(a) 2.5 kW (b) 5 kW (c) 7.5 kW (d) 15 kW

Chapter 3
Basic Electrical Circuits

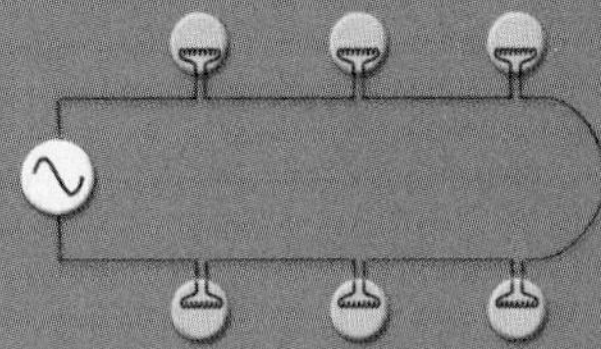

Unit 10 – Series Circuits

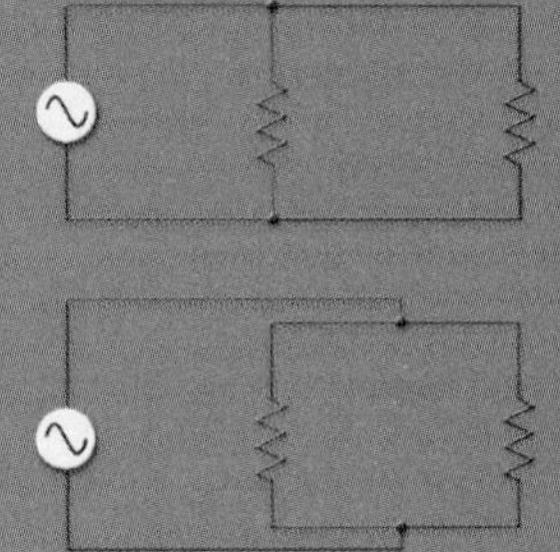

Unit 11 – Parallel Circuits

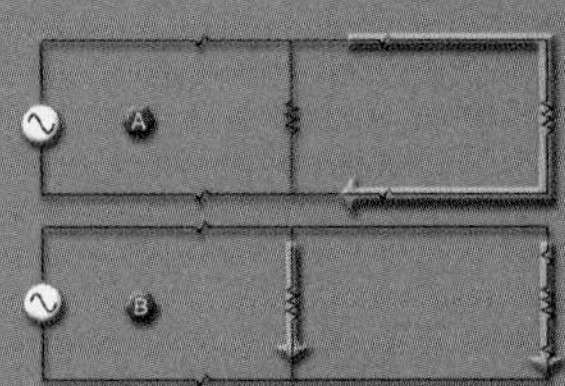

Unit 12 – Series - Parallel Circuits

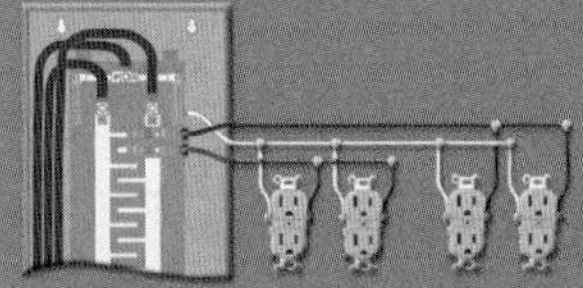

Unit 13 – Multiwire Circuits

Notes

UNIT 10

Series Circuits

Introduction

A series circuit is a circuit in which a specific amount of current leaves the voltage source and flows through every electrical device in a single path before it returns to the voltage source. Figure 10–1

It is important to understand that in a series circuit, current is identical through ALL circuit elements of the circuit.

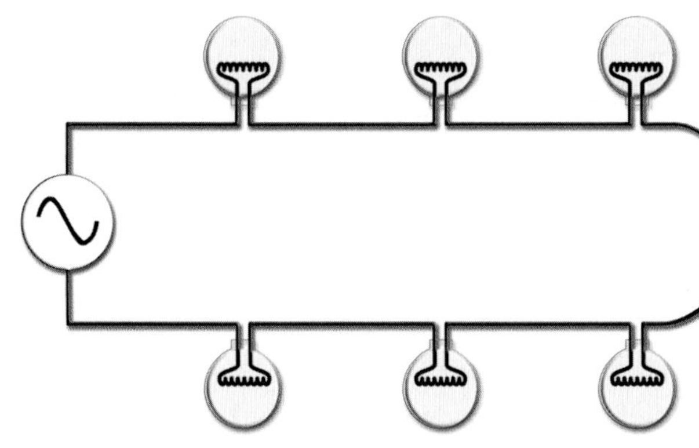

Figure 10–1

10.1 Practical Uses of the Series Circuit

In a series circuit, if any part of the circuit is open, the current in the circuit will stop.

Lighting

A series circuit is not useful for lighting because if one lamp burns out, all the other lamps on the circuit will go out. Figure 10–2

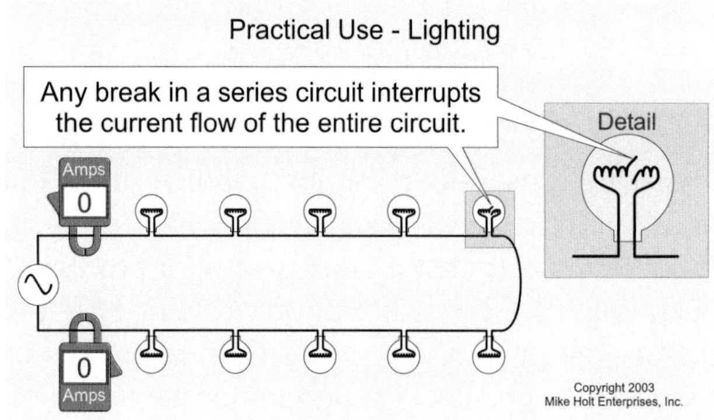

Figure 10–2

Many strings of Christmas lights are made in series circuits—if one bulb burns out, it requires examining EVERY bulb in order to find the bad one because the entire string stops burning when this occurs! Most of the newer Christmas light lamps used in series string lighting have a shorting bar. When one lamp burns out, the lamp leads are shorted together (shorting bar) and the rest of the string stays lit.

AUTHOR'S COMMENT: If, however, there are ten lamps in the string, and one burns out, the rest of the lamps will operate at 10% higher voltage, causing the other nine lamps to burn out even quicker.

For most practical purposes, series circuits, also called closed-loop systems, are not used for building wiring; however, they are often used for control and signal circuits.

Control Circuit

Closed-loop (series) circuits are often used for the purpose of controlling (starting and stopping) electrical equipment. **Figure 10–3**

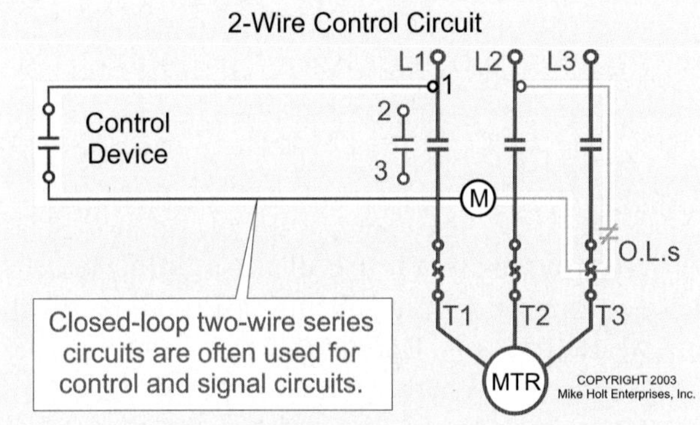

Figure 10–3

Signaling Circuit

Two-wire closed-loop (series) circuits are often used to give a signal that something has occurred. It could indicate that a door is open, a process is operating, or there is fire or smoke. For example the discontinuation of current flow when part of the circuit is opened is important for the operation of burglar alarm circuits. **Figure 10–4**

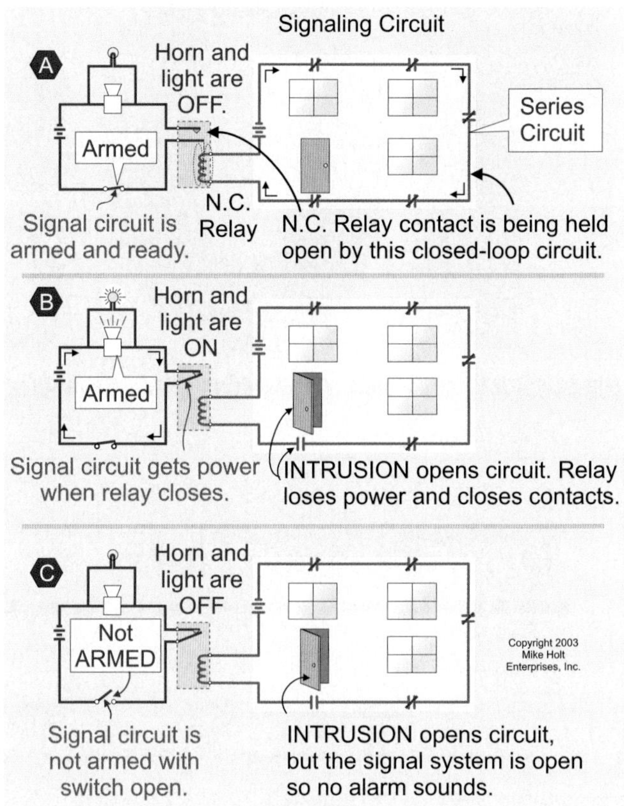

Figure 10–4

Internal Equipment Wiring

The internal wiring of many types of equipment, such as motor windings, will be connected in series. For example, a 115/230V rated motor connected to a 230V circuit must have the windings connected in series so that each winding will receive at least 115V. **Figure 10–5**

10.2 Understanding Series Calculations

It is important to understand the relationship between current, voltage, resistance, and power in series circuits. **Figure 10–6**

Resistance

Resistance opposes the flow of electrons. In a series circuit, the total circuit resistance is equal to the sum of all the series resistances. Resistance is additive: $R_T = R_1 + R_2 + R_3 + R_4$. **Figure 10–7**

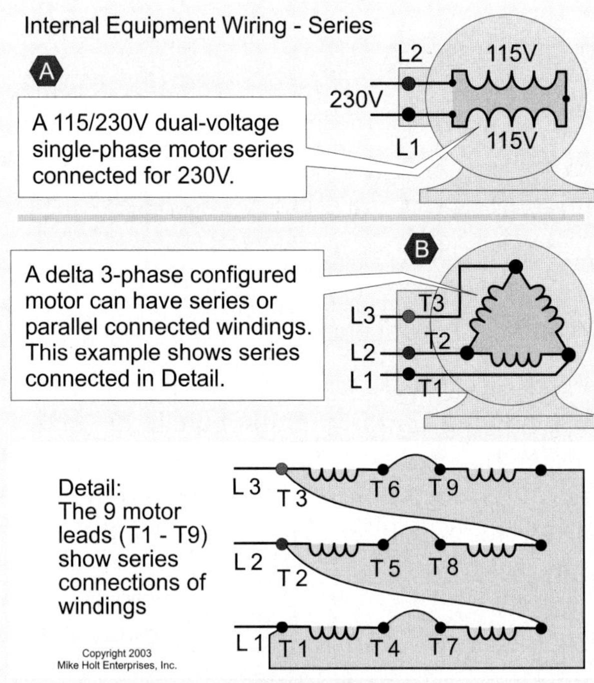

Internal Equipment Wiring - Series
A
A 115/230V dual-voltage single-phase motor series connected for 230V.
L2
115V
230V
L1
115V
B
A delta 3-phase configured motor can have series or parallel connected windings. This example shows series connected in Detail.
L3
T3
L2
T2
L1
T1
Detail:
The 9 motor leads (T1 - T9) show series connections of windings
L3 T3 T6 T9
L2 T2 T5 T8
L1 T1 T4 T7
Copyright 2003 Mike Holt Enterprises, Inc.

Figure 10–5

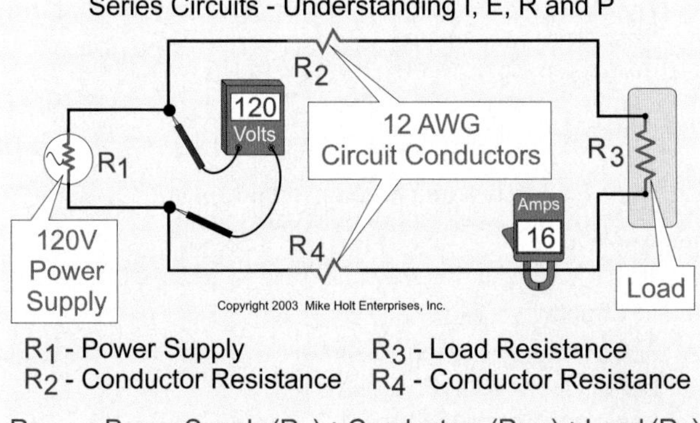

Figure 10–6

Example

R_1 Power Supply	0.05Ω (ohms)
R_2 Conductor No. 1	0.15Ω
R_3 Appliance	7.15Ω
R_4 Conductor No. 2	0.15Ω
R_T Total Resistance	7.50Ω

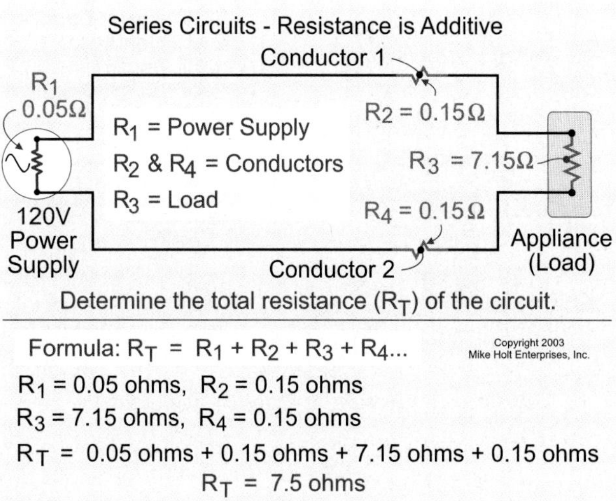

Figure 10–7

Voltage

The voltage, also called electromotive force (EMF), provides the pressure necessary to move electrons through the circuit. However, the power supply, the conductors, and the appliance all have resistance (although the power supply's resistance is usually ignored) that opposes the current flow. The opposition (resistance) to current flow (amperes) results in a voltage drop of the circuit voltage, and can be calculated by the formula $E_{VD} = I \times R$.

Kirchoff's Voltage Law

Kirchoff's Voltage Law states that in a series circuit, the sum of the voltages (or "voltage drops") across all of the resistors in the series circuit is equal to the applied voltage.

The voltage drop across each resistor can be determined by the formula $E_{VD} = I \times R$. Figure 10–8

I = Current of circuit

R = Resistance of resistor

Power Supply	16A x 0.05Ω	=	0.8V
Conductor 1	16A x 0.15Ω	=	2.4V
Appliance	16A x 7.15Ω	=	114.4V
Conductor 2	16A x 0.15Ω	=	2.4V
Total	16A x 7.50Ω	=	120.0V

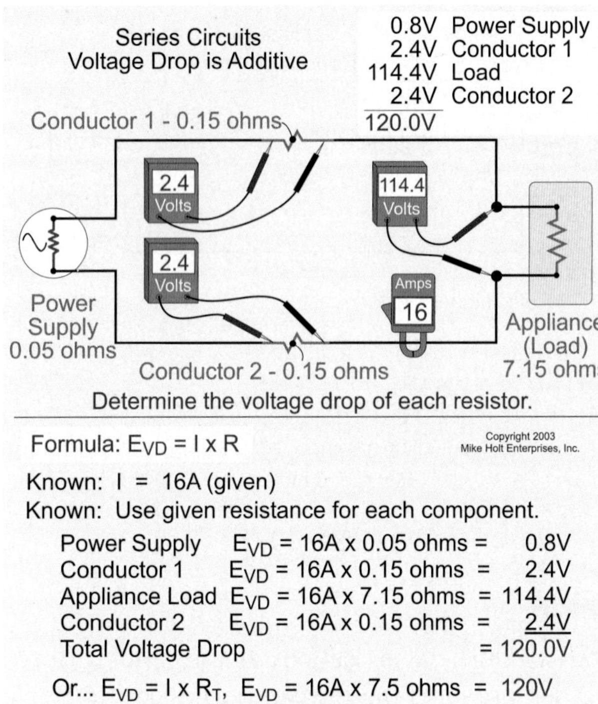

Figure 10–8

In addition, the voltage of the power supply is distributed or divided among the circuit resistances according to the Law of Proportion. The Law of Proportion means that the supply voltage is distributed among all the resistances, according to the proportion of resistance each resistance has relative to the total resistance. Figure 10–9

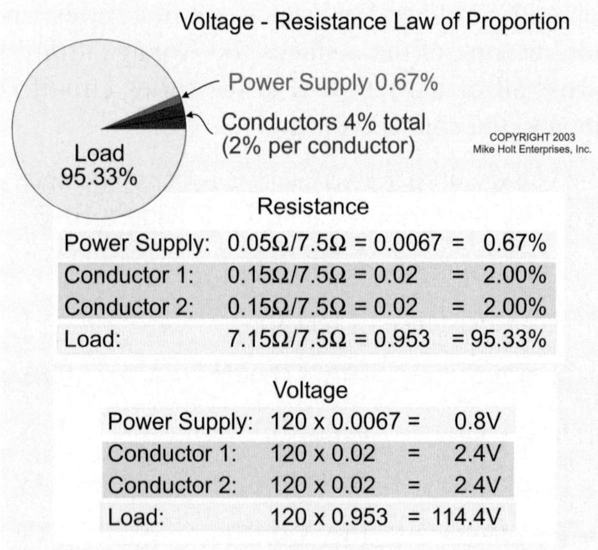

Figure 10–9

	Resistance	Percentage	Voltage
Power Source	0.05Ω	0.67%	0.8V
Conductor No. 1	0.15Ω	2.00%	2.4V
Appliance	7.15Ω	95.34%	114.4V
Conductor No. 2	0.15Ω	2.00%	2.4V
Total	7.50Ω	100%	120.0V

Kirchoff's Current Law

Kirchoff's Current Law states that the sum of currents flowing into a junction equals the sum of currents flowing away from the junction. Another way to say it is, current flowing through each resistor of the series circuit will be the same. Figure 10–10

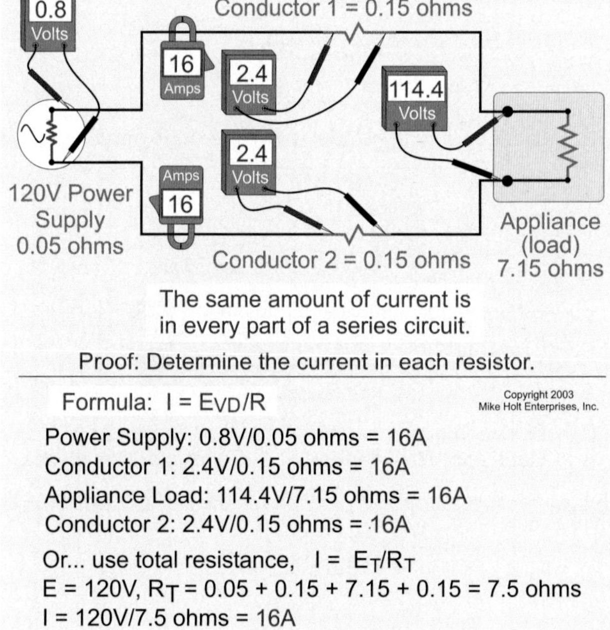

Figure 10–10

To calculate the current in a series circuit, you need to know the power-supply voltage (E_S) and the total circuit resistance (R_T). The current of the circuit can be determined by the formula $I_T = E_S/R_T$. In the following example, the current of the circuit is equal to 120V/7.5Ω = 16A. Since this is a series circuit, every component of the circuit has 16A flowing through it.

AUTHOR'S COMMENT: The current flowing through each resistance can be calculated by I = E/R, where E (voltage) represents the voltage drop across the individual resistances, not the voltage source!

Power Source $I = \frac{0.8V}{0.05\Omega} = 16A$

Conductor No. 1 $I = \frac{2.4V}{0.15\Omega} = 16A$

Appliance $I = \frac{114.4V}{7.15\Omega} = 16A$

Conductor No. 2 $I = \frac{2.4V}{0.15\Omega} = 16A$

Total Resistance $I = \frac{120.0V}{7.5\Omega} = 16A$

Power

The power consumed in a series circuit will equal the sum of the power consumed by all of the resistances in the series circuit. The Law of Conservation of Energy states that the power supply (battery, etc.) will only produce as much power as that consumed by the circuit elements. Power is a result of current flowing through a resistance and is calculated by the formula $P = I^2 \times R$.

Example

Power Source $P = 16A^2 \times 0.05\Omega = 12.8W$

Conductor No. 1 $P = 16A^2 \times 0.15\Omega = 38.4W$

Appliance $P = 16A^2 \times 7.15\Omega = 1,830.4W$

Conductor No. 2 $P = 16A^2 \times 0.15\Omega = 38.4W$

Power can also be calculated according to the law of proportion.

	Resistance	Percentage	Power
Power Source	0.05Ω	0.67%	12.8W
Conductor No. 1	0.15Ω	2.00%	38.4W
Appliance	7.15Ω	95.34%	1,830.0W
Conductor No. 2	0.15Ω	2.00%	38.4W
Total Resistance	7.50Ω	100%	1,920.0W

10.3 Series Circuit Calculations

When performing series circuit calculations, the following steps should be helpful: Figure 10–11

Step 1 Determine the resistance of each resistive element in the circuit. Often, the resistance of each element is given in the problem. If you know the nameplate voltage and power (wattage) rating of the appliance or equipment, you can determine its resistance by the formula $R = E^2/P$.

E = Nameplate voltage rating (squared)

P = Nameplate power rating

Step 2 Calculate the total resistance (R_T) of the circuit, $R_T = R_1 + R_2 + R_3 + R_4$.

Step 3 The current of the circuit can be determined by the formula $I = E_S/R_T$.

E_S = Voltage Source

R_T = Total circuit resistance (Step 2)

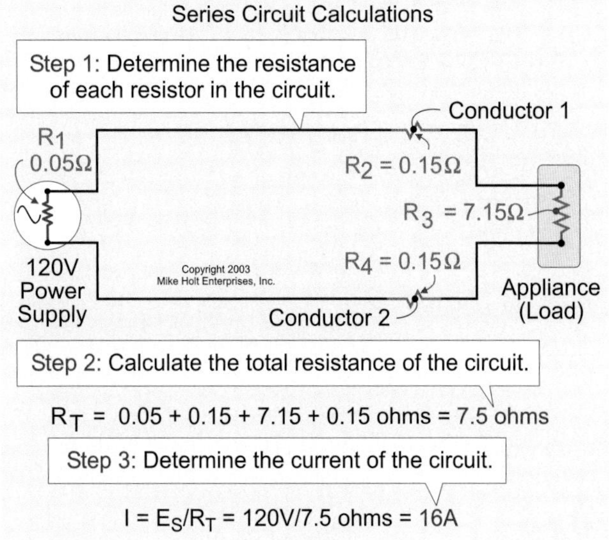
Series Circuit Calculations
Step 1: Determine the resistance of each resistor in the circuit.
Conductor 1
R1
0.05Ω
R2 = 0.15Ω
R3 = 7.15Ω
120V Power Supply
Copyright 2003 Mike Holt Enterprises, Inc.
R4 = 0.15Ω
Appliance (Load)
Conductor 2
Step 2: Calculate the total resistance of the circuit.
RT = 0.05 + 0.15 + 7.15 + 0.15 ohms = 7.5 ohms
Step 3: Determine the current of the circuit.
I = ES/RT = 120V/7.5 ohms = 16A

Figure 10–11

10.4 Power Calculations

If you know the current of the circuit and the resistance of each resistor, the power of each resistor can be determined by the formula $P = I^2 \times R$. Figure 10–12

I^2 = Current of circuit (squared) (Step 3)

R = Resistance of the resistor (Step 1)

The power of the circuit can be determined by adding up the power of all of the resistors or by the formula $P = I^2 \times R_T$.

I^2 = Current of the circuit (squared)

R_T = Resistance total of the circuit

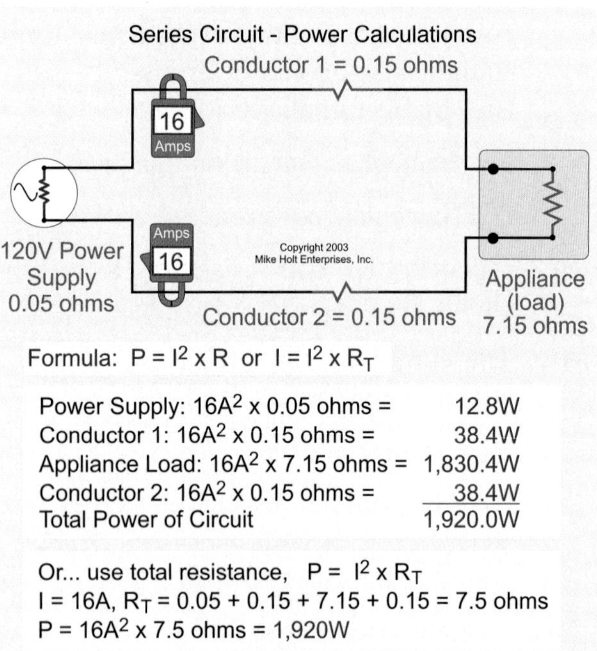

Series Circuit - Power Calculations
Conductor 1 = 0.15 ohms
16
Amps
Amps
16
120V Power Supply 0.05 ohms
Copyright 2003 Mike Holt Enterprises, Inc.
Appliance (load) 7.15 ohms
Conductor 2 = 0.15 ohms
Formula: P = I2 x R or I = I2 x RT
Power Supply: 16A2 x 0.05 ohms = 12.8W
Conductor 1: 16A2 x 0.15 ohms = 38.4W
Appliance Load: 16A2 x 7.15 ohms = 1,830.4W
Conductor 2: 16A2 x 0.15 ohms = 38.4W
Total Power of Circuit 1,920.0W
Or... use total resistance, P = I2 x RT
I = 16A, RT = 0.05 + 0.15 + 7.15 + 0.15 = 7.5 ohms
P = 16A2 x 7.5 ohms = 1,920W

Figure 10–12

10.5 Variations

There are often many different ways to solve an electrical circuit problem involving voltage, current, resistance and power. It is also often possible to verify or check one's work by solving the problem different ways.

10.6 Series Circuit Notes

Note 1: The total resistance of a series circuit is equal to the sum of all of the resistances of the circuit.

Note 2: Current is the same value through all of the resistances.

Note 3: The sum of the voltage drops across all resistances equals the voltage of the source.

Note 4: The sum of the power consumed by all resistors equals the total power consumed by the circuit.

10.7 Series-Connected Power Supplies

When power supplies are connected in series, the voltage of the power supply will be additive (provided the polarities are connected properly). Figure 10–13 and Figure 10–14

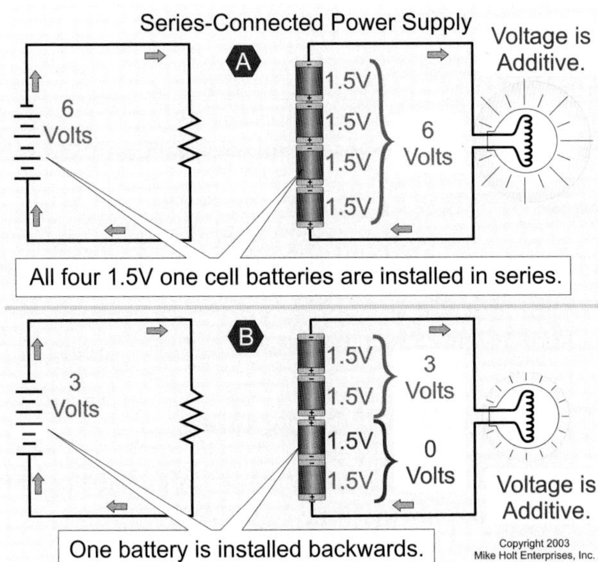

Figure 10–13

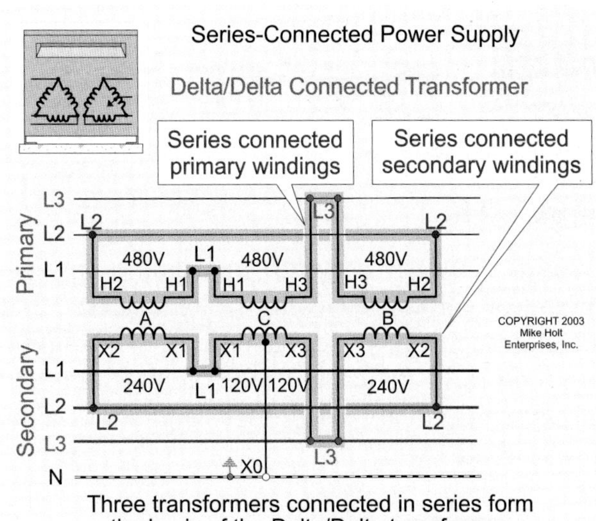

Figure 10–14

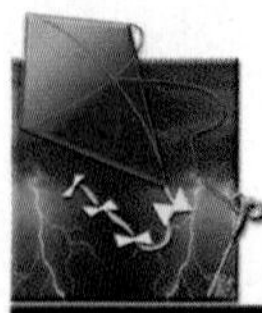

Unit 10 Summary

Introduction

A series circuit is a circuit in which a specific amount of current leaves the voltage source and flows through every electrical device in a single path before it returns to the voltage source. Current is identical through ALL circuit elements of the circuit.

10.1 Practical Uses of the Series Circuit

In a series circuit, if any part of the circuit is open, the current in the circuit will stop. For most practical purposes, series circuits (closed-loop systems) are not used for building wiring; however, they are often used for control and signal circuits.

The internal wiring of many types of equipment, such as motor windings, will be connected in series.

10.2 Understanding Series Calculations

Resistance

In a series circuit, the total circuit resistance is equal to the sum of all the series resistances. Resistance is additive: $R_T = R_1 + R_2 + R_3 + R_4$.

Kirchoff's Voltage Law

Kirchoff's Voltage Law states that in a series circuit, the sum of the voltages (or "voltage drops") across all of the resistors in the series circuit is equal to the applied voltage.

Kirchoff's Current Law

Kirchoff's Current Law states that the sum of currents flowing into a junction equals the sum of currents flowing away from the junction. Another way to say it is, current flowing through each resistor of the series circuit will the same.

Power

The power consumed in a series circuit will equal the sum of the power consumed by all of the resistances in the series circuit.

10.3 Series Circuit Calculations

When performing series circuit calculations, the following steps should be helpful:

Step 1 Determine the resistance of each resistive element in the circuit.

Step 2 Calculate the total resistance (R_T) of the circuit, $R_T = R_1 + R_2 + R_3 + R_4$.

Step 3 The current of the circuit can be determined by the formula: $I = E_S/R_T$.

E_S = Voltage Source

R_T = Total circuit resistance

10.4 Power Calculations

If you know the current of the circuit and the resistance of each resistor, the power of each resistor can be determined by the formula $P = I^2 \times R$.

10.5 Variations

There are often many different ways to solve an electrical circuit problem involving voltage, current, resistance and power.

10.6 Series Circuit Notes

Note 1: The total resistance of a series circuit is equal to the sum of all of the resistances of the circuit.

Note 2: Current is the same value through all of the resistances.

Note 3: The sum of the voltage drops across all resistances equals the voltage of the source.

Note 4: The sum of the power consumed by all resistors equals the total power consumed by the circuit.

10.7 Series-Connected Power Supplies

When power supplies are connected in series, the voltage of the power supply will be additive (provided the polarities are connected properly).

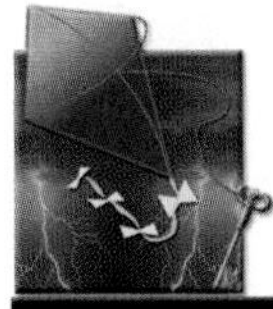

Unit 10 Conclusion

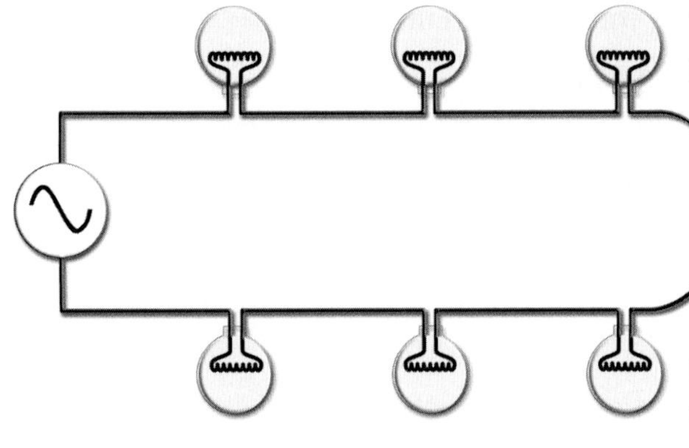

You now understand series circuits. In addition to knowing their uses and limitations, you know how to do calculations involving them. You've also learned Kirchoff's Law—and that means you won't be fooled by the misinformation floating around the industry about grounding versus bonding, as covered in the Annex. Once you work through the following problems, you will be ready to tackle parallel circuits.

Words to Live By: *A man is rich according to what he* is, *not according to what he* has.

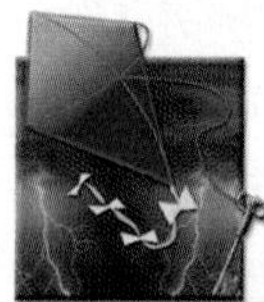

Unit 10 Practice Questions

Introduction

1. A series circuit is a circuit in which a specific amount of current leaves the voltage source and flows through every electrical device in a single path before it returns to the voltage source.

   (a) True (b) False

10.1 Practical Uses of the Series Circuit

2. For most practical purposes, series circuits are used for _____ circuits.

   (a) signal (b) control (c) a and b (d) none of these

3. A 115/230V rated motor connected to a 230V circuit must have the windings connected in series so that each winding will receive at least 230V.

   (a) True (b) False

10.2 Understanding Series Calculations

4. Resistance opposes the flow of electrons. In a series circuit, the total circuit resistance is equal to the sum of all the resistances in series.

   (a) True (b) False

5. The opposition to current flow results in a voltage drop of the circuit voltage.

   (a) True (b) False

6. Kirchoff's Voltage Law states that in a series circuit, the sum of the voltage drops across all of the resistors will equal the applied voltage.

   (a) True (b) False

7. No matter how many resistances there are in a series circuit, the sum of the voltages across all of the resistances will equal the voltage of the source according to the Law of Proportion.

   (a) True (b) False

8. Kirchoff's Current Law states that in a series circuit, the current is _____ through the transformer, the conductors, and the appliance.

   (a) proportional (b) distributed (c) additive (d) the same

9. The power consumed in a series circuit is equal to the power consumed by the largest resistance in the series circuit.

(a) True (b) False

10.3 Series Circuit Calculations

10. To determine the resistance of each resistive element in the circuit, use the formula $R = E^2/P$.

(a) True (b) False

11. To calculate the total resistance of the circuit: $R_T = R_1 + R_2 + R_3 + ...$

(a) True (b) False

12. The current of the circuit can be determined by the formula $I = E_S/R_T$.

(a) True (b) False

10.4 Power Calculations

13. If you know the current of the circuit and the resistance of each resistor, the power of each resistor can be determined by the formula $P = I^2 \times R$.

(a) True (b) False

10.5 Variations

14. There can never be variations in the formulas used or the order in which they are used for series circuits.

(a) True (b) False

10.7 Series-Connected Power Supplies

15. When power supplies are connected in series, the circuit voltage remains the same as when only one power supply is connected to it, provided that all the polarities are connected properly.

(a) True (b) False

UNIT 11 Parallel Circuits

Introduction

"Parallel" is a term used to describe a method of connecting electrical components so that there are two or more paths on which current may flow. Figure 11–1

A parallel circuit is one with several different paths for the electricity to travel. It's like a river that has been divided up into smaller streams and all the streams come back to form the river once again.

A parallel circuit has extremely different characteristics than a series circuit. For one, the total resistance of a parallel circuit is not equal to the sum of the resistors. The total resistance in a parallel circuit is always less than any of the branch resistances. Adding more parallel resistances to the paths cause the total resistance in the circuit to decrease.

11.1 Practical Uses of the Parallel Circuits

For most purposes, parallel circuits are used for building wiring.

Receptacle

When wiring receptacles on a circuit, they are connected in parallel to each other. Figure 11–2

Lighting

Another example would be lights connected in parallel to each other. Figure 11–3A

The major advantage of a parallel circuit is that if any branch of the circuit is opened or turned off, the power supply continues to provide voltage to the remaining parts of the circuit. Figure 11–3B

Other Uses

Parallel circuits, also called open-loop systems, are used for fire alarm pull stations and smoke detectors. If any initiating device (pull station or smoke detector) closes, the signal circuit is complete and the alarm will sound. Figure 11–4

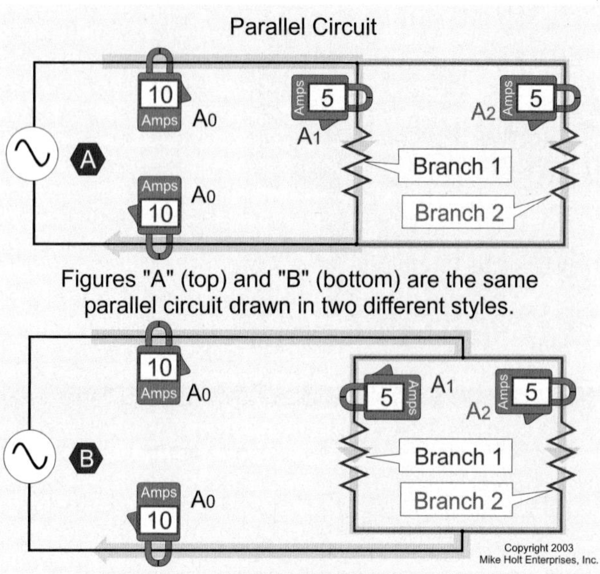
Parallel Circuit
10
Amps
Ao
5
Amps
A1
A2
5
Branch 1
Branch 2
A
B
Figures "A" (top) and "B" (bottom) are the same parallel circuit drawn in two different styles.
Copyright 2003 Mike Holt Enterprises, Inc.

Figure 11–1

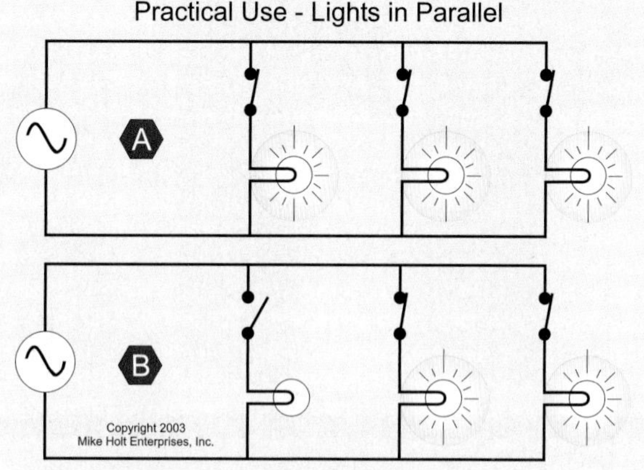
Practical Use - Lights in Parallel
A
B
Copyright 2003 Mike Holt Enterprises, Inc.
An advantage of parallel circuits is that if any part of the circuit is opened, the remaining portion of the circuit is still operable.

Figure 11–3

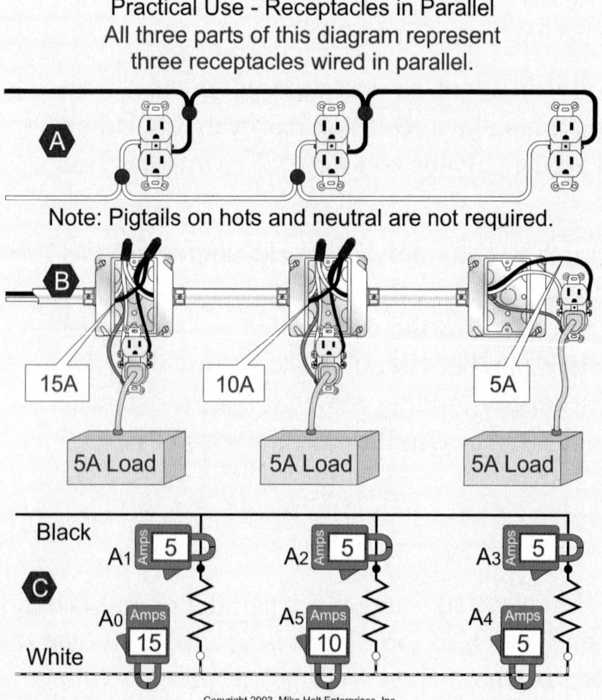
Practical Use - Receptacles in Parallel
All three parts of this diagram represent three receptacles wired in parallel.
A
Note: Pigtails on hots and neutral are not required.
B
15A
10A
5A
5A Load
5A Load
5A Load
Black
A1
A2
A3
C
Ao
A5
A4
15
10
5
White
Copyright 2003 Mike Holt Enterprises, Inc.

Figure 11–2

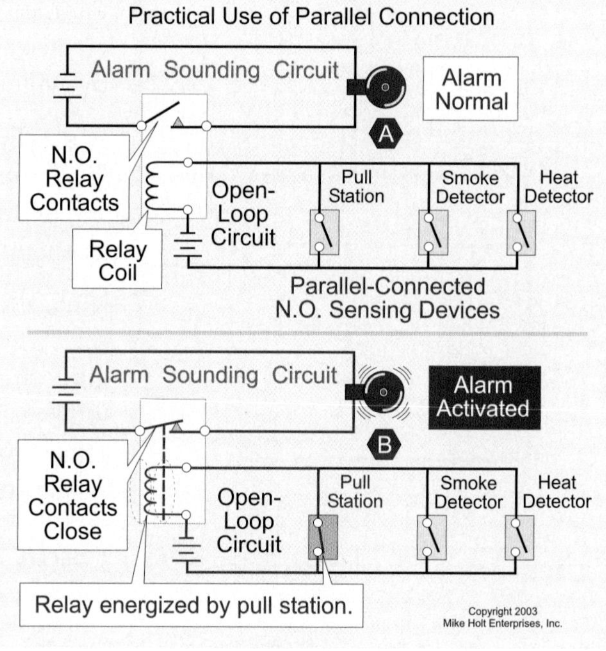
Practical Use of Parallel Connection
Alarm Sounding Circuit
Alarm Normal
A
N.O. Relay Contacts
Relay Coil
Open-Loop Circuit
Pull Station
Smoke Detector
Heat Detector
Parallel-Connected N.O. Sensing Devices
Alarm Sounding Circuit
Alarm Activated
B
N.O. Relay Contacts Close
Open-Loop Circuit
Pull Station
Smoke Detector
Heat Detector
Relay energized by pull station.
Copyright 2003 Mike Holt Enterprises, Inc.

Figure 11–4

Often electrical components within appliances, such as water heaters and motors, have their components connected in parallel. **Figure 11–5**

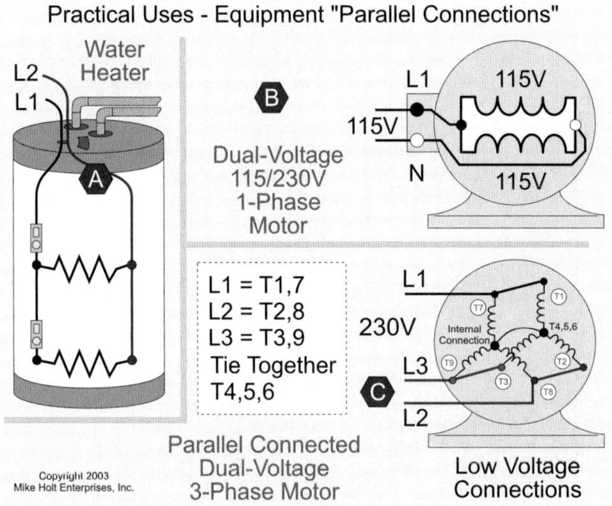

Figure 11–5

11.2 Understanding Parallel Calculations

It is important to understand the relationship between voltage, current, power, and resistance of a parallel circuit.

Voltage

In a pure parallel circuit (one with no resistors in series with the parallel resistors), the voltage drop across each resistance is equal to the voltage supplied by the power source (ignoring any voltage drop in the source and conductors). **Figure 11–6**

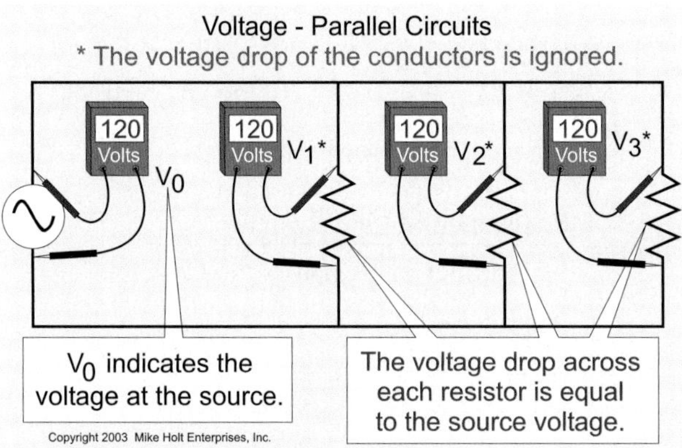

Figure 11–6

For the moment, we will ignore the voltage drop and power loss effects of the conductor and power supply as it is usually much, much smaller than the drop across the resistive elements.

Kirchoff's Current Law

In a parallel circuit, current from the power source will branch in different directions and magnitudes. The current in each branch is dependent on the resistance of each branch. Kirchoff's Current Law states that the total current provided by the source to a parallel circuit will be equal to the sum of the currents of all of the branches.

The current in each branch can be calculated by the formula I = E/R. **Figure 11–7**

E = Voltage of each branch.

R = Resistance of each branch (appliance).

The current of each branch is as follows: I = E/R

Coffee Pot (R_1) P = 120V/16Ω = 7.50A

Skillet (R_2) P = 120V/13Ω = 9.17A

Blender (R_3) P = 120V/36Ω = 3.33A

Total Current = 20.00A

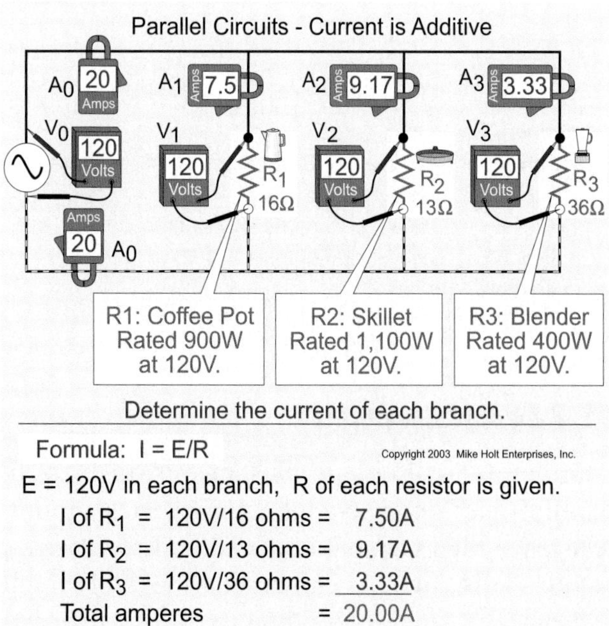

Figure 11–7

AUTHOR'S COMMENT: The resistance and currents have been rounded off.

Power

When current flows through a resistor, power is consumed. The power consumed by each branch of the parallel circuit can be determined by the formulas: $P = I^2 \times R$, $P = E \times I$, or $P = E^2/R$.

The total power consumed in a parallel circuit will equal the sum of the branches' powers. **Figure 11–8** Using the following formula $P = I^2 \times R$, determine the power of each resistor:

Coffee Pot	$P =$	$7.50A^2 \times 16\Omega$	= 900W
Skillet	$P =$	$9.17A^2 \times 13\Omega$	= 1,100W
Blender	$P =$	$3.33A^2 \times 36\Omega$	= 400W
Total Circuit Power			= 2,400W

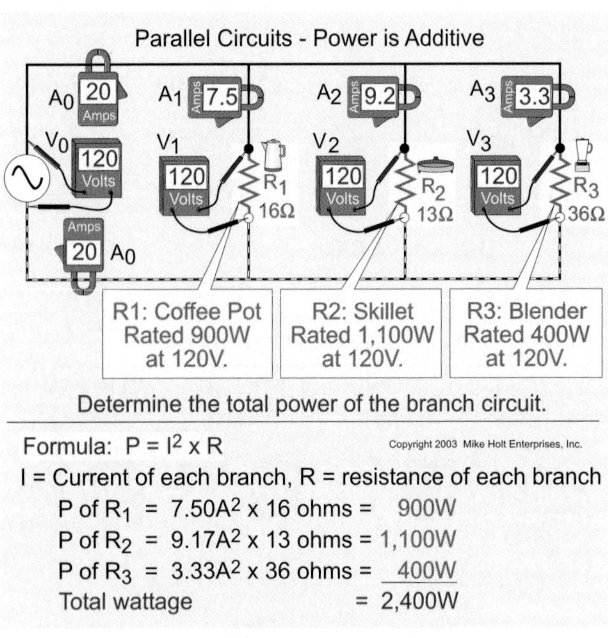

Figure 11–8

11.3 Circuit Resistance

Calculating total circuit resistance is different in parallel and series circuits. In a series circuit, resistance total is equal to the sum of resistances, **Figure 11–9A**. In a parallel circuit, the total circuit resistance is always less than the smallest resistance. **Figure 11–9B**

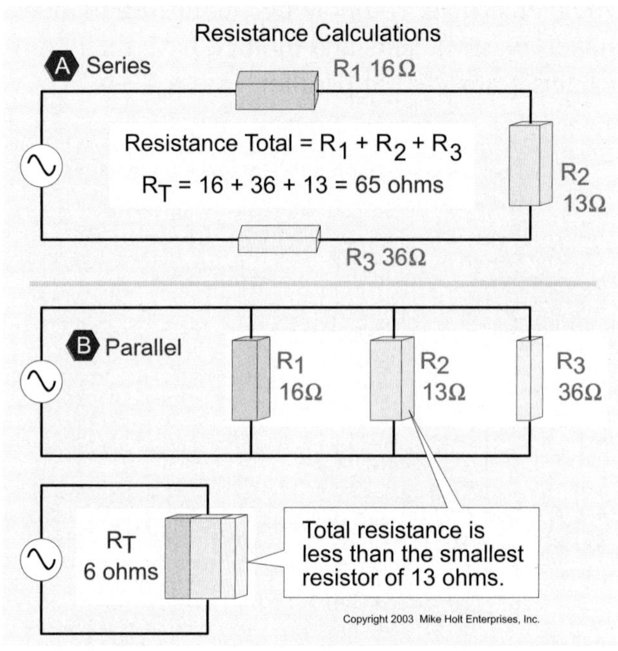

Figure 11–9

There are three basic methods of calculating the total resistance of a parallel circuit; the Equal Resistance method, the Product-Over-Sum method, and the Reciprocal method.

Equal Resistance Method

When all of the resistances of the parallel circuit have the same resistance, the total resistance is found by dividing the resistance of one resistive element by the total number of resistors in parallel.

Example A

The total resistance of three 10Ω resistors in parallel is _____. **Figure 11–10**

(a) 10Ω (b) 20Ω
(c) 30Ω (d) none of these

• Answer: (d) none of these

$$R_T = \frac{\text{Resistance of One Resistor}}{\text{Number of Resistors}}$$

$$R_T = \frac{10\Omega}{3}$$

$$R_T = 3.33\Omega$$

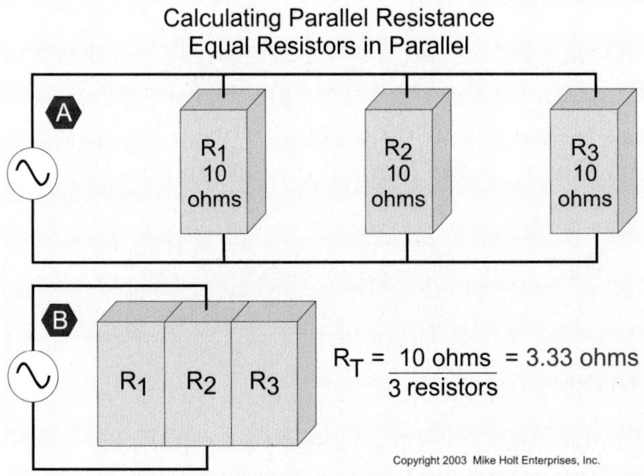

Figure 11–10

Example B

The total resistance of ten 10Ω resistors in parallel is _____.

(a) 10Ω (b) 100Ω
(c) 50Ω (d) none of these

• Answer: (d) none of these

$$R_T = \frac{\text{Resistance of One Resistor}}{\text{Number of Resistors}}$$

$$R_T = \frac{10\Omega}{10}$$

$$R_T = 1\Omega$$

Product-Over-Sum Method

This method is used to calculate the resistance of two resistances at a time:

$$R_T = \frac{R_1 \text{ x } R_2 \text{ (product)}}{R_1 + R_2 \text{ (sum)}}$$

AUTHOR'S COMMENT: The term "product" means the answer obtained when numbers are multiplied. The term "sum" means the answer obtained by adding a group of numbers.

Example

The resistance of a 900W coffee pot is 16Ω and the resistance of a 1,100W skillet is approximately 13Ω; the appliances are connected in parallel. What is the total resistance of the two appliances? **Figure 11–11, A and B**

(a) 16Ω (b) 13Ω
(c) 29Ω (d) 7.2Ω

• Answer: (d) 7.2Ω

The total resistance of a parallel circuit is always less than the smallest resistance.

$$R_T = \frac{(R_1 \text{ x } R_2)}{(R_1 + R_2)}$$

$$R_T = \frac{(16 \text{ x } 13)}{(16 + 13)}$$

$$R_T = 7.20\Omega$$

The "product-over-sum" method can be used to determine the resistance total for more than two resistors in a parallel circuit, but only two resistors can be dealt with at a time. If more than two resistances are in parallel, the "product-over-sum" method must be applied several times, each time considering the equivalent resistance of the last two resistances looked at as a "new" resistance for the equation.

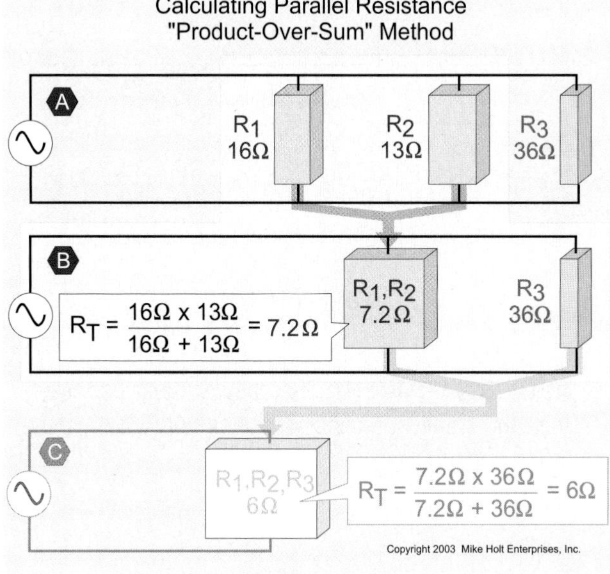

Figure 11–11

Example

What is the total resistance of a 16Ω, 13Ω, and 36Ω resistor connected in parallel? **Figure 11–12**

(a) 43Ω (b) 65Ω
(c) 6Ω (d) 26Ω

• Answer: (c) 6Ω

The 16 and 13Ω resistors are treated as an "equivalent" single resistor of 7.2Ω (previous example). The resistance of the circuit would be calculated as follows: **Figure 11–12, B and C**

$$R_T = \frac{R_{1,2} \text{ x } R_3}{R_{1,2} \text{ x } R_3}$$

$$R_T = \frac{7.2 \text{ x } 36}{7.2 \text{ x } 36}$$

$$R_T = 6\Omega$$

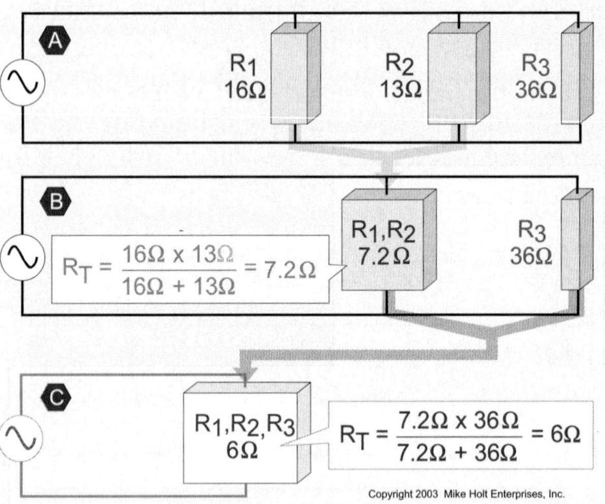

Figure 11–12

AUTHOR'S COMMENT: The answer must be less than the smallest resistor of the circuit (13Ω).

Reciprocal Method

The advantage of the "reciprocal" method in determining the total resistance of a parallel circuit is that this formula can be used for as many resistances as the parallel circuit contains.

$$R_T = \frac{1}{(1/R_1 + 1/R_2 + 1/R_3 \ldots)}$$

Example

What is the resistance total of a 16Ω, 13Ω, and 36Ω resistor connected in parallel?

(a) 13Ω (b) 16Ω
(c) 36Ω (d) 6Ω

• Answer: (d) 6Ω

$$R_T = \frac{1}{(1/_{16}\Omega + 1/_{13}\Omega + 1/_{36}\Omega)}$$

$$R_T = \frac{1}{(0.0625\Omega + 0.0769\Omega + 0.0278\Omega)}$$

$$R_T = \frac{1}{(0.1672\Omega)}$$

$$R_T = 6\Omega$$

11.4 Parallel Circuit Notes

A parallel circuit has the following characteristics:

Note 1: Resistance total is less than the smallest resistance and you can find total resistance in a parallel circuit with the following formula:

$$R_T = \frac{1}{(1/R_1 + 1/R_2 + 1/R_3 \ldots)}$$

Note 2: The sum of the currents through each path is equal to the total current that flows from the source.

Note 3: Power total is equal to the sum of the branches' powers.

Note 4: Voltage is the same across each component of the parallel circuit.

Note 5: A parallel circuit has two or more paths for current to flow through.

11.5 Parallel-Connected Power Supplies

When power supplies are connected in parallel, the voltage remains the same, but the current, or in the case of batteries the amp-hour capacity, will be increased. To place batteries in parallel to each other, connect them with the proper polarity, which is (+) to (+) and (–) to (–). Figure 11–13A

AUTHOR'S COMMENT: When jumping a car battery, place the red cables on the positive (+) terminals and the black cables on the negative (–) terminals. Figure 11–13B

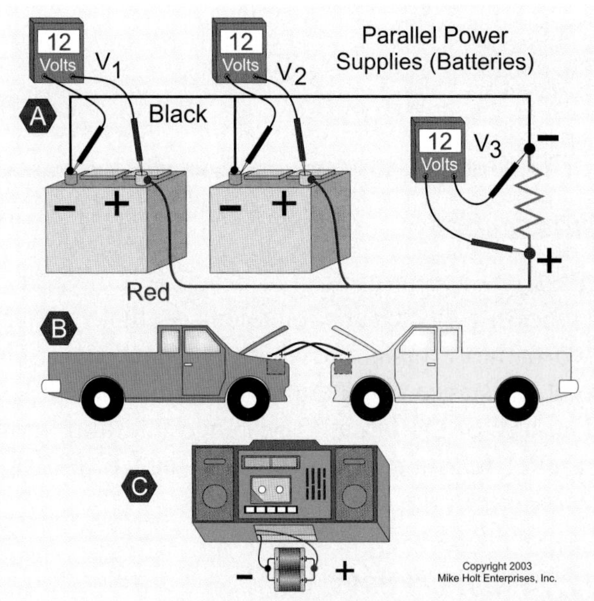

Figure 11–13

Batteries are often connected in parallel in radios, toys and other appliances that operate on dc power. Figure 11–13C

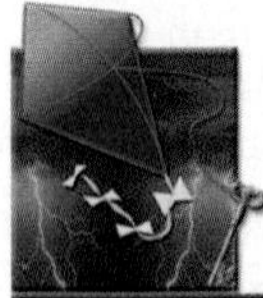

Unit 11 Summary

Introduction

"Parallel" is a term used to describe a method of connecting electrical components so that there are two or more paths on which current flows. The total resistance of a parallel circuit is always less than any of the branch resistances. Adding more parallel resistances to the paths cause the total resistance in the circuit to decrease.

11.1 Practical Uses

For most purposes, parallel circuits are used for building wiring. The major advantage of a parallel circuit is that if any one branch of the circuit is opened or turned off, the current will continue to provide power on the remaining part of the circuit.

Parallel circuits (open-loop systems) are often used for fire alarm pull stations and smoke detectors. If any initiating device (pull station or smoke detector) closes, the signal circuit is complete and the alarm will sound.

11.2 Understanding Parallel Calculations

It is important to understand the relationship between voltage, current, power, and resistance of a parallel circuit.

Voltage

In a pure parallel circuit, the voltage drop across each resistance is equal to the voltage supplied by the power source.

Kirchoff's Current Law

In a parallel circuit, current from the power source will branch in different directions and magnitudes. The current in each branch is dependent on the resistance of each branch. Kirchoff's Current Law states that the total current provided by the source to a parallel circuit will be equal to the sum of the currents of all of the branches.

Power

The total power consumed in a parallel circuit will equal the sum of the branches' powers.

11.3 Circuit Resistance

In a parallel circuit, the total circuit resistance is always less than the smallest resistance. There are three basic methods of calculating the total resistance of a parallel circuit: the Equal Resistance method, the Product-Over-Sum method, and the Reciprocal method.

Equal Resistance Method

When all the resistances of the parallel circuit have the same resistance, the total resistance is found by dividing the resistance of one resistive element by the total number of resistors in parallel.

Product-Over-Sum Method

The "product-over-sum" method can be used to determine the resistance total for more than two resistors in a parallel circuit, but only two resistors can be dealt with at a time. If more than two resistances are in parallel, the "product-over-sum" method must be applied several times, each time considering the equivalent resistance of the last two resistances looked at as a "new" resistance for the equation.

$$R_T = \frac{R_1 \text{ x } R_2 \text{ (product)}}{R_1 + R_2 \text{ (sum)}}$$

Reciprocal Method

The advantage of the "reciprocal method" in determining the total resistance of a parallel circuit is that this formula can be used for as many resistances as the parallel circuit contains.

$$R_T = \frac{1}{(1/R_1 + 1/R_2 + 1/R_3 \ldots)}$$

11.4 Parallel Circuit Notes

A parallel circuit has the following characteristics:

Note 1: Resistance total is less than the smallest resistance.

Note 2: The sum of the currents through each path is equal to the total current that flows from the source.

Note 3: Power total is equal to the sum of the branches' powers.

Note 4: Voltage is the same across each component of the parallel circuit.

Note 5: A parallel circuit has two or more paths for current to flow through.

11.5 Parallel-Connected Power Supplies

When power supplies are connected in parallel, the voltage remains the same, but the current or amp-hour capacity will be increased. To place batteries in parallel to each other, connect them with the proper polarity, which is (+) to (+) and (–) to (–).

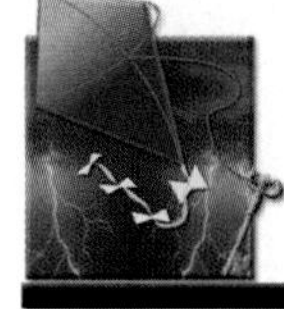

Unit 11 Conclusion

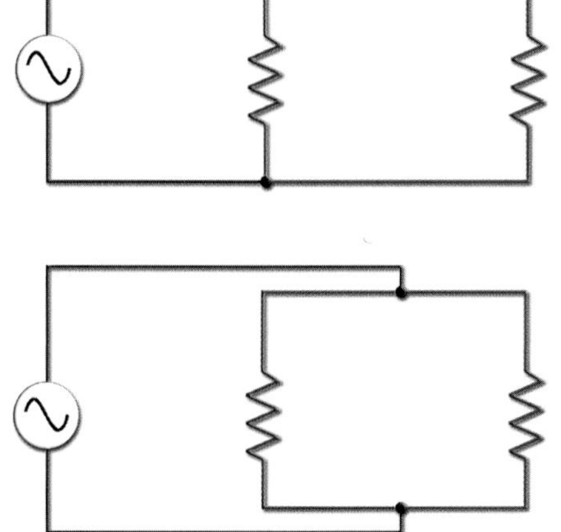

You've now studied series circuits and parallel circuits. While it's important to understand both kinds of circuits, their applications, and calculations involving them, you need to take this knowledge to the next level. You need to understand circuits that combine series and parallel. After you work through the parallel circuit problems, we'll look at those combination circuits.

Words to Live By: ***Sometimes we are so busy adding up our troubles that we forget to count our blessings.***

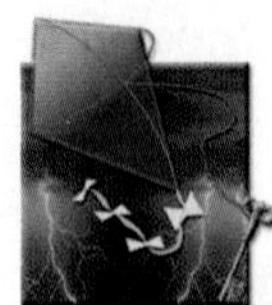

Unit 11 Practice Questions

Introduction

1. A parallel circuit is a circuit where there are two or more paths on which current may flow.

   (a) True (b) False

11.2 Understanding Parallel Calculations

2. In a parallel circuit, the voltage drop across each resistance is equal to the sum of the voltage drops of each of the resistors in parallel.

   (a) True (b) False

3. According to Kirchoff's Current Law, the total current provided by the source to a parallel circuit will equal the sum of the currents of all of the branches.

   (a) True (b) False

4. The total power consumed in a parallel circuit equals the sum of the branches' powers.

   (a) True (b) False

11.3 Circuit Resistance

5. In a parallel circuit, the total circuit resistance is always greater than the smallest resistance.

   (a) True (b) False

6. The total resistance of a parallel circuit can be calculated by the _____ method.

   (a) equal resistance (b) product-over-sum (c) reciprocal (d) any of these

7. According to the equal resistance method, when all the resistances of the parallel circuit have the same resistance, divide the resistance of one element by the largest resistor in parallel.

   (a) True (b) False

8. The product-over-sum method is used to calculate the resistance of _____ resistance(s) at a time.

   (a) one (b) two (c) three (d) four

9. The advantage of the reciprocal method is that the formula can be used for as many resistances as the parallel circuit contains.

   (a) True (b) False

11.5 Parallel-Connected Power Supplies

10. When power supplies are connected in parallel, the voltage remains the same, but the current or amp-hour capacity will be increased.

    (a) True (b) False

Notes

UNIT 12 Series-Parallel Circuits

Introduction

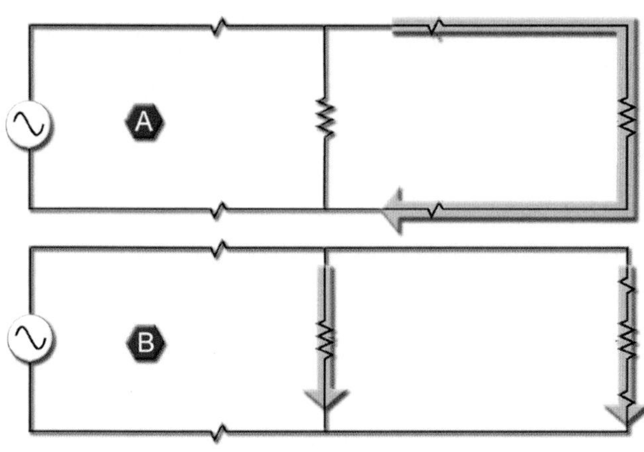

A series-parallel circuit is a circuit that contains some resistances in series and some in parallel to each other. That portion of the series-parallel circuit that contains resistances in series must comply with the rules for series circuits. That portion of the series-parallel circuit that contains resistances in parallel must comply with the rules for parallel circuits. In all cases, however, it's good to remember that Ohm's Law always prevails. Figure 12–1

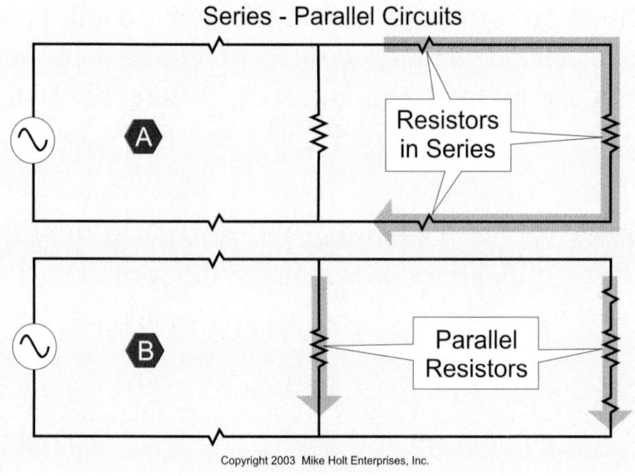

Figure 12–1

12.1 Review of Series and Parallel Circuits

To understand series-parallel circuits, we must review the rules for series and parallel circuits.

Series Circuit Review, Figure 12–2

Note 1: The total resistance of the series circuit is equal to the sum of all of the resistances of the circuit.

Note 2: Current is constant.

Note 3: The sum of the voltage drop of all resistances must equal the voltage of the source.

Note 4: The sum of the power consumed by all resistances equals the total power of the circuit.

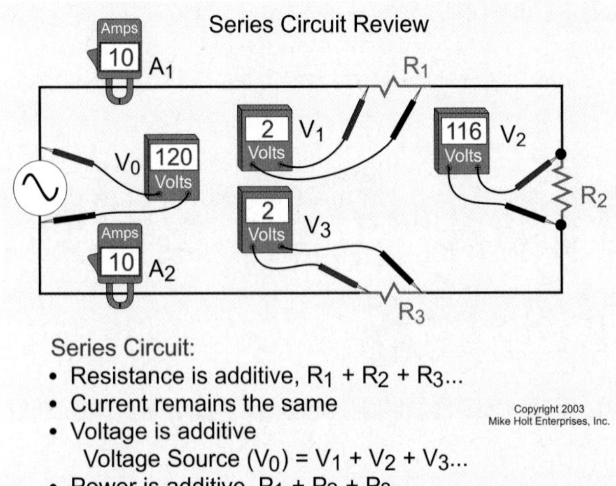

Series Circuit Review
Series Circuit:
• Resistance is additive, R1 + R2 + R3...
• Current remains the same
• Voltage is additive
Voltage Source (V0) = V1 + V2 + V3...
• Power is additive, P1 + P2 + P3...
Copyright 2003 Mike Holt Enterprises, Inc.

Figure 12–2

Parallel Circuit Review, Figure 12–3

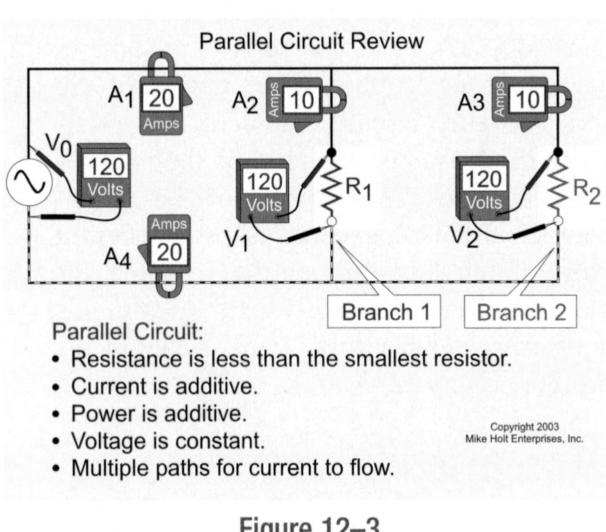

Parallel Circuit Review
Branch 1
Branch 2
Parallel Circuit:
• Resistance is less than the smallest resistor.
• Current is additive.
• Power is additive.
• Voltage is constant.
• Multiple paths for current to flow.
Copyright 2003 Mike Holt Enterprises, Inc.

Figure 12–3

Note 1: Resistance total is less than the smallest resistance and you can find total resistance in a parallel circuit with the following formula:

$$R_T = \frac{1}{(1/R_1 + 1/R_2 + 1/R_3 ...)}$$

Note 2: The sum of the currents through each path is equal to the total current that flows from the source.

Note 3: Power total is equal to the sum of the branches' powers.

Note 4: Voltage is the same across each component of the parallel circuit.

Note 5: A parallel circuit has two or more paths for current to flow through.

12.2 Working Series-Parallel Circuits

When working with series-parallel circuits, it is best to redraw the circuit so you can see the series components and the parallel branches. Each circuit should be examined to determine the best plan of attack—some turn out to be easier to analyze if you tackle the parallel elements first and then combine them with the series elements. Figure 12–4

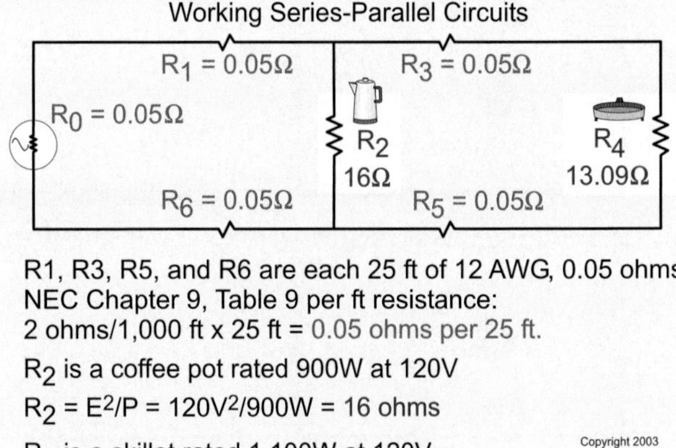

Figure 12–4

Other circuits are best worked by combining series elements first and then combining the result with the parallel resistances. In Figure 12–4, the series combination of R_3, R_4, and R_5 is the first step.

Step 1 Series: Determine the resistance total of each series branch using the formula:

$R_T = R_3 + R_4 + R_5$. Figure 12–5A

R_3 Conductor (25 ft of 12 AWG)	=	0.05Ω
R_4 Skillet (1,100W)	=	13.09Ω
R_5 Conductor (25 ft of 12 AWG)	=	0.05Ω
		13.19Ω

The circuit can now be redrawn showing the relationship between the two conductors and the two parallel branches. **Figure 12–5B**

Step 2 Parallel: Determine the resistance total of the two parallel branches. **Figure 12–5B**

AUTHOR'S COMMENT: The resistance total of the two branches will be less than that of the smallest branch (13.19Ω). Since we are only trying to determine the total resistance of two parallel branches, the Product-Over-Sum method can determine the resistance.

$$R\ Total = \frac{(R_2 \times R_{3,4,5})}{(R_2 + R_{3,4,5})}$$

$$R\ Total = \frac{(16\Omega \times 13.19\Omega)}{(16\Omega + 13.19\Omega)}$$

$$R\ Total = 7.23\Omega$$

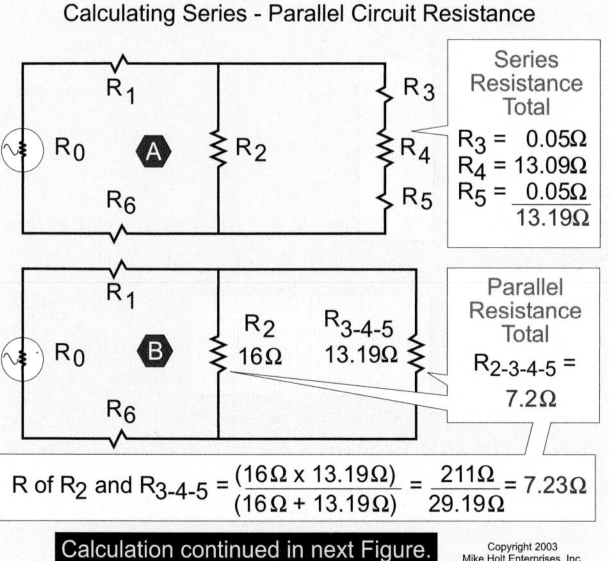

Figure 12–5

AUTHOR'S COMMENT: When working series-parallel circuits, keep breaking the circuit down from series to parallel to series to parallel, etc., until you have only one resistance. **Figure 12–6**

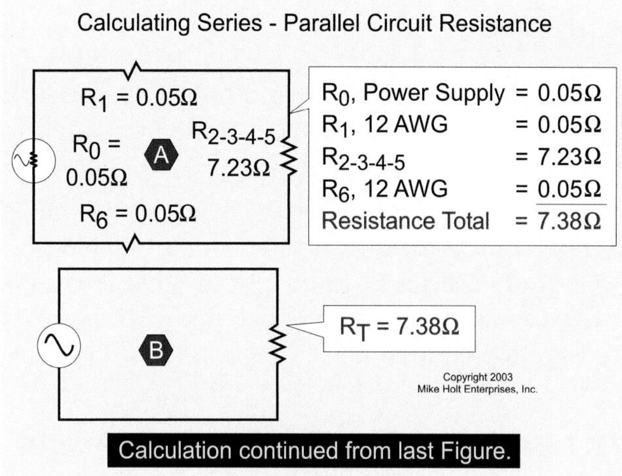

Figure 12–6

12.3 Voltage

Even though the current is different in the different resistors, remember that Ohm's Law always works. Every complicated problem is really just a series of easy problems that are waiting to be worked out. To calculate the voltage of each resistor, simply consider each one on a case by case basis and multiply its value by the current flowing through it.

AUTHOR'S COMMENT: Determining the current flowing through each resistor is very complicated and beyond the scope of this textbook.

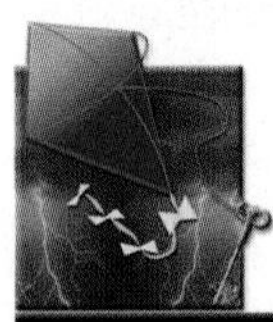

Unit 12 Summary

Introduction

A series-parallel circuit is a circuit that contains some resistances in series and some in parallel to each other. That portion of the series-parallel circuit that contains resistances in series must comply with the rules for series circuits. That portion of the series-parallel circuit that contains resistances in parallel must comply with the rules for parallel circuits.

12.1 Review of Series and Parallel Circuits

Series Circuit Review

Note 1: The total resistance of the series circuit is equal to the sum of all of the resistances of the circuit.

Note 2: Current is constant.

Note 3: The sum of the voltage drop of all resistances must equal the voltage of the source.

Note 4: The sum of the power consumed by all resistances equals the total power of the circuit.

Parallel Circuit Review

Note 1: Resistance total is less than the smallest resistance and you can find total resistance in a parallel circuit with the following formula:

$$R_T = \frac{1}{(^1/_{R_1} + {}^1/_{R_2} + {}^1/_{R_3} \ldots)}$$

Note 2: The sum of the currents through each path is equal to the total current that flows from the source.

Note 3: Power total is equal to the sum of the branches' powers.

Note 4: Voltage is the same across each component of the parallel circuit.

Note 5: A parallel circuit has two or more paths for current to flow through.

12.2 Working Series-Parallel Circuits

When working with series-parallel circuits, it is best to redraw the circuit so you can see the series components and the parallel branches. When working series-parallel circuits, keep breaking the circuit down from series to parallel to series to parallel, etc., until you have only one resistance.

12.3 Voltage

Even though the current is different in the different resistors, remember that Ohm's Law always works. Every complicated problem is really just a series of easy problems that are waiting to be worked out. To calculate the voltage of each resistor, simply consider each one on a case by case basis and multiply its value by the current flowing through it.

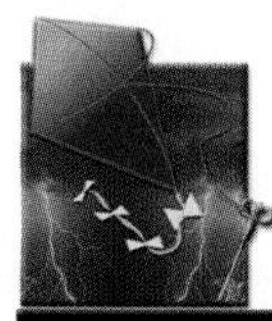

Unit 12 Conclusion

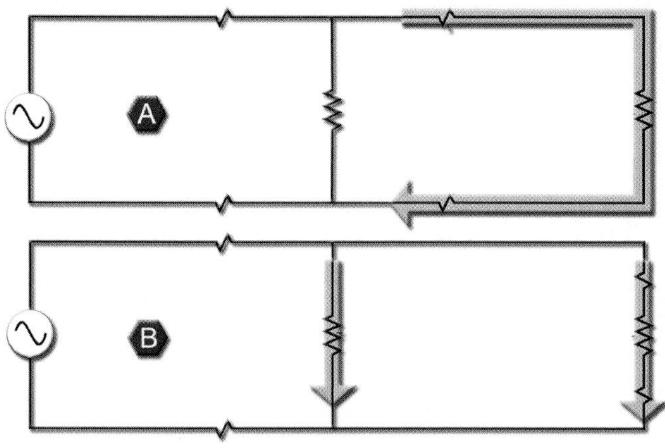

You may recall from Unit 1 that when elements combine to form compounds, the result is something that has the characteristics of neither element. In a mixture, on the other hand, the elements retain their individual characteristics. As you can see, series-parallel circuits act like mixtures. You can separate out the individual series and parallel circuits.

Words to Live By: *The trouble with the guy who talks too fast is that he often says something he hasn't thought of yet.*

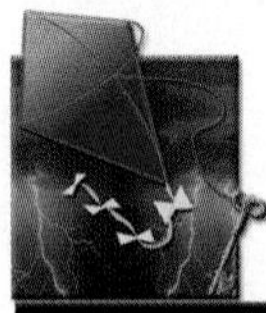

Unit 12 Practice Questions

Introduction

1. A _____ is a circuit that contains some resistances in series and some resistances in parallel with each other.

   (a) parallel circuit (b) series circuit (c) series-parallel circuit (d) none of these

2. That portion of the series-parallel circuit that contains resistances in series must comply with the rules for series circuits.

   (a) True (b) False

3. That portion of the series-parallel circuit that contains resistances in parallel must comply with the rules for parallel circuits.

   (a) True (b) False

12.2 Working Series-Parallel Circuits

4. When working with series-parallel circuits, it is best to redraw the circuit so you can see the series components and the parallel branches.

   (a) True (b) False

UNIT 13

Multiwire Circuits

Introduction

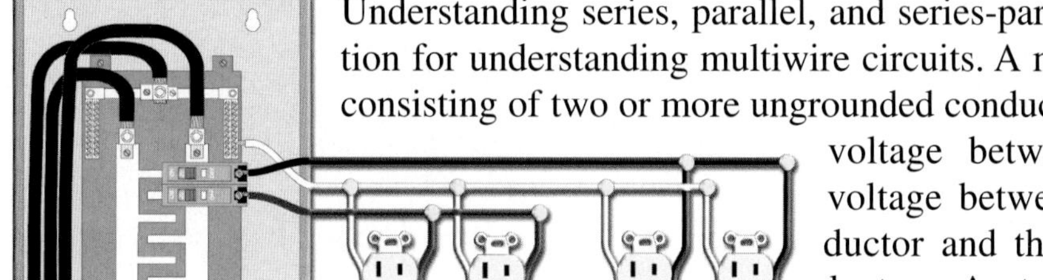

Understanding series, parallel, and series-parallel circuits is the foundation for understanding multiwire circuits. A multiwire circuit is a circuit consisting of two or more ungrounded conductors (hot wires) that have a voltage between them, and an equal voltage between each ungrounded conductor and the grounded (neutral) conductor. A typical 3-wire, 120/240V, single-phase (1Ø) circuit is an example. Figure 13–1

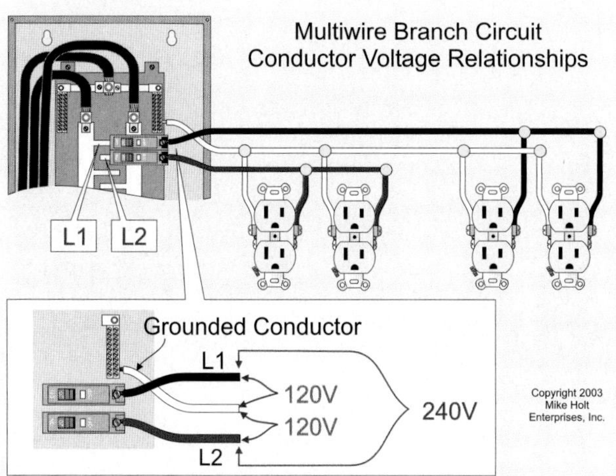

Figure 13–1

13.1 Neutral Conductor

According to the IEEE Dictionary, a neutral conductor is the conductor that has an equal potential difference between it and the other output conductors of a 3- or 4-wire system. Therefore, a neutral conductor would be the white/gray wire from a 3-wire, 120/240V, single-phase (1Ø), or a 4-wire, 120/208V, three-phase (3Ø) system. Figure 13–2

AUTHOR'S COMMENT: Since a neutral conductor can only be from a 3- or 4-wire system, the white wire of a 2-wire, 120V, single-phase or 4-wire, 120/240V, three-phase high-leg delta system is not a neutral conductor—it's a grounded conductor. Figure 13–3

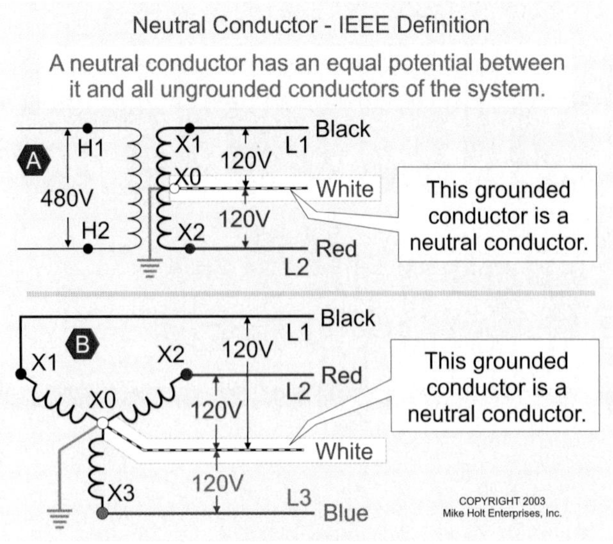

Figure 13–2

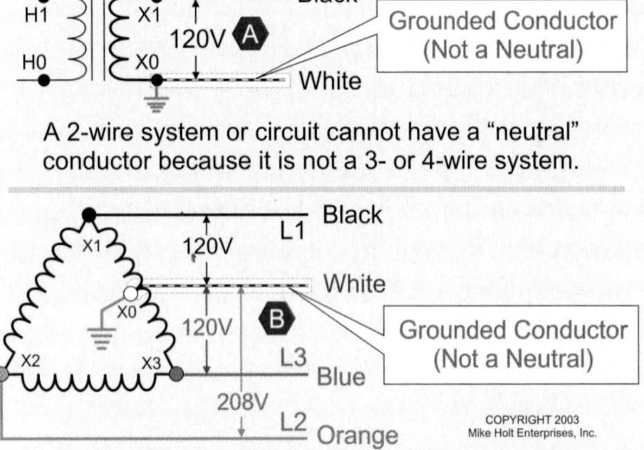

Figure 13–3

13.2 Grounded Conductor

The grounded conductor, according to the *NEC*, is a conductor that is intentionally grounded. In the case of home wiring (3-wire, 120/240V, single-phase), the grounded conductor is often called the neutral conductor, and it will be either white or gray in color in accordance with the *National Electrical Code*.

AUTHOR'S COMMENT: For convenience, I will refer to the neutral and the grounded conductor as the grounded (neutral) conductor.

13.3 Current Flow on the Grounded (Neutral) Conductor

To understand the current flow on the grounded (neutral) conductor, review the following circuits.

2-Wire Circuit

The current flowing in the grounded (neutral) conductor of a 2-wire circuit will be the same as the current flowing in the ungrounded (hot) conductor. **Figure 13–4**

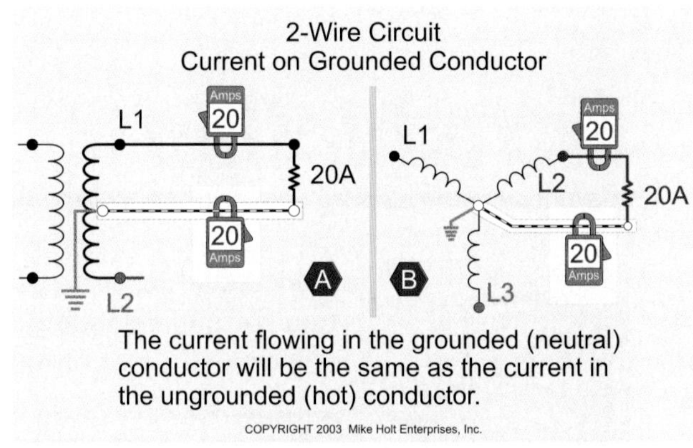

Figure 13–4

3-Wire, 120/240V, Single-Phase Circuit

The current flowing in the grounded (neutral) conductor of a 3-wire, 120/240V, single-phase circuit will equal the difference in current flowing in the ungrounded conductors ($I_N = I_{Line1} - I_{Line2}$). **Figure 13–5**

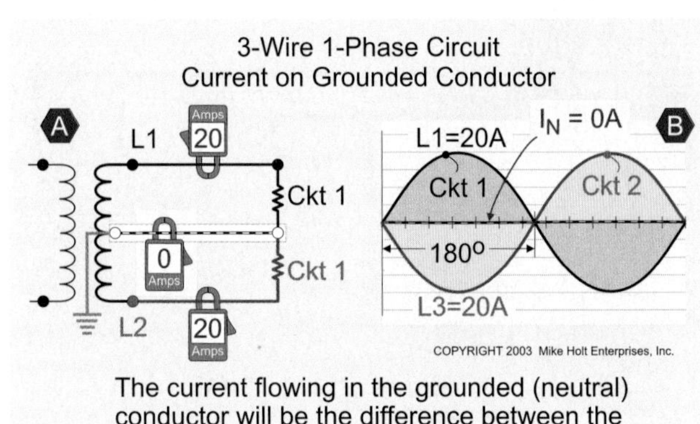

Figure 13–5

The current on the grounded (neutral) conductor is equal to the difference in ungrounded conductor current because at any instant the currents on the two ungrounded conductors oppose each other. **Figure 13–6**

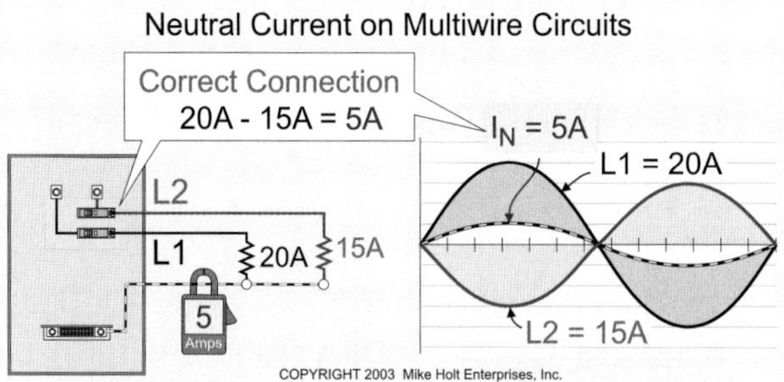

Currents on the grounded (neutral) conductor cancel because the current flowing through the grounded (neutral) conductor at any instant from the two phase conductors oppose each other.

Figure 13–6

CAUTION: *If the ungrounded conductors of a multiwire circuit are not terminated to different phases, the currents on the ungrounded conductors will not cancel, but will add on the grounded (neutral) conductor. This can cause the neutral current to be in excess of the grounded (neutral) conductor rating.* **Figure 13–7**

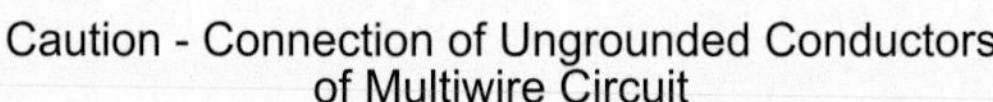

Caution - Connection of Ungrounded Conductors of Multiwire Circuit

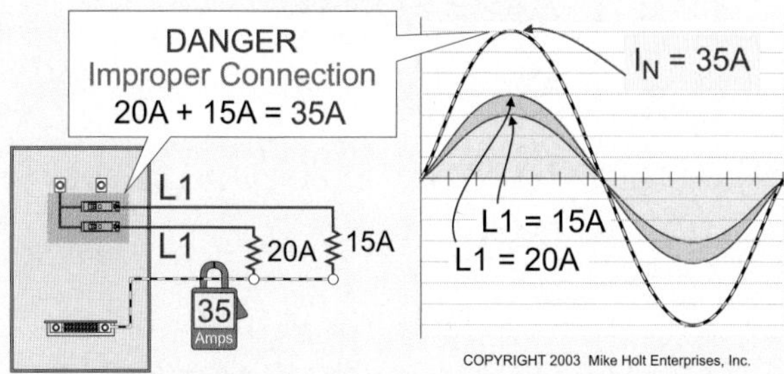

If the ungrounded conductors of a multiwire circuit are not terminated to different phases, the current on the grounded (neutral) conductor will add instead of cancel, which can overload the grounded (neutral) conductor.

Figure 13–7

AUTHOR'S COMMENT: This is one reason white neutral conductors sometimes turn brown or black.

13.4 Balanced Systems

If the current in each ungrounded conductor of a multiwire circuit is the same, the grounded (neutral) conductor will carry 0A. This applies to 3-wire, 120/240V, single-phase and all three-phase circuits, regardless of configuration or voltage. **Figure 13–8**

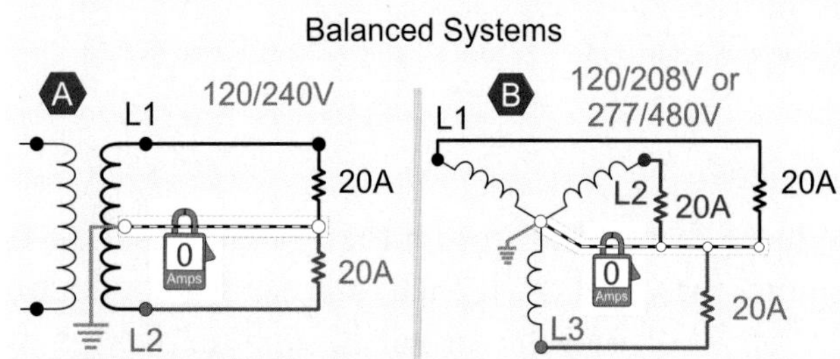

If the current flow in each line of a multiwire circuit is the same, the grounded (neutral) conductor will carry zero amperes.

Figure 13–8

13.5 Unbalanced Current

The current flowing on the grounded (neutral) conductor of a multiwire circuit is called "unbalanced current."

3-Wire, 120/240V, Single-Phase Circuit

The neutral conductor of a 3-wire, 120/240V, single-phase circuit will only carry current when the current on the ungrounded conductors is not identical. The unbalanced current is equal to: $I_{Line1} - I_{Line2}$. **Figure 13–9**

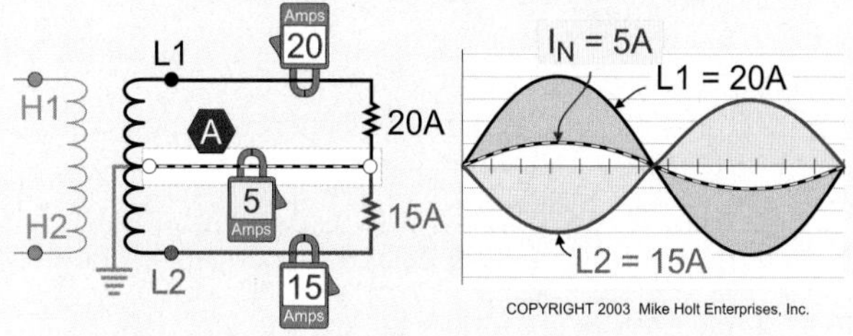

The grounded (neutral) conductor of a 3-wire 120/240V circuit will carry current only when the ungrounded conductors do not have identical current flow. The unbalanced current is the difference between line 1 and line 2.

Figure 13–9

3-Wire Circuit from a 4-wire, Three-Phase System

The grounded (neutral) conductor of a 3-wire, 120/208V or 277/480V, three-phase circuit from a 4-wire, three-phase system will always carry neutral current. The current on the grounded (neutral) conductor of a 3-wire circuit supplied from a 4-wire, three-phase system is determined by the following formula:

$$I_N=\sqrt{(L1^2 + L2^2 + L3^2) - [(L1 \times L2) + (L2 \times L3) + (L1 \times L3)]}$$

Example

What is the neutral current for a 3-wire, 120/208V, single-phase circuit, if each ungrounded conductor carries 20A, and the circuit is supplied from a 4-wire, 120/208V, 3Ø system? **Figure 13–10**

(a) 80A (b) 100A
(c) 20A (d) 0A

• Answer: (c) 20A

$$I_N = \sqrt{(20^2 + 20^2 + 0) - (20^2 + 0 + 0)}$$

$$I_N = \sqrt{400}$$

$$I_N = 20A$$

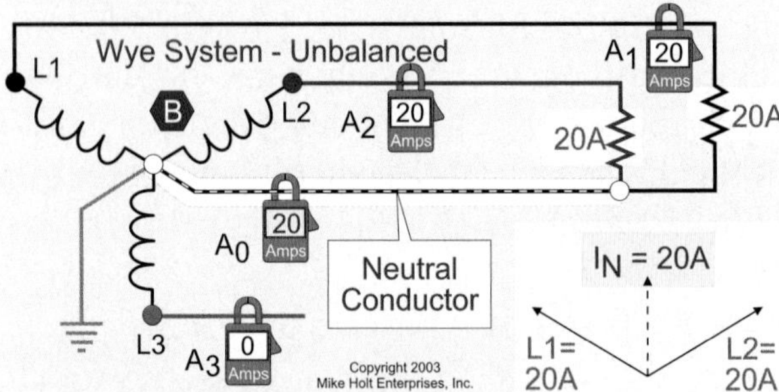

The neutral of a 3-wire circuit from a 4-wire wye system carries about the same current as the phase conductors.

$$I_N = \sqrt{(L1^2 + L2^2 + L3^2) - [(L1 \times L2) + (L2 \times L3) + (L1 \times L3)]}$$

$$I_N = \sqrt{(20^2 + 20^2 + 0^2) - [(20 \times 20) + (20 \times 0) + (20 \times 0)]}$$

$$I_N = \sqrt{(400 + 400 + 0) - (400 + 0 + 0)}$$

$$I_N = \sqrt{800 - 400} \quad I_N = \sqrt{400} \quad I_N = 20A$$

Figure 13–10

4-Wire, Three-Phase Circuit

The neutral conductor of a 4-wire, 120/208V or 277/480V, three-phase system will have neutral current when the ungrounded conductors are not identically loaded. The current on the grounded (neutral) conductor of a 4-wire circuit supplied from a 4-wire system is determined by the following formula:

$$I_N=\sqrt{(L1^2 + L2^2 + L3^2) - [(L1 \times L2) + (L2 \times L3) + (L1 \times L3)]}$$

Example

What is the neutral current for a 4-wire, 120/208V, 3Ø circuit, if Line 1 = 100A, Line 2 = 100A and Line 3 = 50A? **Figure 13–11**

(a) 50A (b) 100A
(c) 125A (d) 0A

• Answer: (a) 50A

$$I_N=\sqrt{(100^2 + 100^2 + 50^2) - (100 \times 100 \times 100 \times 50 + 100 \times 50)}$$

$$I_N = \sqrt{2500}$$

$$I_N = 50A$$

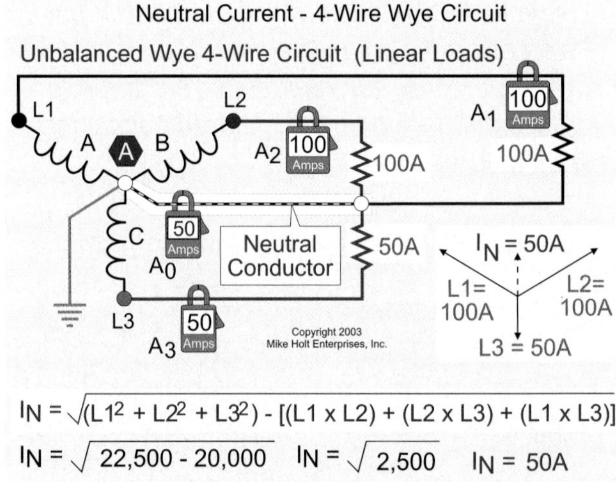

Figure 13–11

13.6 Multiwire Branch Circuit

Multiwire branch circuits are more cost-effective than 2-wire circuits in that they have fewer conductors for a given number of circuits, which enables the use of a smaller raceway. In addition, multiwire branch circuits result in lower circuit voltage drop.

Reduced Number of Conductors. Instead of four conductors for two 2-wire circuits, three conductors can be used with single-phase wiring, and instead of six conductors for three 2-wire circuits, four conductors can be used with three-phase wiring.

Reduced Raceway Size. If the number of circuit conductors is reduced, the size of the raceway can often be reduced. Reducing the number of conductors and installing a smaller raceway is very cost-effective. The cost savings include the material and labor, as well as overhead.

Reduced Circuit Voltage Drop. The voltage drop of the circuit conductors is dependent upon the magnitude of current and conductor resistance: $E_{VD} = I \times R$.

2-Wire Circuit Voltage Drop

A typical 2-wire circuit will have current flow over both the ungrounded and grounded (neutral) conductors. Therefore, the circuit voltage drop includes the voltage drop of both conductors.

Example

What is the voltage drop of two 12 AWG conductors, each 75 ft long, supplying a 2-wire, 20A load? **Figure 13–12**

(a) 2V (b) 4V
(c) 3V (d) 6V

• Answer: (d) 6V

$E_{VD} = I \times R$

$I = 20A$

$$R = \frac{2\Omega \text{ per } 1{,}000 \text{ ft}}{1{,}000} \times 75 \text{ ft} \times 2 \text{ wires}$$

$R = 0.30\Omega$

$E_{VD} = 20A \times 0.30\Omega$

$E_{VD} = 6V$

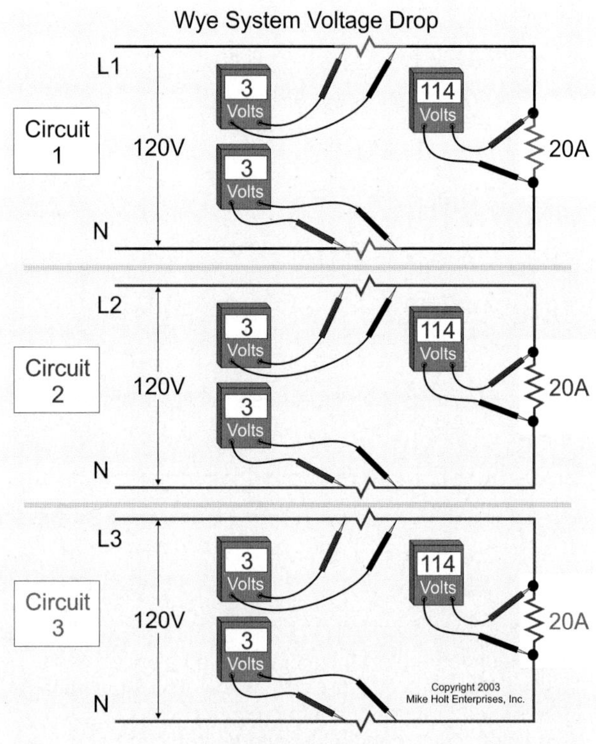

Figure 13–12

Multiwire Circuit Voltage Drop

A balanced 3-wire, single-phase or 4-wire, three-phase multiwire branch circuit will have current flow only on the ungrounded circuit conductors. Therefore, the circuit voltage drop only includes the voltage drop of one conductor.

Example

What is the circuit voltage drop over each line conductor of a balanced 4-wire multiwire circuit? Each conductor is 12 AWG, 75 ft long, supplying a 20A load. **Figure 13–13**

(a) 2V (b) 4V
(c) 3V (d) 6V

• Answer: (c) 3V

The grounded (neutral) conductor in a balanced 4-wire system effectively has 0A of current flow (the three return currents cancel each other out because of their phase relationship). Thus, by Ohm's Law, the voltage drop over this conductor is 0V. The remaining phase conductor voltage drop can be calculated as follows:

$E_{VD} = I \times R$

$I = 20A$

$R = \frac{2\Omega \text{ per } 1{,}000 \text{ ft}}{1{,}000} \times 75 \text{ ft} \times 1 \text{ wire}$

$R = 0.15\Omega$

$E_{VD} = 20A \times 0.15\Omega$

$E_{VD} = 3V$

The grounded (neutral) conductor in a balanced 4-wire system effectively has no current flow. Thus, the voltage drop on the grounded (neutral) conductor is 0V. The remaining phase conductor voltage drop can be calculated as follows:

E_{VD} = IR, I = 20A,
R = 2 ohms per 1,000 ft = 0.15 ohms for 75 ft
E_{VD} = 20A x 0.15 ohms = 3 volts dropped

Figure 13–13

13.7 Dangers of Multiwire Circuits

As in life, there are no benefits without risk. Yes, multiwire circuits offer fewer conductors, reduced raceway size and voltage drop; however, improper wiring or mishandling of multiwire circuits can cause a fire hazard because of conductor overloading and/or the destruction of equipment connected because of over, as well as under, operating voltage.

Fire Hazard

Failure to terminate the ungrounded conductors to separate phases could cause the grounded (neutral) conductor to become overloaded from excessive neutral current, and the insulation could be damaged or destroyed. Conductor overheating is known to decrease insulating material service life, potentially resulting in a fire from arcing faults in hidden locations. We do not know just how long conductor insulation will last, but heat does decrease its life span. **Figure 13–14**

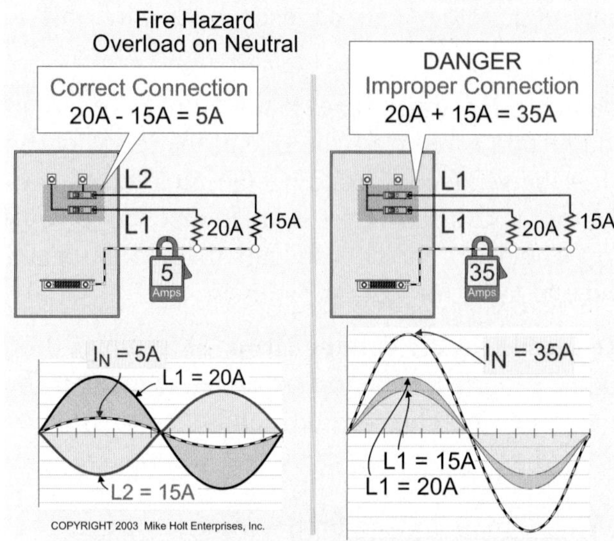

Failure to terminate the ungrounded (hot) conductors to different phases can cause the grounded (neutral) conductor to be overloaded, which can cause a fire.

Figure 13–14

Destruction of Equipment as Well as Fire Hazard

The opening of the ungrounded or grounded (neutral) conductor of a 2-wire circuit during the replacement of a device does not cause a safety hazard, so pigtailing of these conductors is not required.

If the continuity of the grounded (neutral) conductor of a multiwire circuit is interrupted (open), there could be a fire and/or destruction of electrical equipment resulting from overvoltage or undervoltage.

Example:

A 3-wire, 120/240V circuit supplies a 1,200W, 120V hair dryer and a 600W, 120V television. If the grounded (neutral) conductor is interrupted, it will cause the 120V television to operate at 160V and consume 1,067W of power (instead of 600W) for only a few seconds before it burns up. **Figure 13–15**

Step 1 Determine the resistance of each appliance, $R = E^2/P$.

Hair Dryer

$$R = \frac{120V^2}{1{,}200W}$$

$$R = 12\Omega$$

Television

$$R = \frac{120V^2}{600W}$$

$$R = 24\Omega$$

Step 2 Determine the current of the circuit.

$$I = \frac{E}{R}$$

$$I = \frac{240V}{(12\Omega + 24\Omega)}$$

$$I = 6.7A$$

Step 3 Determine the operating voltage for each appliance, $E = I \times R$.

Hair Dryer Operates at = 6.7A x 12Ω
Hair Dryer Operates at = 80V

Television Operates at = 6.7A x 24Ω
Television Operates at = 160V

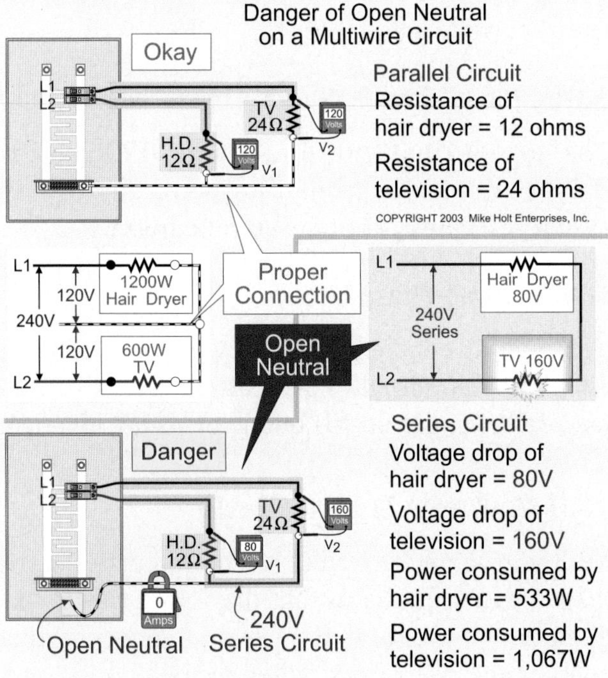

Figure 13–15

13.8 NEC Requirements

Because of the dangers associated with an open grounded (neutral) conductor, the *NEC* specifies that the continuity of the grounded (neutral) conductor cannot be dependent upon any wiring device. In other words, the grounded (neutral) conductors of a multiwire circuit should be spliced together, and a wire brought out to the device. This way, if the receptacle was removed, it would not result in an open grounded (neutral) conductor. **Figure 13–16**

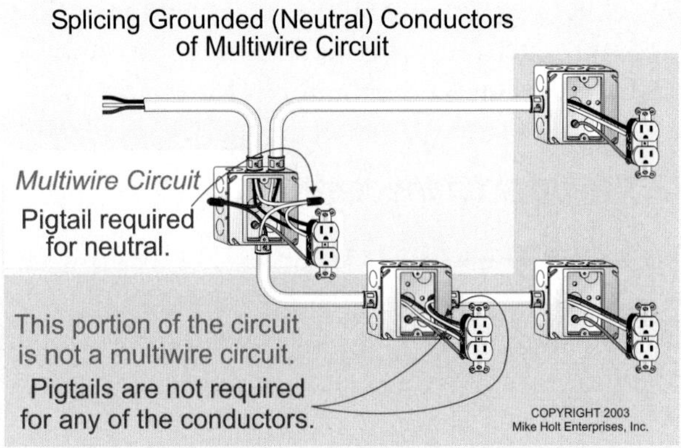

Because of the dangers associated with an open grounded (neutral) conductor, the NEC specifies that the grounded (neutral) conductors of a multiwire circuit be spliced together.

Figure 13–16

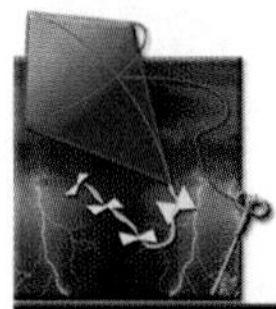

Unit 13 Summary

Introduction

Understanding series, parallel, and series-parallel circuits is the foundation for understanding multiwire circuits.

A multiwire circuit is a circuit consisting of two or more ungrounded conductors (hot wires) that have a voltage between them, and an equal voltage between each ungrounded conductor and the grounded (neutral) conductor.

13.1 Neutral Conductor

According to the IEEE Dictionary, a neutral conductor is the conductor that has an equal potential difference between it and the other output conductors of a 3- or 4-wire system.

13.2 Grounded Conductor

The grounded (neutral) conductor, according to the *NEC*, is a conductor that is intentionally grounded to the earth. In the case of single-phase home wiring (120/240V), the grounded conductor is often called the neutral conductor.

13.3 Current Flow on the Grounded (Neutral) Conductor

2-Wire Circuit

The current flowing on the grounded (neutral) conductor will be the same as the current on the ungrounded conductors.

3-Wire, 120/240V, Single-Phase Circuit

The current flowing on the grounded (neutral) conductor will be the difference between the current flowing on the ungrounded conductors. The currents cancel because the currents flowing through the grounded (neutral) conductor at any instant from the ungrounded conductors oppose each other.

CAUTION: *If the ungrounded conductors of a multiwire circuit are not terminated to different phases, the currents on the grounded (neutral) conductor will not cancel, but will add, which can cause an overload on the grounded (neutral) conductor.*

13.4 Balanced Systems

If the current flow in each line of a multiwire circuit is the same, the grounded (neutral) conductor will carry 0A.

13.5 Unbalanced Current

When current flows on the grounded (neutral) conductor of a multiwire circuit, it is called the unbalanced current.

3-Wire, 120/240V, Single-Phase Circuit

The neutral of a 3-wire, 120/240V circuit will carry current only when the ungrounded conductors do not have identical current flow. The unbalanced current is equal to: $I_{Line1} - I_{Line2.}$

3-Wire Circuit from a 4-wire, Three-Phase System

The neutral conductor of a 3-wire, 120/208V or 277/480V circuit from a 4-wire, three-phase system will always carry neutral current.

4-Wire, Three-Phase Circuit

The neutral conductor of a 4-wire, 120/208V or 277/480V circuit will have current flow when the load on the ungrounded conductors is not identical.

13.6 Multiwire Branch Circuit

Multiwire branch circuits are more cost-effective than 2-wire circuits in that they have fewer conductors for a given number of circuits, which enables the use of a smaller raceway and lower conductor voltage drop.

13.7 Dangers of Multiwire Circuits

Fire Hazard

Failure to terminate the ungrounded conductors to separate phases could cause the grounded (neutral) conductor to become overloaded from excessive neutral current, and the insulation could be damaged or destroyed.

Destruction of Equipment as Well as Fire Hazard

The opening of the ungrounded or grounded (neutral) conductor of a 2-wire circuit during the replacement of a device does not cause a safety hazard, so pigtailing of these conductors is not required.

If the continuity of the grounded (neutral) conductor of a multiwire circuit is interrupted (open), there could be a fire and/or destruction of electrical equipment resulting from overvoltage or undervoltage.

13.8 NEC Requirements

Because of the dangers associated with an open grounded (neutral) conductor, the *NEC* specifies that the grounded (neutral) conductors of a multiwire circuit be spliced together, and a wire brought out to the device. This way, if the receptacle was removed, it would not result in an open grounded (neutral) conductor.

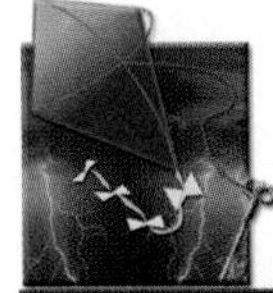

Unit 13 Conclusion

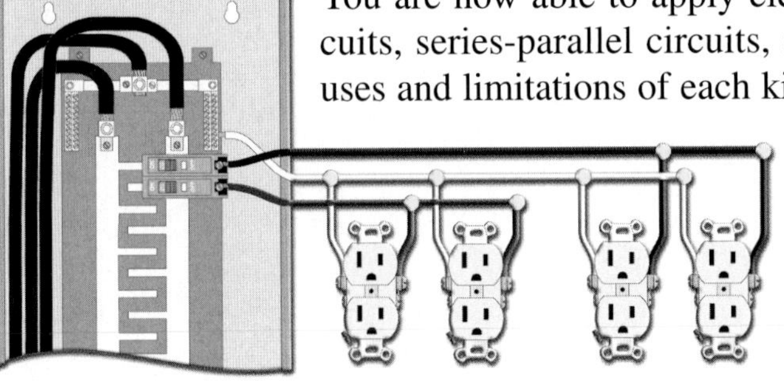

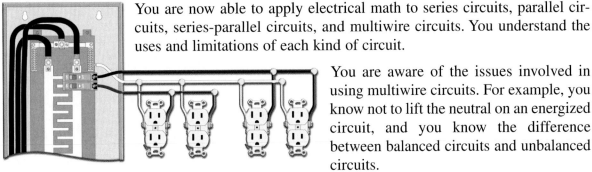

You are now able to apply electrical math to series circuits, parallel circuits, series-parallel circuits, and multiwire circuits. You understand the uses and limitations of each kind of circuit.

You are aware of the issues involved in using multiwire circuits. For example, you know not to lift the neutral on an energized circuit, and you know the difference between balanced circuits and unbalanced circuits.

Words to Live By: *The best way to get the last word is to apologize.*

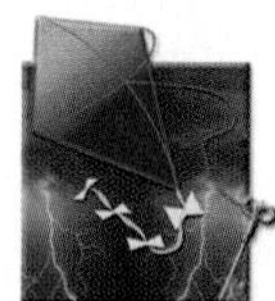

Unit 13 Practice Questions

Introduction

1. A multiwire circuit has two or more ungrounded conductors having a potential difference between them, and having an equal difference of potential between each ungrounded conductor and the grounded (neutral) conductor.

   (a) True (b) False

2. According to the IEEE Dictionary, a neutral conductor has the same equal potential between it and all ungrounded conductors of a _____ system.

   (a) 2-wire (b) 3-wire (c) 4-wire (d) b or c

13.1 Neutral Conductor

3. A 2-wire, 120V circuit contains a(n) _____.

   (a) neutral conductor (b) grounded (neutral) conductor
   (c) ungrounded conductor (d) b and c

4. A 3-wire, 120/240V circuit from a 3Ø delta transformer contains a(n) _____.

   (a) neutral conductor (b) grounded (neutral) conductor
   (c) ungrounded conductor (d) b and c

13.2 Grounded Conductor

5. The grounded conductor is a conductor that is intentionally grounded to the earth.

   (a) True (b) False

13.3 Current Flow on the Grounded (Neutral) Conductor

6. The current on the grounded (neutral) conductor of a 2-wire circuit will be _____ of the current on the ungrounded conductor.

   (a) 0% (b) 70% (c) 80% (d) 100%

7. A balanced 3-wire, 120/240V, 1Ø circuit is connected so that the ungrounded conductors are from different transformer phases (Line 1 and Line 2). The current on the grounded (neutral) conductor will be _____ of the ungrounded conductor current.

   (a) 0% (b) 70% (c) 80% (d) 100%

8. The grounded (neutral) conductor of a 3-wire, 120/240V, 1Ø circuit will only carry the unbalanced current when the circuit is not balanced.

(a) True (b) False

9. If the ungrounded conductors of a multiwire circuit are not terminated to different phases, this can cause the neutral current to be in excess of the grounded (neutral) conductor rating.

(a) True (b) False

13.4 Balanced Systems

10. If the current in each ungrounded conductor of a multiwire circuit is the same, the grounded (neutral) conductor will carry 0A.

(a) True (b) False

11. What is the neutral current for a 4-wire, 120/208V circuit, where L1 = 20A, L2 = 20A, and L3 = 20A?

(a) 0A (b) 10A (c) 20A (d) none of these

13.5 Unbalanced Current

12. The current flowing on the grounded (neutral) conductor of a multiwire circuit is called unbalanced current.

(a) True (b) False

13. The neutral conductor of a 3-wire, 120/240V, 1Ø circuit will only carry current when the current on the ungrounded conductors is not identical.

(a) True (b) False

14. The neutral conductor of a 3-wire, 120/208V or 277/480V circuit supplied from a 4-wire, 3Ø system will never carry neutral current.

(a) True (b) False

15. The neutral conductor of a 4-wire, 120/208V or 277/480V, 3Ø system will have neutral current flow when the ungrounded conductors are equally loaded.

(a) True (b) False

13.6 Multiwire Branch Circuit

16. Multiwire branch circuits have more conductors for a given number of circuits, which requires the use of a larger raceway.

(a) True (b) False

17. A balanced multiwire branch circuit will have current flow only on the ungrounded conductors.

(a) True (b) False

18. What is the voltage drop of two 12 AWG conductors, each 100 ft in length, supplying a 2-wire, 16A load? The resistance of 12 AWG conductors is 2Ω per 1,000 ft.

(a) 4.2V (b) 6.4V (c) 7.2V (d) 9.6V

19. What is the voltage drop of each conductor of a 4-wire multiwire circuit? Each conductor is 12 AWG, 100 ft in length, supplying a 16A load.

(a) 3.2V (b) 6.4V (c) 7.2V (d) 9.6V

13.7 Dangers of Multiwire Circuits

20. Improper wiring or mishandling of multiwire branch circuits can cause _____ connected to the circuit.

(a) overloading of the ungrounded conductors
(b) overloading of the grounded (neutral) conductors
(c) destruction of equipment because of overvoltage
(d) b and c

21. The opening of the ungrounded or grounded (neutral) conductor of a _____ circuit during the replacement of a device does not cause a safety hazard, so pigtailing of these conductors is not required.

(a) 2-wire (b) 3-wire (c) 4-wire (d) all of these

13.8 NEC Requirements

22. Because of the dangers associated with an open grounded (neutral) conductor, the continuity of the _____ conductor cannot be dependent upon the receptacle.

(a) ungrounded (b) grounded (c) a and b (d) none of these

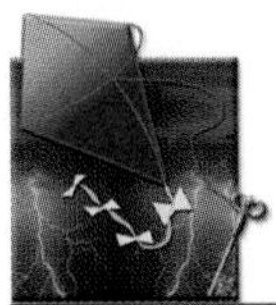

Chapter 3 Final Exam

Unit 10—Series Circuits

Introduction

1. A series circuit is a circuit in which a specific amount of current leaves the voltage source and flows through every electrical device in a single path before it returns to the voltage source.

   (a) True (b) False

10.1 Practical Uses of the Series Circuit

2. For practical purposes, series circuits are often used for _______.

   (a) signal (b) control (c) a and b (d) None of these

10.2 Understanding Series Calculations

3. Resistance opposes the flow of electrons. In a series circuit, the total circuit resistance is equal to the sum of all the resistances in series.

   (a) True (b) False

4. The opposition to current flow results in a voltage drop of the circuit voltage.

   (a) True (b) False

5. Kirchoff's Voltage Law states that in a series circuit, the sum of the voltage drops across all of the resistors will equal the applied voltage.

   (a) True (b) False

6. No matter how many resistances there are in a series circuit, the sum of the voltages across all of the resistances will equal the voltage of the source according to the Law of Proportion.

   (a) True (b) False

7. Kirchoff's Current Law states that in a series circuit, the current is _____ through the transformer, the conductors, and the appliance.

   (a) proportional (b) distributed (c) additive (d) the same

10.3 Series Circuit Calculations

8. To determine the resistance of each resistive element in the circuit, use the formula $R = E^2/P$.

   (a) True (b) False

9. The current of the circuit can be determined by the formula $I = E_S/R_T$

   (a) True (b) False

10.7 Series-Connected Power Supplies

10. When power supplies are connected in series, the circuit voltage remains the same as when only one power supply is connected to it, provided that all the polarities are connected properly.

    (a) True (b) False

Unit 11—Parallel Circuits

11.2 Understanding Parallel Calculations

11. In a parallel circuit, the voltage drop across each resistance is equal to the sum of the voltage drops of each of the resistors in parallel.

    (a) True (b) False

12. According to Kirchoff's Current Law, the total current provided by the source to a parallel circuit will equal the sum of the currents of all of the branches.

    (a) True (b) False

11.3 Circuit Resistance

13. In a parallel circuit, the total circuit resistance is always greater than the smallest resistance.

    (a) True (b) False

14. The total resistance of a parallel circuit can be calculated by the _____ method.

    (a) equal resistance (b) product-over-sum (c) reciprocal (d) any of these

15. According to the equal resistance method, when all the resistances of the parallel circuit have the same resistance, divide the resistance of one element by the largest resistor in parallel.

    (a) True (b) False

16. The product-over-sum method is used to calculate the resistance of _____ resistance(s) at a time.

(a) one (b) two (c) three (d) four

17. The advantage of the reciprocal method is that the formula can be used for as many resistances as the parallel circuit contains.

(a) True (b) False

11.5 Parallel-Connected Power Supplies

18. When power supplies are connected in parallel, the voltage remains the same, but the current or amp-hour capacity will be increased.

(a) True (b) False

Unit 12—Series-Parallel Circuits

Introduction

19. A _____ is a circuit that contains some resistances in series and some resistances in parallel with each other.

(a) parallel circuit (b) series circuit (c) series-parallel circuit (d) none of these

20. That portion of the series-parallel circuit that contains resistances in series must comply with the rules for series circuits.

(a) True (b) False

21. That portion of the series-parallel circuit that contains resistances in parallel must comply with the rules for parallel circuits.

(a) True (b) False

12.2 Working Series-Parallel Circuits

22. When working with series-parallel circuits, it is best to redraw the circuit so you can see the series components and the parallel branches.

(a) True (b) False

Unit 13—Multiwire Circuits

Introduction

23. A multiwire circuit has two or more ungrounded conductors having a potential difference between them, and having an equal difference of potential between each ungrounded conductor and the grounded (neutral) conductor.

    (a) True (b) False

13.3 Current Flow on the Grounded (Neutral) Conductor

24. A balanced 3-wire, 120/240V, 1Ø circuit is connected so that the ungrounded conductors are from different transformer phases (Line 1 and Line 2). The current on the grounded (neutral) conductor will be _____ of the ungrounded conductor current.

    (a) 0% (b) 70% (c) 80% (d) 100%

25. The grounded (neutral) conductor of a 3-wire, 120/240V, 1Ø circuit will only carry the unbalanced current when the circuit is not balanced.

    (a) True (b) False

26. If the ungrounded conductors of a multiwire circuit are not terminated to different phases, this can cause the neutral current to be in excess of the grounded (neutral) conductor rating.

    (a) True (b) False

13.4 Balanced Systems

27. If the current in each ungrounded conductor of a multiwire circuit is the same, the grounded (neutral) conductor will carry 0A.

    (a) True (b) False

13.5 Unbalanced Current

28. The current flowing on the grounded (neutral) conductor of a multiwire circuit is called unbalanced current.

    (a) True (b) False

29. The neutral conductor of a 3-wire, 120/240V, 1Ø circuit will only carry current when the current on the ungrounded conductors is not identical.

    (a) True (b) False

13.6 Multiwire Branch Circuit

30. Multiwire branch circuits have more conductors for a given number of circuits, which requires the use of a larger raceway.

(a) True (b) False

31. A balanced multiwire branch circuit will have current flow only on the ungrounded conductors.

(a) True (b) False

32. What is the voltage drop of two 12 AWG conductors, each 100 ft in length, supplying a 2-wire, 16A load? The resistance of 12 AWG conductors is 2Ω per 1,000 ft.

(a) 4.2V (b) 6.4V (c) 7.2V (d) 9.6V

13.7 Dangers of Multiwire Circuits

33. Improper wiring or mishandling of multiwire branch circuits can cause _____ connected to the circuit.

(a) overloading of the ungrounded conductors
(b) overloading of the grounded (neutral) conductors
(c) destruction of equipment because of overvoltage
(d) b and c

13.8 NEC Requirements

34. Because of the dangers associated with an open grounded (neutral) conductor, the continuity of the _____ conductor cannot be dependent upon the receptacle.

(a) ungrounded (b) grounded (c) a and b (d) none of these

Chapter 4
Electrical Systems and Protection

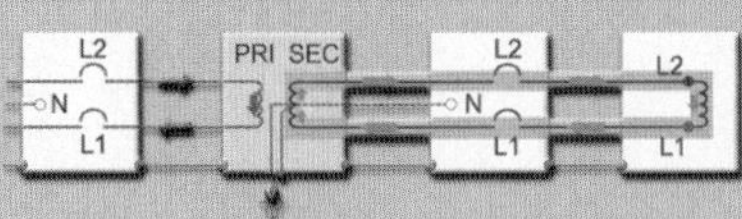

Unit 14 – The Electrical System

Unit 15 – Protection Devices

Notes

UNIT

14 The Electrical System

Introduction

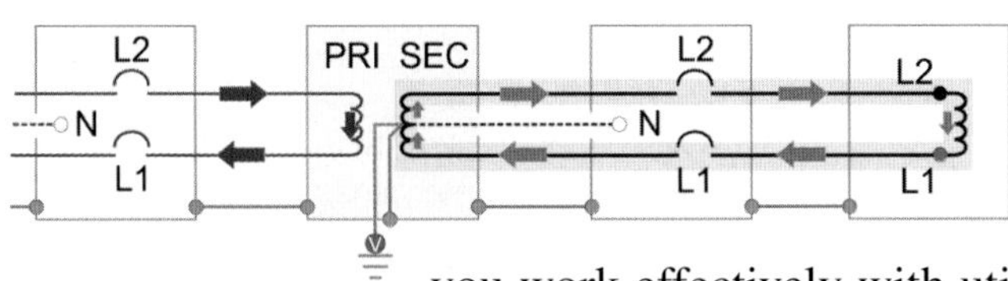

Knowing how the electricity gets from the generating station to your service entrance gives you a better sense of "the big picture" in your electrical work. It also helps you work effectively with utility people when resolving service entrance and critical load issues.

For example, if you need to install a service-entrance transformer, what should the primary voltage be? Will the total load of your facility require a different local step-down transformer? Do load conditions require you to be on your own substation? The ability to answer questions like that can be a major influence on the quality and reliability of the installation you provide.

Though service installations and critical load installations often have engineering oversight, the electrician is the last line of defense to ensure the design matches the transmission system and load requirements.

14.1 Current Flow

Electrons leaving a power supply are always trying to return to the same power supply; they are not trying to go into the earth. When alternating current is applied to the primary of a transformer, it induces a voltage in the secondary. This induced secondary voltage causes electrons to leave one end of the transformer's secondary, travel over the circuit's conductors through the load, and return over the remaining circuit's conductors to the other end of the transformer's secondary. Figure 14–1

14.2 Utility Neutral Current Path

The electric utility grounds the primary and secondary neutral conductor to the earth at multiple locations to create a parallel path so as to reduce the ac resistance (impedance) of the return neutral current path.

Multipoint Neutral Ground

This multipoint grounded neutral is intended to help reduce primary utility neutral voltage drop, assist in clearing line-to-neutral/ground utility faults, and to reduce elevated line-to-neutral voltage caused by line-to-neutral/ground faults. **Figure 14–2**

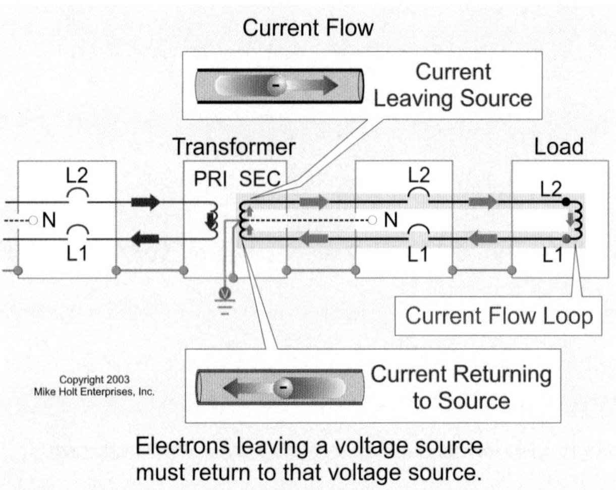

Figure 14–1

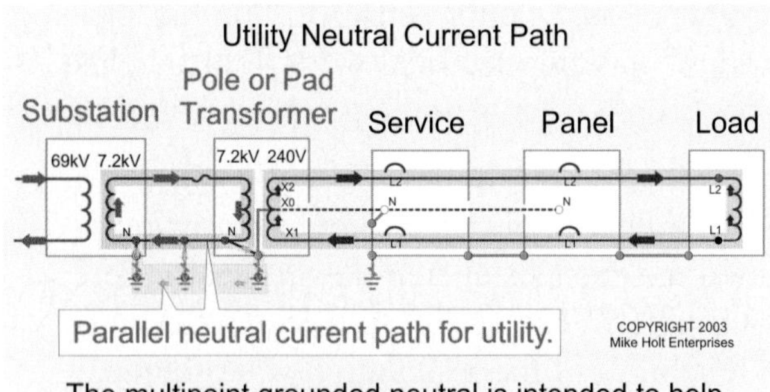

Figure 14–2

14.3 Utility Ground-Fault Current Path

Metal parts of the electric utility equipment (transformer and capacitor cases, guy wires, luminaires, etc.) are bonded to the utility neutral (which is grounded to the earth) to provide a low-impedance (ac resistance) path to the power supply for the purpose of clearing a line-to-case fault.

If the utility neutral conductor is inadvertently opened, the earth itself should have low enough impedance to permit sufficient fault current to return to the source, thereby opening the utility's circuit protection device (blow the fuse) so that the high-voltage fault can be cleared.

For example, a 7,200V line is typically protected by a 3A to 5A fuse (depending on wire size). The earth, having a resistance of 25Ω, would have no problem carrying sufficient fault current to blow a 5A fuse. (I = E/R, I = 7,200V/25Ω, I = 288A). **Figure 14–3**

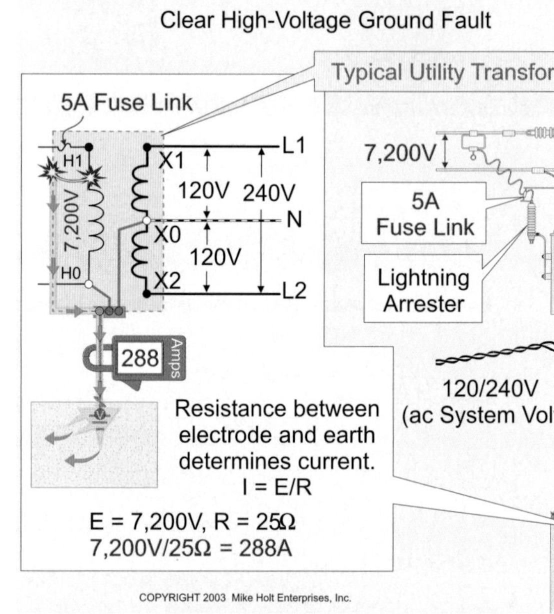

Figure 14–3

14.4 Premises Neutral Current Path

To prevent fires and electric shock, the *NEC* specifies that neutral current must only flow in the insulated grounded (neutral) conductor. **Figure 14–4**

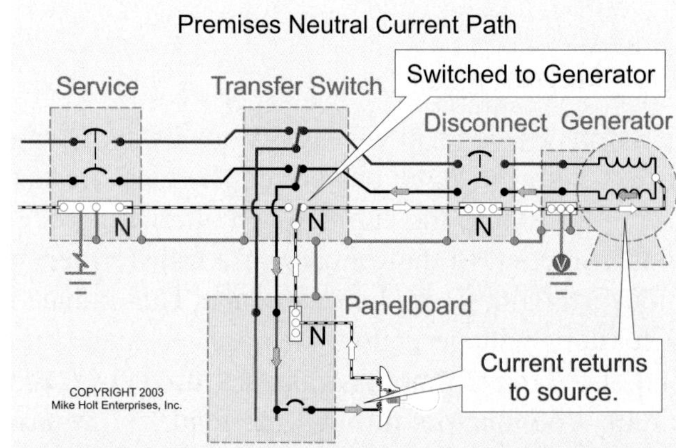

Figure 14–4

Single Point Neutral Bond

Neutral current is not permitted to flow on metal parts of the electrical installation; therefore, premises wiring utilizes the "single point neutral ground system," not the "multipoint neutral ground system" of electric utilities.

14.5 Premises Ground-Fault Current Path

Metal parts of premises wiring are bonded to a low-impedance path designed and intended to carry fault current from the point of a line-to-case fault on a wiring system to the grounded (neutral) conductor at the electrical supply source. This low-impedance fault-current path ensures that the opening of the circuit protection device will quickly clear the ground fault. **Figure 14–5**

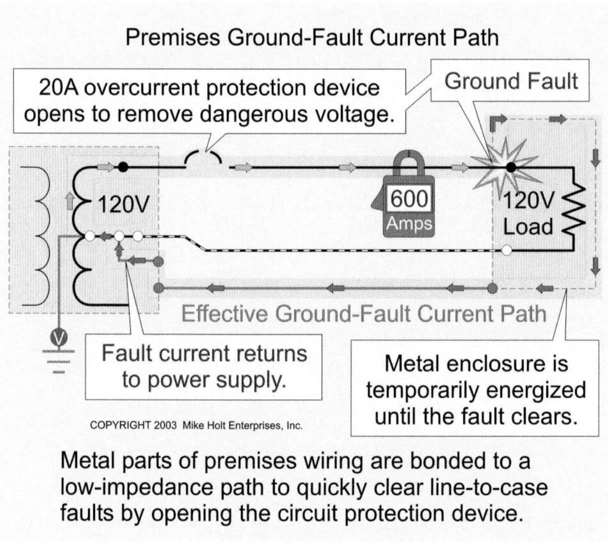

Premises Ground-Fault Current Path
20A overcurrent protection device opens to remove dangerous voltage.
Ground Fault
120V
600 Amps
120V Load
Effective Ground-Fault Current Path
Fault current returns to power supply.
Metal enclosure is temporarily energized until the fault clears.
COPYRIGHT 2003 Mike Holt Enterprises, Inc.
Metal parts of premises wiring are bonded to a low-impedance path to quickly clear line-to-case faults by opening the circuit protection device.

Figure 14–5

AUTHOR'S COMMENT: The only current that should ever flow on the low-impedance fault path is fault current. Neutral currents should never exist on this path.

Earth as Ground-Fault Path for Systems 600V or Less

Because of the earth's high resistance to current flow, it cannot be used for the purpose of clearing a line-to-case ground fault. A separate, properly sized bonding jumper is required for this purpose. **Figure 14–6**

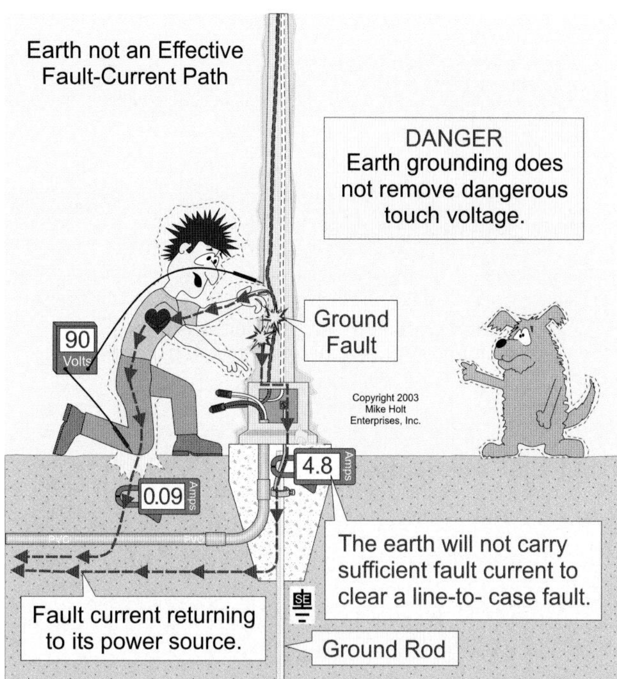

Figure 14–6

For example, a 120V fault to a ground rod having a resistance of 25Ω will only draw 4.8A (I = E/Z, I = 120V/25Ω, I = 4.8A), not enough to open a 15A protection device. **Figure 14–6**

14.6 Utility High-Voltage Transmission Lines

Electric power is typically generated and transmitted across long transmission lines to the electrical substation. Here the voltage is stepped down and delivered over distribution lines to the customer. These conductors have relatively low resistance, but because of their length, the total resistance can cause significant conductor voltage drop and power losses.

14.7 Conductor Voltage Drop

Conductor voltage drop is directly proportional to the length of the conductor because conductor resistance is directly proportional to the conductor length. For example, the ac resistance of 4/0 aluminum is 0.10Ω per 1,000 feet or about 0.53Ω per mile. If the conductor length is doubled, the resistance will be doubled, and the voltage drop will also double: $E_{VD} = I \times R$. **Figure 14–7**

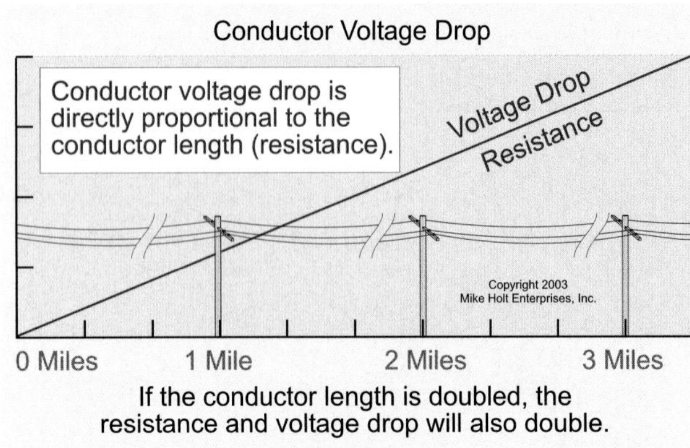
Conductor Voltage Drop
Conductor voltage drop is directly proportional to the conductor length (resistance).
Voltage Drop
Resistance
Copyright 2003
Mike Holt Enterprises, Inc.
0 Miles
1 Mile
2 Miles
3 Miles
If the conductor length is doubled, the resistance and voltage drop will also double.

Figure 14–7

Conductor Voltage Example

What is the voltage drop per mile on a 4/0 aluminum power line (0.53Ω) carrying 50A?

(a) 13 VD (b) 26 VD
(c) 39 VD (d) 53 VD

• Answer: (b) 26 VD

E = I x R
I = 50A
R - 0.53Ω
E = 50A x 0.53Ω
E = 26V per mile

AUTHOR'S COMMENT: 4/0 aluminum carrying 50A will have a voltage drop of 26V per mile, therefore the voltage drop over three miles will be 26V x 3 = 78V.

14.8 Conductor Power Loss

Conductor power losses are directly proportional to the length of the conductor and the square of the current: $P = I^2 \times R$. So if the length of the conductors were doubled, the power loss would double.

Conductor Power Loss Example A

What is the power loss per mile for a 4/0 aluminum power line carrying 50A?

(a) 500W (b) 1,000W
(c) 1,300W (d) 1,800W

• Answer: (c) 1,300W

$P = I^2 \times R$
$P = 50A^2 \times 0.53\Omega$
P = 2,500 x 0.53Ω
P = 1,325W per mile

Current

Because power is relative to the square of the current ($P = I^2 \times R$), if the current is decreased to one-tenth of its original level, the power loss will be 100 times less. Then again, if the current is doubled, the power loss will be increased by 400 percent (2^2)! **Figure 14–8**

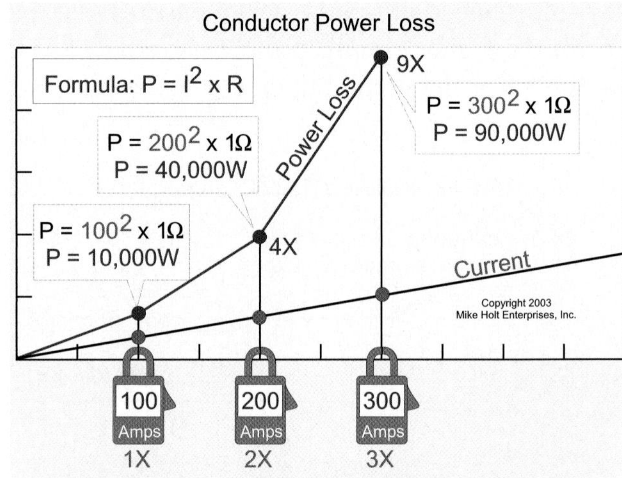
Conductor Power Loss
Formula: $P = I^2 \times R$
$P = 200^2 \times 1\Omega$
P = 40,000W
$P = 100^2 \times 1\Omega$
P = 10,000W
$P = 300^2 \times 1\Omega$
P = 90,000W
Power Loss
9X
4X
Current
Copyright 2003
Mike Holt Enterprises, Inc.
100 Amps
200 Amps
300 Amps
1X
2X
3X
Because power is relative to the square of the current ($P = I^2R$), if the current were doubled, the power loss would be increased by 400 percent (2^2).

Figure 14–8

Power Loss Example B

What is the power loss per mile for a 4/0 aluminum power line carrying 100A?

(a) 1,000W (b) 2,100W
(c) 4,200W (d) 5,300W

• Answer: (d) 5,300W

$P = I^2 \times R$
$P = 100A^2 \times 0.53\Omega$
P = 10,000 x 0.53Ω
P = 5,300W

AUTHOR'S COMMENT: 4/0 aluminum carrying 50A will have a power loss of 1,325W per mile, but this increases by a factor of four (to 5,300W per mile) if the current is doubled.

14.9 Reducing Voltage Drop and Power Loss

The most effective way to reduce conductor voltage drop and power loss is to lower the current flowing through the conductors and this is accomplished by increasing the circuit voltage.

138 kV Transmission Line

A transmission line operating at 138,000V, three-phase can transmit one million watts of three-phase power with a current of just over 4A!

$$I = \frac{P}{(E \times \sqrt{3})}$$

$$I = \frac{1{,}000{,}00W}{(138{,}000V \times 1.732)}$$

$$I = \frac{1{,}000{,}000W}{239{,}016}$$

$$I = 4.18A$$

Primary Distribution Line (13,200V, three-phase)

$$I = \frac{1{,}000{,}000W}{(13{,}200V \times 1.732)}$$

$$I = \frac{1{,}000{,}000W}{22{,}862}$$

$$I = 43.74A$$

Secondary Distribution Line (480V, three-phase)

$$I = \frac{1{,}000{,}000W}{(480V \times 1.732)}$$

$$I = \frac{1{,}000{,}000W}{831}$$

$$I = 1{,}203A$$

14.10 Generating Plants

The electrical system begins at a generating plant where it converts energy from fossil fuels (coal or oil) or nuclear power to steam, which turns the turbine of an electric generator. Typically, a steam turbine is directly connected to an electrical generator, which produces 13.8 kV, three-phase power. **Figure 14–9**

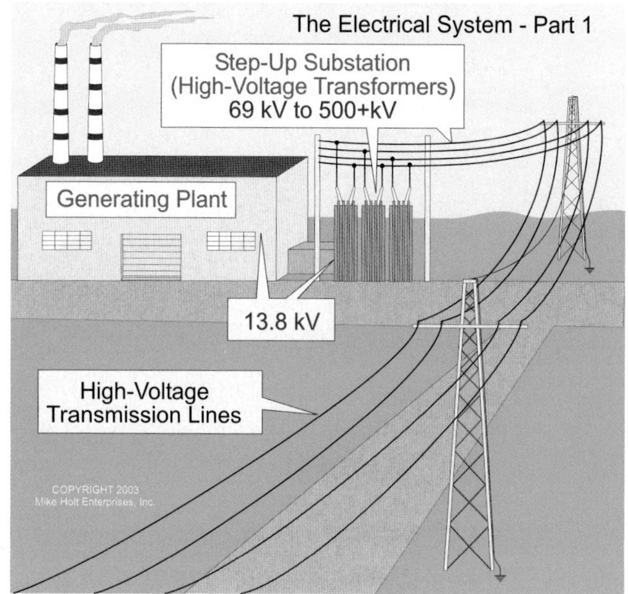

Figure 14–9

AUTHOR'S COMMENT: Water or wind power can also be used to turn the turbine of the generator.

14.11 Step-Up Substation at Generating Plant

As discussed earlier, the most economical way to transfer electrical power over long distances is with high voltage, because for a given power, the current decreases in direct proportion to the increase in voltage level. Thus, conductor voltage drop and power losses (wasted energy) are lower when transferring power over great distances.

A step-up substation is located at the generating facilities for the purpose of transforming the 13.8 kV generator output to 69 kV, 500 kV or even higher. **Figure 14–9**

AUTHOR'S COMMENT: Some transmission voltages are one million volts!

14.12 Transmission Line

High-voltage transmission lines carry the 69 kV or higher voltage from the generating plant step-up substation to various step-down substations. Figure 14–9 and Figure 14–10

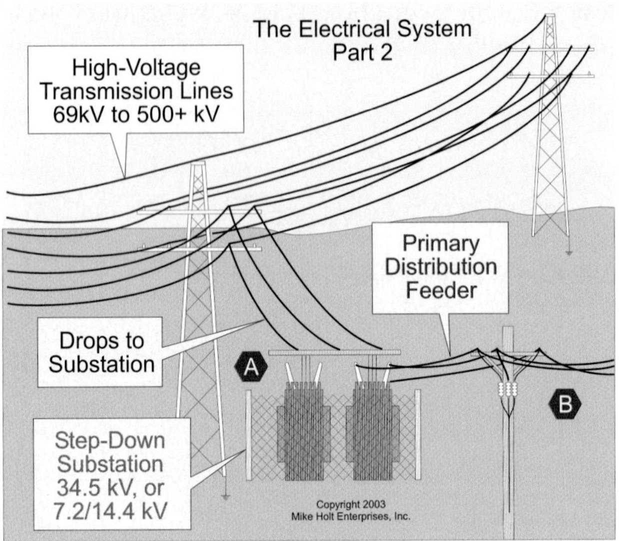

Figure 14–10

AUTHOR'S COMMENT: High-voltage transmission lines are usually connected to transmission lines from other generating plants. This system of connecting high-voltage transmission lines is known as an interconnected system or an electrical power grid.

14.13 Step-Down Substation

Step-down substations reduce the voltage from the high-voltage transmission lines to 34.5 kV, 14.4 kV, or sometimes as low as 4,160V. This reduced voltage is known as primary distribution voltage. Figure 14–10

AUTHOR'S COMMENT: Primary distribution voltage can also be 13.2 kV.

14.14 Primary Distribution Feeders

Distribution feeders transfer the primary distribution voltage to distribution transformers, which are often mounted on poles or on the ground next to the building being served. Figure 14–11

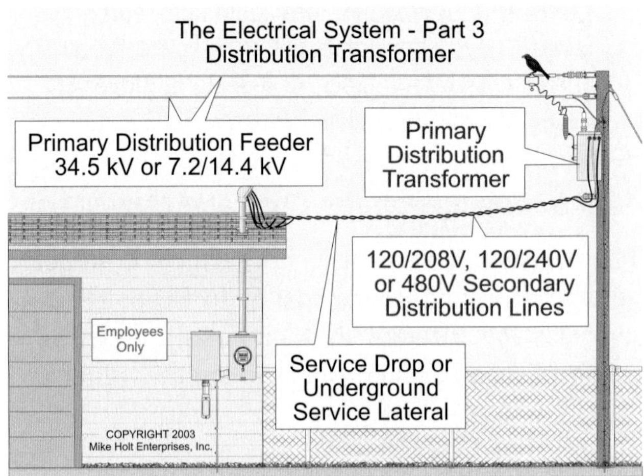

Figure 14–11

14.15 Distribution Transformer

Distribution transformers reduce the primary distribution voltage from 34.5 kV or 13.8 kV to secondary distribution voltage, such as 120/208V, 120/240V or 480V. Figure 14–11

14.16 Secondary Distribution Line

The customer's power is transferred from the utility's distribution transformer to the customer via the overhead service drop or underground service lateral. Overhead service-drop conductors are typically installed and maintained by the electric utility power company, whereas underground service-lateral conductors are often installed and maintained by the customer. Figure 14–12

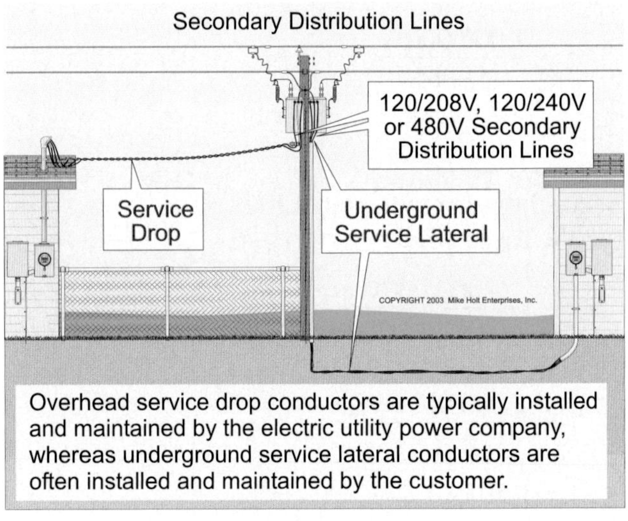

Figure 14–12

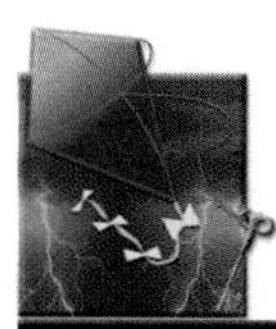

Unit 14 Summary

14.1 Current Flow

Electrons leaving a power supply are always trying to return to the same power supply; they are not trying to go into the earth.

14.2 Utility Neutral Current Path

The electric utility grounds the primary and secondary neutral conductor to the earth at multiple locations to create a parallel path so as to reduce the impedance of the return neutral current path. This multipoint grounded neutral helps in reducing primary utility neutral voltage drop, the clearing of utility line-to-neutral faults, and in reducing elevated line-to-neutral voltage caused by line-to-ground faults.

14.3 Utility Ground-Fault Current Path

Metal parts of the electric utility equipment (transformer and capacitor cases, guy wires, luminaires, etc.) are grounded to the earth and bonded to the grounded (neutral) conductor to provide a low-impedance parallel path for the purpose of clearing a line-to-case ground fault. If the utility grounded (neutral) conductor is inadvertently opened, the earth itself should still have low enough impedance to permit sufficient fault current to flow to blow the fuse, thereby clearing the high-voltage ground fault.

14.4 Premises Neutral Current Path

Neutral current should only flow on the grounded (neutral) conductor, not on metal parts of the electrical installation.

14.5 Premises Ground-Fault Current Path

Metal parts of premises wiring are bonded to a low-impedance path designed and intended to carry fault current from the point of a line-to-case fault on a wiring system to the grounded (neutral) conductor at the electrical supply source.

This low-impedance fault-current path ensures that the opening of the circuit protection device will quickly clear the ground fault.

For systems operating at 600V or less, the earth will not carry sufficient fault current to clear a line-to-case ground fault.

14.6 Utility High-Voltage Transmission Lines

Electric power is typically generated and transmitted across long transmission lines to the electrical substation. Here the voltage is stepped down and delivered over distribution lines to the customer. These conductors have relatively low resistance, but because of their length, the total resistance can cause significant conductor voltage drop and power losses.

14.7 Conductor Voltage Drop

The voltage drop over a conductor is directly proportional to the length of the conductor because conductor resistance is directly proportional to the conductor length.

14.8 Conductor Power Loss

Conductor power losses are directly proportional to the length of the conductor and the square of the current: $P = I^2 \times R$. So if the length of the conductors were doubled, the power loss would double.

Because power is relative to the square of the current ($P = I^2 \times R$), if the current is decreased to one-tenth of its original level, the power loss will be 100 times less. Then again, if the current is doubled, the power loss will be increased by 400 percent (2^2)!

14.9 Reducing Voltage Drop and Power Loss

The most effective way to reduce conductor voltage drop and power loss is to lower the current flowing through the conductors and this is accomplished by increasing the circuit voltage.

14.10 Generating Plants

The electrical system begins at a generating plant that converts energy from fossil fuels (coal or oil) or nuclear power to steam, which turns the turbine of an electric generator. Typically, a steam turbine is directly connected to an electrical generator, which produces 13.8 kV, three-phase power.

14.11 Step-Up Substation at Generating Plant

The most economical way to transfer electrical power over long distances is with high voltage, because for a given power, the current decreases in direct proportion to the increase in voltage level. Thus, conductor voltage drop and power losses (wasted energy) are lower when transferring power over great distances.

At the step-up substation, the 13.8 kV generated voltage is transformed to 69 kV, 500 kV or even higher.

14.12 Transmission Line

High-voltage transmission lines are used to carry 69 kV or higher voltage to the various step-down substations.

14.13 Step-Down Substation

Step-down substations reduce the voltage from the high-voltage transmission lines to 34.5 kV, 13.8 kV, or sometimes as low as 4,160V. This reduced voltage is known as primary distribution voltage.

14.14 Primary Distribution Feeders

Various distribution feeders transfer the primary distribution voltage from step-down substations to distribution transformers, which are often mounted on poles or on the ground next to the building being served.

14.15 Distribution Transformer

Distribution transformers further reduce the primary distribution voltage from 34.5 kV or 13.8 kV to 240V or 480V, three-phase for the average moderate-sized commercial or small industrial customer.

14.16 Secondary Distribution Line

The customer's power is transferred from the utility's distribution transformer to the customer via the overhead service drop or underground service lateral. Overhead service-drop conductors are typically installed and maintained by the electric utility power company, whereas underground service-lateral conductors are often installed and maintained by the customer.

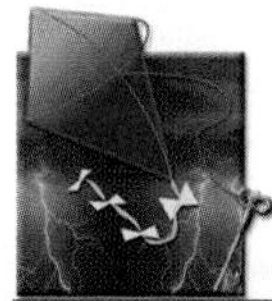

Unit 14 Conclusion

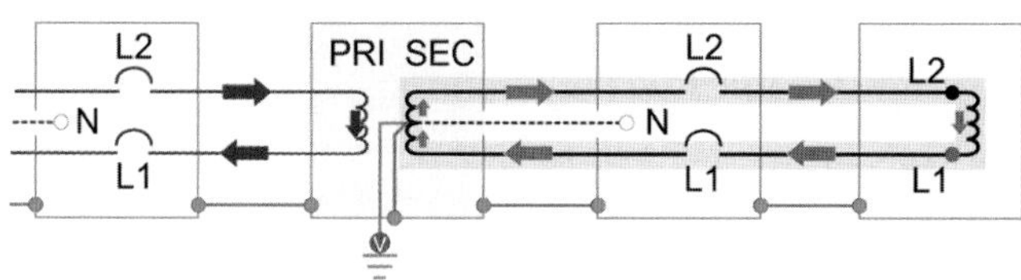

Now you know a bit about how utilities produce and distribute electrical power. You also know that when someone refers to a "14 kV line," that person is referring to the 13.8 kV distribution line. You're also aware that 13.8 kV is just one of many distribution voltages.

The typical electrician never works on equipment at these voltages. Electric utilities have their own crews to install, troubleshoot, and maintain transmission equipment. However, some electricians work for electrical testing firms that do work with this equipment.

Words to Live By: *The train of failure usually runs on the track of laziness.*

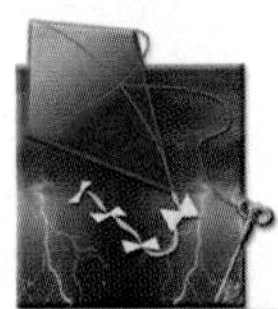

Unit 14 Practice Questions

14.1 Current Flow

1. Electrons leaving a power supply are always trying to return to the same power supply; they are not trying to go into the earth.

   (a) True (b) False

2. When ac is applied to the secondary of a transformer, it induces voltage in the primary, which causes electrons to travel through the primary circuit.

   (a) True (b) False

14.2 Utility Neutral Current Path

3. The electric utility grounds the primary and secondary neutral conductor to the earth at multiple locations for the purpose of reducing the _____ of the return current path.

   (a) ac resistance (b) dc resistance (c) a or b (d) none of these

4. The multipoint grounded neutral is intended to reduce the _____ neutral voltage drop, assist in clearing _____ line-to-neutral faults, and reduce elevated voltage caused by line-to-ground faults.

   (a) primary (b) secondary (c) a or b (d) none of these

14.3 Utility Ground-Fault Current Path

5. Metal parts of the electric utility equipment are bonded to the utility neutral to provide a _____ path to the power source to assist in clearing a line-to-case fault.

   (a) high-resistive (b) low-impedance (c) ground (d) none of these

6. The earth generally has low enough impedance to permit sufficient fault current to return to the source, thereby opening the utility's circuit protection device.

   (a) True (b) False

14.4 Premises Neutral Current Path

7. To prevent fires and electric shock, the *NEC* specifies that neutral current can flow on metal parts of the electrical system.

   (a) True (b) False

14.5 Premises Ground-Fault Current Path

8. Metal parts of premises wiring must be bonded to a low-impedance path designed so that the circuit protection device will quickly open and clear a ground fault.

   (a) True (b) False

9. Because of the earth's high resistance to current flow, it cannot be used for the purpose of clearing a line-to-case ground fault for _____ wiring.

   (a) utility (b) premises (c) a or b (d) none of these

14.6 Utility High-Voltage Transmission Lines

10. Electrical power is generated and transmitted across long transmission lines to the customer. These conductors have a very low resistance, but because of their length, the conductor _____ losses can be significant.

    (a) voltage drop (b) power (c) current (d) a and b

14.7 Conductor Voltage Drop

11. The voltage drop over a conductor is directly proportional to the _____ of the conductor.

    (a) area (b) circular mils (c) length (d) none of these

14.8 Conductor Power Loss

12. Conductor power losses are directly proportional to the length of the conductor and the square of the current. If the current is doubled, the power loss will be increased by _____.

    (a) 100% (b) 200% (c) 300% (d) 400%

14.9 Reducing Voltage Drop and Power Loss

13. The most effective way to reduce conductor voltage drop and power loss is to lower the current flowing through the conductors. This is accomplished by _____ the transmission voltage.

    (a) reducing (b) applying (c) increasing (d) none of these

14.10 Generating Plants

14. The electrical system usually begins at the generating plant that converts energy to _____, 3Ø power.

    (a) 13.2 kV (b) 13.8 kV (c) 69 kV (d) 138 kV

14.11 Step-Up Substation at Generating Plant

15. A step-up substation located at the generating facilities transforms the 13.8 kV generator output to _____.

(a) 13.2 kV (b) 13.8 kV (c) 69 kV or higher (d) none of these

14.12 Transmission Line

16. High-voltage transmission lines are usually connected to transmission lines from other generating plants. This is known as a(n) _____.

(a) interconnected system (b) electrical power grid
(c) power system (d) a or b

14.13 Step-Down Substation

17. Step-down substations reduce the voltage from the high-voltage transmission lines to a primary distribution voltage of _____.

(a) 4 – 35 kV (b) 50 – 60 kV (c) 69 – 100 kV (d) 169+ kV

14.14 Primary Distribution Feeders

18. Distribution feeders transfer the primary distribution voltage to distribution _____ mounted on poles or on the ground next to the building being served.

(a) capacitors (b) generators (c) transformers (d) all of these

14.15 Distribution Transformer

19. Distribution transformers reduce the primary distribution voltage to secondary distribution voltage, such as _____.

(a) 120/208V (b) 120/240V (c) 277/480V (d) any of these

14.16 Secondary Distribution Line

20. The customer's power is transferred from the utility's distribution transformer to the customer via the _____.

(a) overhead service drop (b) underground service lateral
(c) a or b (d) none of these

UNIT 15 Protection Devices

Introduction

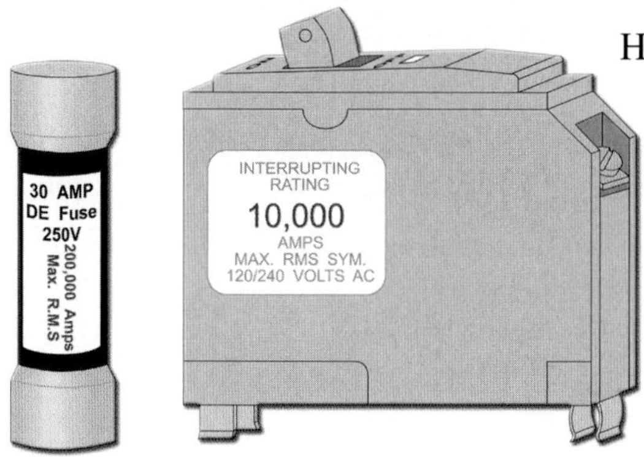

How does a fuse differ from a circuit breaker? How do you select a circuit breaker, and what actually makes it work? In this unit, you will learn the answers to those questions. You'll learn about the interrupting rating and the short-circuit rating—two very different, but often confused—overcurrent protection terms. Perhaps most importantly, you'll understand the role of circuit overcurrent protection in clearing ground faults and some critical facts about grounding.

PART A—OVERCURRENT PROTECTION DEVICES

15.1 Overcurrent Protection

The purpose of overcurrent protection is to protect conductors and equipment against excessive or dangerous temperatures due to current in excess of the rated ampacity of equipment or conductors. These conditions may result from overload, short circuit, or ground fault. Figure 15–1

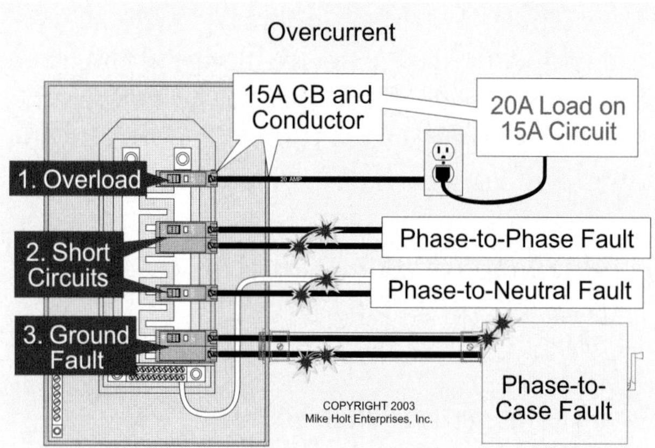

Overcurrent: Any current in excess of the rated current of equipment or materials. Causes of overcurrent are overloads, short circuits and ground faults.

Figure 15–1

Overload

An overload is a condition where equipment or conductors carry current in excess of their rated ampacity. An example of an overload is plugging two hair dryers, each rated 1,500W, into a circuit wired with 12 AWG wire. Each dryer draws

12.5A, and 12 AWG wire is not permitted to be protected by a protection device greater than 20A.

Ground Fault

A ground fault is the electrical connection between any ungrounded conductors of the electrical system and any noncurrent-carrying metal object. During the period of a ground fault, dangerous voltages and larger currents exist.

Short Circuit

A short circuit is the electrical connection between any two conductors of the electrical system from line-to-line or from line-to-neutral.

15.2 Clearing Faults

To protect against electric shock from dangerous voltages on metal parts of electrical equipment, and to prevent a fire from an overload, ground fault or short circuit, the fault must quickly be removed by the opening of the circuit's overcurrent protection device.

Time—Current Curves

The opening time for an overcurrent protection device is inversely proportional to the magnitude of the current. The greater the current value, the less time it takes for the protection device to open.

For example, a 20A circuit breaker with an overload of 40A (twice the device rating) would trip in 25 to 150 seconds. If the overload were five times the rating of the breaker (100A) the breaker would trip in 5 to 20 seconds. **Figure 15–2**

> **AUTHOR'S COMMENT:** A circuit breaker can open in three to five cycles if current is twenty times its rating.

Remove Dangerous Touch Voltage

To remove dangerous touch voltage on metal parts from a ground fault, the fault-current path must have sufficiently low impedance to allow the fault current to quickly rise to facilitate the opening of the branch-circuit overcurrent protection device.

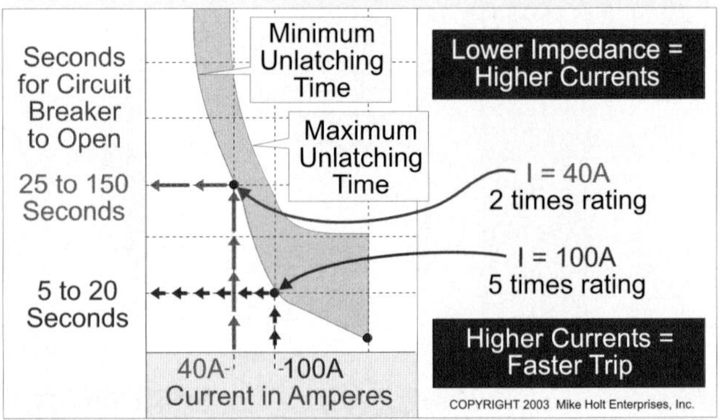

Figure 15–2

Example

The approximate ground-fault current for the following will be _____.

- Ungrounded circuit conductors—200 ft of 3 AWG at 0.05Ω
- Equipment bonding conductor—200 ft of 8 AWG at 0.156Ω. **Figure 15–3**

(a) 100A (b) 200A
(c) 600A (d) 800A

- Answer: (c) 600A

Fault Current = E/Z
E = 120V
Z* = 0.05Ω + 0.156Ω = 0.206Ω
Fault Current = 120V/0.206Ω = 583A
* See Section 14.4.

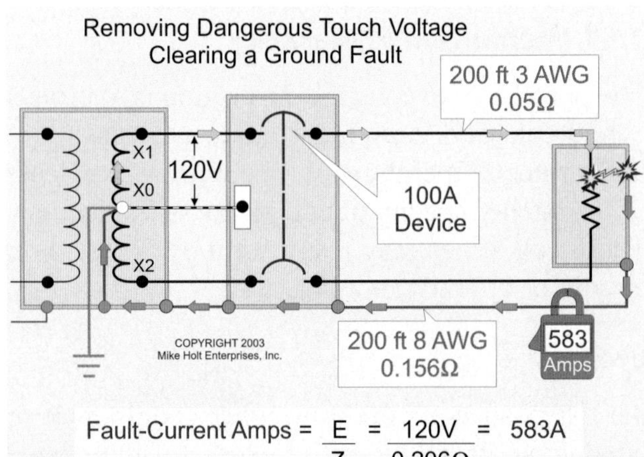

100A overcurrent device quickly opens, clears the ground fault and removes dangerous voltage from metal parts.

Figure 15–3

15.3 Overcurrent Protection Device Types

The most common types of overcurrent protection are fuses and circuit breakers.

AUTHOR'S COMMENT: Two additional protection devices, the Ground-Fault Circuit Interrupter (GFCI) and the Arc-Fault Circuit Interrupter (AFCI) protect against electric shock and fires.

15.4 Fuse

Construction

A typical fuse consists of an element electrically connected to the end blades, called the ferrules. The conductive element provides a path for current through the fuse. The element is enclosed in a tube and surrounded by a non-conductive filler material. Figure 15–4

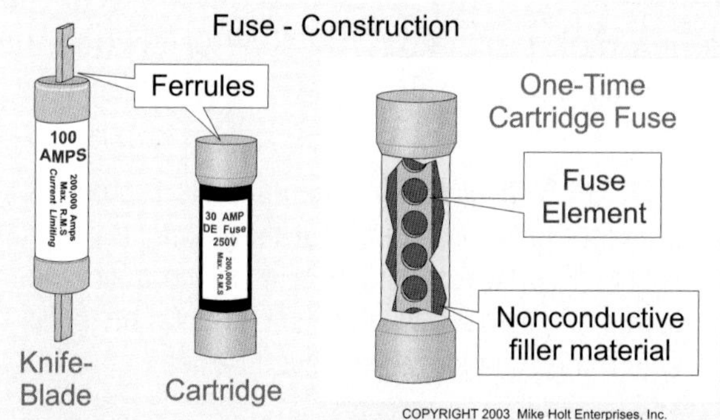

A typical fuse consists of an element electrically connected to the ferrules. The conductive element provides a path for current through the fuse. The element is enclosed in a tube surrounded by a nonconductive filler material.

Figure 15–4

Overload Protection

When current flows through the element of a fuse, it generates heat. During normal operation, the filler material absorbs this heat. When a sustained overload occurs, the heat melts a portion of the element stopping the flow of current. Figure 15–5

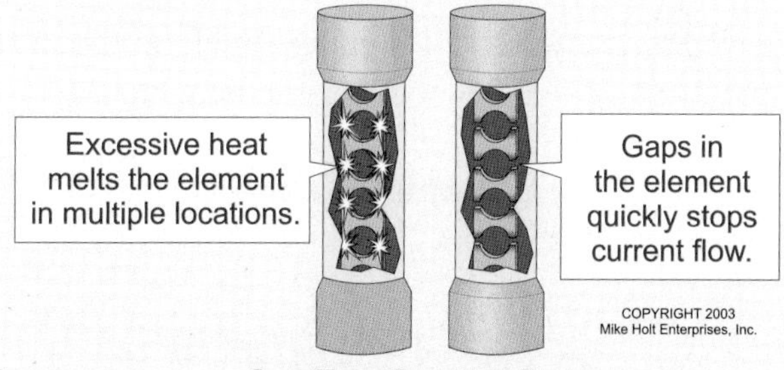

Short circuits and ground faults can be in the thousands of amperes. Several element segments can melt at the same time removing the current, typically, in less than half of a cycle.

Figure 15–5

Short-Circuit and Ground-Fault Protection

Short-circuit and ground-fault current can be in the thousands of amperes. When a short circuit or ground fault occurs, several element segments melt at the same time removing the load from the source very quickly. Typically, circuit breakers and fuses are designed to open or clear short-circuit and ground-fault current in less than one cycle. Figure 15–6

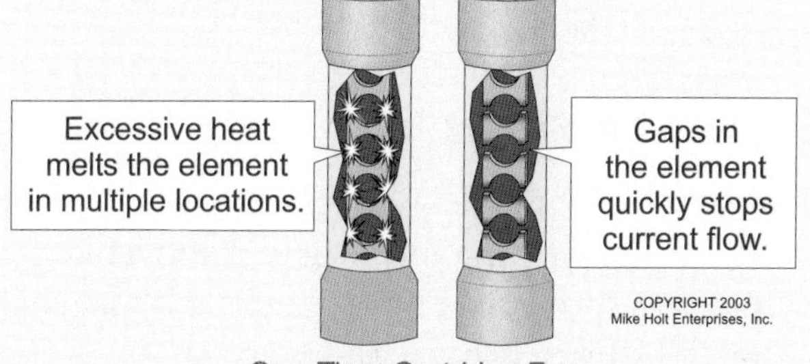

Short circuits and ground faults can be in the thousands of amperes. Several element segments can melt at the same time removing the current, typically, in less than half of a cycle.

Figure 15–6

15.5 Circuit Breaker Trip Elements

Electromagnetic circuit breakers open on the principle of thermo and electromagnetism. Figure 15–7

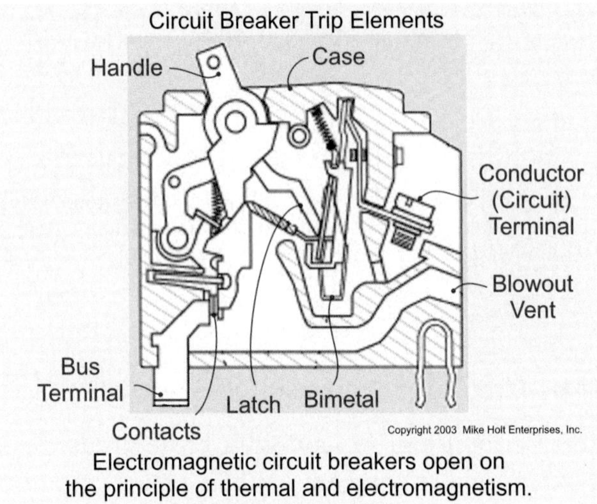

Electromagnetic circuit breakers open on the principle of thermal and electromagnetism.

Figure 15–7

Thermal Trip Element

Thermal circuit breakers are dependent upon temperature rise in the sensing element for actuation. In normal operation, the thermal sensing element (bimetal) will cause the circuit breaker to open when a predetermined calibration temperature is reached.

Magnetic Trip Element

The magnetic time-delay circuit breaker operates on the solenoid principle where a movable core held with a spring, in a tube, is moved by the magnetic field caused by a short circuit or ground fault.

15.6 Circuit Breaker Types

Inverse-Time

Inverse-time breakers operate on the principle that as the current increases, the time it takes for the devices to open decreases. This type of breaker provides overcurrent protection (overload, short circuit and ground fault).

Adjustable-Trip

Adjustable-trip breakers permit the thermo trip setting to be adjusted. The adjustment is often necessary to coordinate the operation of the circuit breakers with other overcurrent protection devices.

AUTHOR'S COMMENT: Coordination means that the devices with the lowest ratings, closest to the fault, operate and isolate the fault and disruption, if possible, so that the rest of the system can remain energized and functional.

Instantaneous-Trip

Instantaneous-trip breakers operate on the principle of electromagnetism only and are used for very large motors; sometimes these devices are called motor-circuit protectors (MCPs). This type of protection device does not provide overload protection. It only provides short-circuit and ground-fault protection; overload protection must be provided separately.

AUTHOR'S COMMENT: Instantaneous-trip circuit breakers have no intentional time delay and are sensitive to current inrush, and to vibration and shock. Consequently, they should not be used where these factors are known to exist.

15.7 Available Short-Circuit Current

Available short-circuit current (SCA) is the current in amperes that is available at a given point in the electrical system. This available short-circuit current is first determined at the secondary terminals of the utility transformer. Thereafter, the available short-circuit current is calculated at the terminals of the service equipment, branch-circuit and branch-circuit load panelboard.

The available short-circuit current is different at each point of the electrical system, it is highest at the utility transformer and lowest at the branch-circuit load.

The available short-circuit current is dependent on the impedance of the circuit, which increases downstream from the utility transformer. The

greater the circuit impedance (utility transformer and the additive impedances of the circuit conductors), the lower the available short-circuit current. Figure 15–8

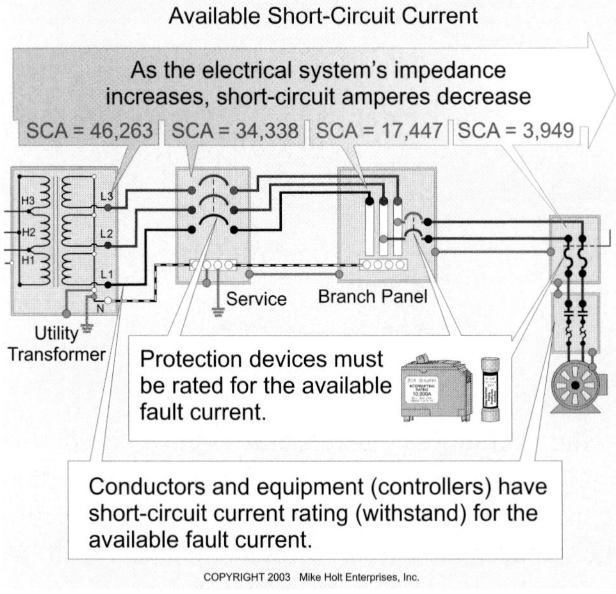

Available Short-Circuit Current
As the electrical system's impedance increases, short-circuit amperes decrease
SCA = 46,263
SCA = 34,338
SCA = 17,447
SCA = 3,949
H3
H2
H1
L3
L2
L1
N
Service
Branch Panel
Utility Transformer
Protection devices must be rated for the available fault current.
Conductors and equipment (controllers) have short-circuit current rating (withstand) for the available fault current.
COPYRIGHT 2003 Mike Holt Enterprises, Inc.

Figure 15–8

Factors that impact the available short-circuit current at the utility transformer include the system voltage, the transformer kVA rating and its impedance (as expressed in a percentage). Properties that impact the impedance of the circuit include the conductor material (copper versus aluminum), the conductor size, and its length.

15.8 Interrupting Rating

Overcurrent protection devices such as circuit breakers and fuses are intended to interrupt the circuit, and they shall have an ampere interrupting rating (AIR) sufficient for the available short-circuit current. They shall have an interrupting rating, such as 10K, 22K, 65K RMS sufficient for the nominal circuit voltage and the short-circuit current available at the line terminals of the equipment. Figure 15–9

AUTHOR'S COMMENT: Amperes Interrupting Rating (AIR) is also described as "Amperes Interrupting Capacity" (AIC) by many in the industry.

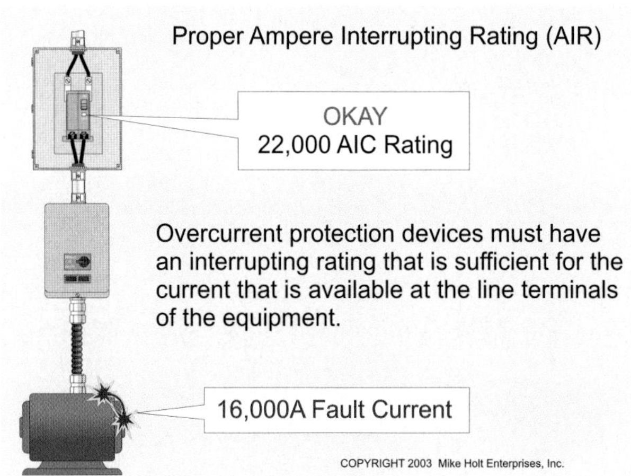

Proper Ampere Interrupting Rating (AIR)
OKAY
22,000 AIC Rating
Overcurrent protection devices must have an interrupting rating that is sufficient for the current that is available at the line terminals of the equipment.
16,000A Fault Current
COPYRIGHT 2003 Mike Holt Enterprises, Inc.

Figure 15–9

Unless marked otherwise, the ampere interrupting rating for circuit breakers is 5,000A and 10,000A for fuses. Figure 15–10

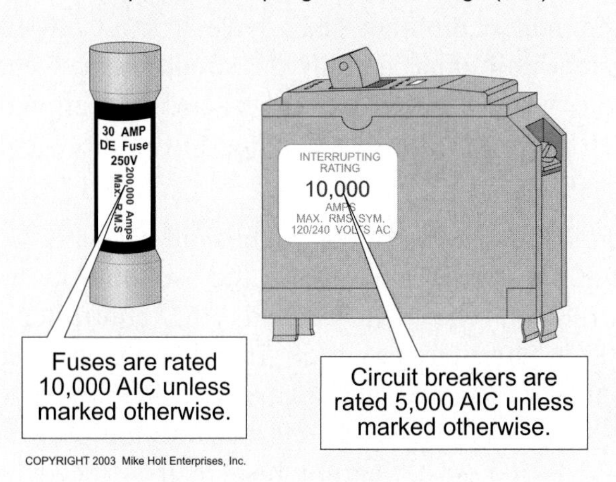

Figure 15–10

DANGER: ***Extremely high values of current flow (caused by short circuits or ground faults) produce tremendously destructive thermal and magnetic forces. If the circuit overcurrent protection device is not rated to interrupt the current at the available fault values at its listed voltage rating, it could explode while attempting to clear the fault. Naturally this can cause serious injury or death, as well as property damage.*** Figure 15–11

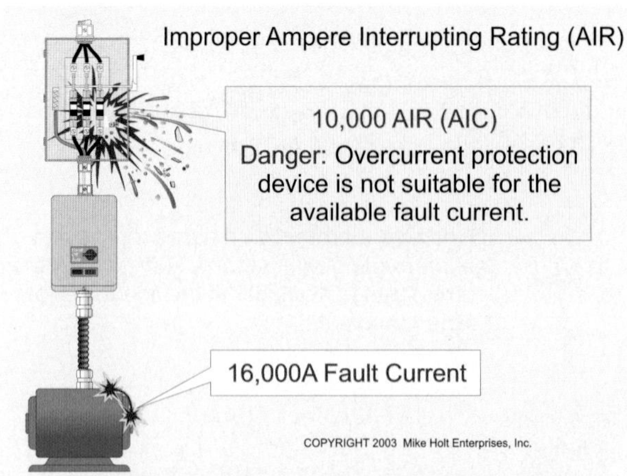
Improper Ampere Interrupting Rating (AIR)
10,000 AIR (AIC)
Danger: Overcurrent protection device is not suitable for the available fault current.
16,000A Fault Current
COPYRIGHT 2003 Mike Holt Enterprises, Inc.
Short circuits and ground faults produce extremely high current flow that is tremendously destructive. Overcurrent protection not properly rated for the available short-circuit and ground-fault values of the circuit could explode attempting to clear the fault.

Figure 15–11

15.9 Short-Circuit Current Rating

Electrical equipment shall have a short-circuit current rating that permits the circuit overcurrent protection device to clear a short circuit or ground fault without extensive damage to the electrical components of the circuit.

For example, a motor controller shall have a sufficient short-circuit rating for the available fault-current. If the fault exceeds the controller's 5,000A short-circuit current rating, the controller could explode, endangering persons and property. To solve this problem, a current-limiting protection device (fast-clearing fuse) can be used to reduce the let-through current to less than 5,000A. Figure 15–12

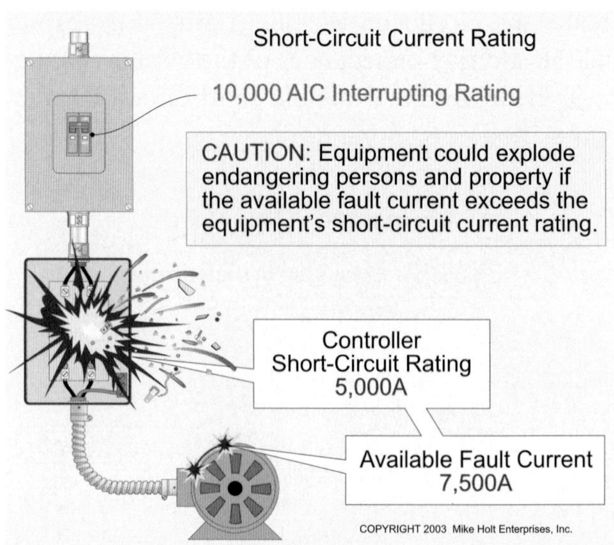
Short-Circuit Current Rating
10,000 AIC Interrupting Rating
CAUTION: Equipment could explode endangering persons and property if the available fault current exceeds the equipment's short-circuit current rating.
Controller Short-Circuit Rating 5,000A
Available Fault Current 7,500A
COPYRIGHT 2003 Mike Holt Enterprises, Inc.

Figure 15–12

If the available short-circuit current exceeds the equipment/conductor short-circuit current rating, then the thermal and magnetic forces can cause the equipment circuit conductors, as well as grounding conductors, to vaporize. The only solution to the problem of excessive available fault current is to:

(1) Install equipment that has a higher short-circuit rating.

(2) Protect the components of the circuit by a current-limiting protection device such as a fast-clearing fuse, which can reduce the let-through energy.

15.10 Current-Limiting Protection

A current-limiting type fuse is a fuse designed for operations relating to short circuits only. When a fuse operates in its current-limiting range, it will clear a bolted short circuit in less than half a cycle. This type of fuse limits the instantaneous peak let-through current to a value substantially less than that obtainable in the same circuit if that fuse was replaced with a solid conductor of equal impedance.

AUTHOR'S COMMENT: A breaker or a fuse does limit current, but it may not be listed as a current-limiting device. A thermal-magnetic circuit breaker will typically clear fault current in less than three to five cycles when subjected to a short circuit or ground fault of twenty times its rating. A standard fuse would clear the fault in less than one cycle and a current-limiting fuse should clear the same fault in less than one-quarter of one cycle. Figure 15–13

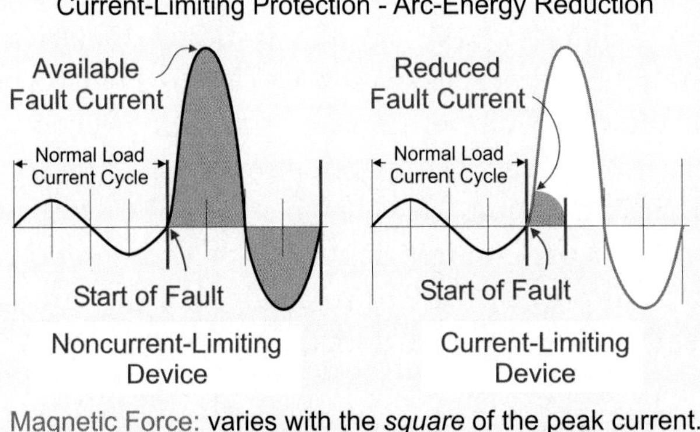

Figure 15–13

PART B—GROUND-FAULT CIRCUIT INTERRUPTERS

15.11 How a GFCI Works

A ground-fault circuit interrupter (GFCI) is specifically designed to protect persons against electric shock from an electrical system. A GFCI protection device operates on the principle of monitoring the imbalance of current between the circuit's ungrounded and grounded (neutral) conductors. **Figure 15–14**

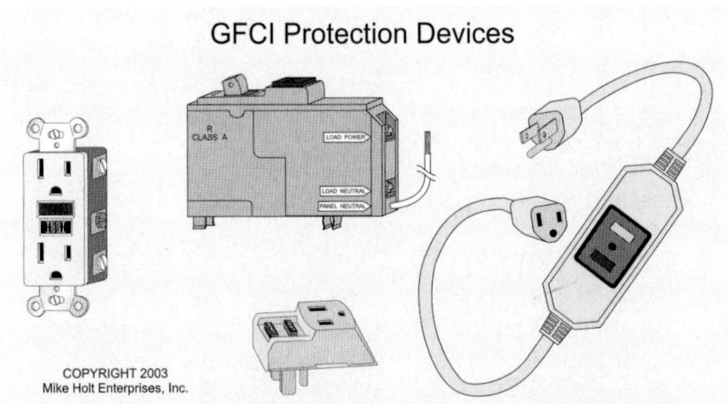

A GFCI is designed to protect persons against electric shock. It operates on the principle of monitoring the unbalanced current between the ungrounded and grounded (neutral) conductor.

Figure 15–14

An interesting point about these devices is that despite their name, they will operate on a circuit with or without an equipment grounding conductor. **Figure 15–15**

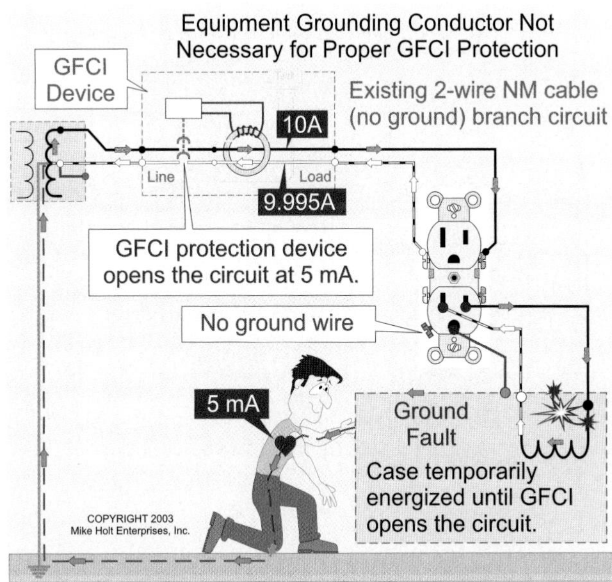

Figure 15–15

During the normal operation of a typical 2-wire circuit, the current returning to the power supply will be equal to the current leaving the power supply. If the difference between the current leaving and returning through the current transformer of the GFCI protection device exceeds 5 mA (± 1 mA), the solid-state circuitry opens the switching contacts and de-energizes the circuit.

The abbreviation "mA" (used above) stands for one thousandth of an ampere, so 5 mA is equal to $^{5}/_{1,000th}$ of an ampere.

15.12 Neutral-to-Case Detection

Another function of a GFCI device is the detection of downstream neutral-to-case connections. A second current transformer in the GFCI induces a voltage on the circuit conductors. If there is a neutral-to-case connection on the load side of the GFCI protection device, the GFCI will sense the imbalance of the current returning on the equipment grounding conductor and prevent the GFCI device from being turned on. This feature can give the appearance of a "defective" GFCI device because it trips when the circuit is energized, even with no loads on or connected. **Figure 15–16**

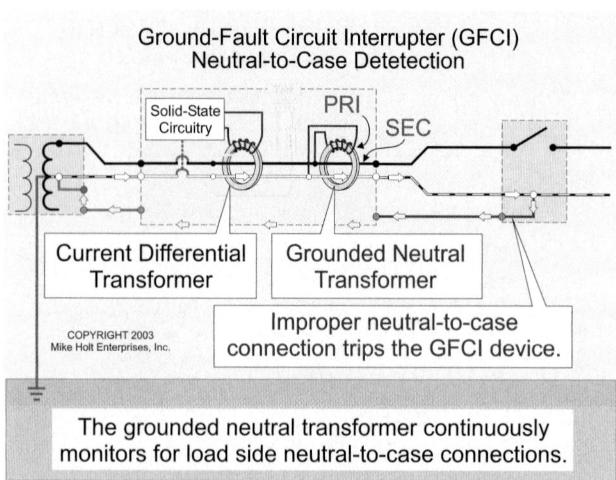

Figure 15–16

According to the *GFCI Field Test Survey Report,* dated January 2001 by the National Electrical Manufacturers Association (NEMA), 11 percent of the GFCI circuit breakers protecting receptacles located indoors did not provide GFCI protection. In addition, 20 percent of the GFCI circuit breakers protecting receptacles located outdoors, did not provide GFCI protection. Yet the circuit remained energized without GFCI protection!

AUTHOR'S COMMENT: Eight percent of GFCI receptacles also failed to provide GFCI protection, yet the receptacle remained energized.

The failures of the GFCI sensing circuits were many, but the greatest percentage related to damage of the internal transient voltage surge protectors (metal-oxide varistors) that protect the GFCI sensing circuit. This damage resulted from voltage transients from lightning and other sources. **Figure 15–18**

15.13 Line-to-Neutral Shock Hazard

Severe electric shock or death can occur if a person touches the ungrounded and grounded (neutral) conductors at the same time, even if the circuit is GFCI protected. This is because the current transformer within the GFCI protection device does not sense an imbalance between the departing and returning current. **Figure 15–17**

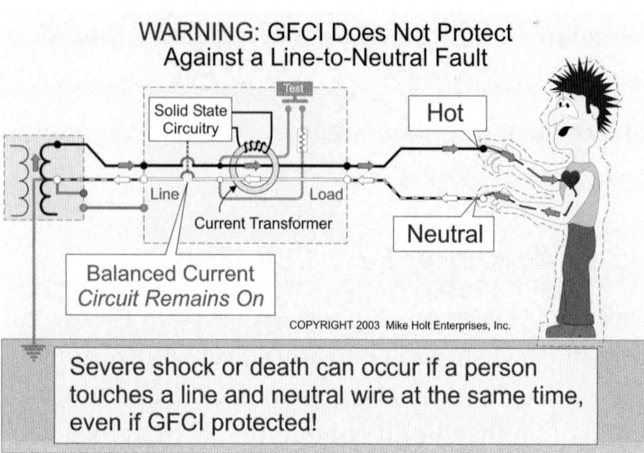

Figure 15–17

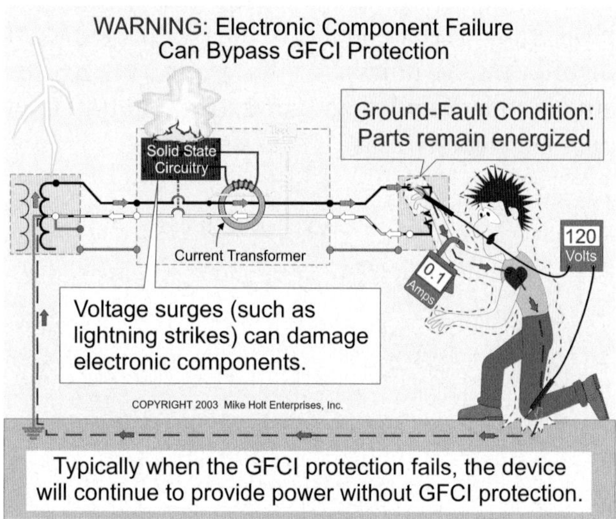

Figure 15–18

15.14 GFCI Fails—Circuit Remains Energized

Typically, when a GFCI protection device fails, the switching contacts remain closed and the device will continue to provide power without GFCI protection!

At least one leading manufacturer markets a listed 15A, 125V GFCI receptacle that cannot be reset if the GFCI circuit no longer provides ground-fault protection. As an added safety improvement, this particular GFCI receptacle has a built-in line load reversal feature that prevents the GFCI from resetting if the installer mistakenly reverses the load and line connections.

15.15 GFCI Test Button

One final thought on GFCI protection is that you should press the test feature of the GFCI protection device to ensure that it turns the power off to the connected load. Do not assume that a GFCI protection device is operational unless you properly test it!

PART C—ARC-FAULT CIRCUIT INTERRUPTER

15.16 Arcing Definition

Arcing is defined as a luminous discharge of electricity across an insulating medium. Electric arcs operate at temperatures between 5,000 and 15,000°F and expel small particles of very hot molten materials. Higher current arcs are more likely to cause a fire because of the higher thermal energy contained in the arc. Greater current will melt more of the conductor metal and therefore expel more hot molten particles. Figure 15–19

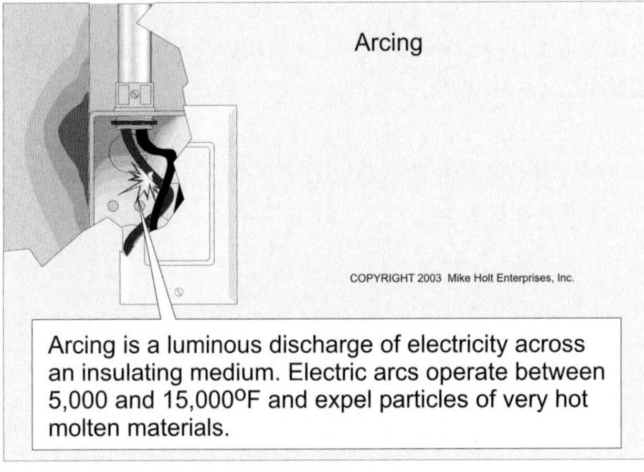
Arcing
COPYRIGHT 2003 Mike Holt Enterprises, Inc.
Arcing is a luminous discharge of electricity across an insulating medium. Electric arcs operate between 5,000 and 15,000°F and expel particles of very hot molten materials.

Figure 15–19

15.17 Series Versus Parallel Arc

In electrical circuits, unsafe arcing faults can occur in one of two ways, as series arcing faults or as parallel arcing faults. The most dangerous is the parallel arcing fault.

Series Arc

A series arc can occur when the conductor in series with the load is unintentionally broken. Examples might be a frayed conductor in a cord that has pulled apart. A series arc-fault current is load limited; the arc's current cannot be greater than the load current the conductor serves. Typically, series arcs do not develop sufficient thermal energy to create a fire.

Parallel Arc

Parallel arcing faults occur in one of two ways, as a short circuit or as a ground fault.

Short-Circuit Parallel Arc. A short-circuit arc might occur if the wire's insulation is damaged by an excessively or incorrectly driven staple in nonmetallic sheath cable, or the insulation of the cord is damaged by a conductive object such as a metal table leg placed on the cord. The result is a decrease in the dielectric strength of insulation separating the conductors allowing a high-impedance low current arcing fault to develop. This arcing fault carbonizes the conductor's insulation further decreasing the dielectric of the insulation separating the conductors. The result is an increase in current, an exponential increase in thermal energy heat, and the likelihood of a fire.

The current flow in a short-circuit type arc is limited by the system impedance and the impedance of the arcing fault itself. Typically, at a receptacle, fault current will be above 75A, but not likely above 450A. This short-circuit arc is reported as being more common in older homes where the appliance cords and the building wiring have deteriorated due to the negative effects of aging. This type of arcing fault can be quickly cleared by an AFCI circuit protective device.

AUTHOR'S COMMENT: The RMS current value for parallel arc faults will likely be less than that of a solid bolted-type fault; therefore, a typical 15A or 20A circuit protective device might not clear this fault before a fire is ignited.

Ground-Fault Parallel Arc. A ground-fault type parallel arc fault can only occur when a ground path is present. This type of arcing fault can be quickly cleared by either a GFCI or AFCI circuit protective device.

15.18 AFCI and the NEC

To help reduce the hazard of electrical fires from a parallel arcing fault in the branch-circuit wiring, the *NEC* requires a listed AFCI protection device to be installed to protect the branch-circuit wiring for dwelling unit bedrooms. Figure 15–20

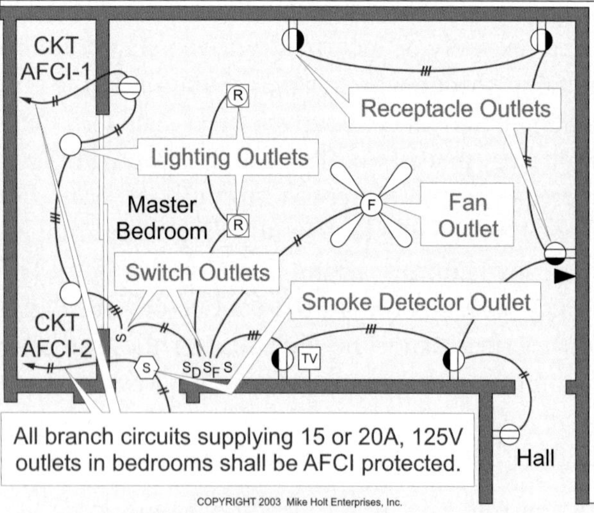

Figure 15–20

15.19 AFCI—How They Operate

An AFCI protection device provides protection from an arcing fault by recognizing the characteristics unique to an arcing fault and by functioning to de-energize the circuit when a parallel arc fault is detected.

AUTHOR'S COMMENT: This topic is beyond the scope of this textbook.

PART D—GROUND-FAULT PROTECTION OF EQUIPMENT

15.20 Ground-Fault Protection of Equipment Definition

Ground-fault protection of equipment is a system intended to provide protection of equipment from damaging ground-fault currents by opening all ungrounded conductors of the faulted circuit. This protection is provided at current levels less than those required to protect conductors from damage through the operation of a supply circuit overcurrent device. This type of protective device is not intended to protect persons, only connected utilization equipment.

AUTHOR'S COMMENT: GFPE is beyond the scope of this textbook.

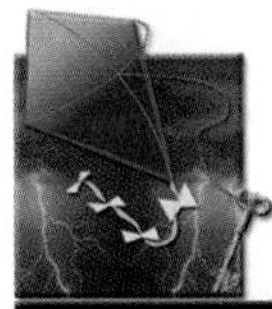

Unit 15 Summary

PART A—OVERCURRENT PROTECTION DEVICES

15.1 Overcurrent Protection

The purpose of overcurrent protection is to protect conductors and equipment against excessive or dangerous temperatures due to current in excess of the rated ampacity of equipment or conductors. These conditions may result from overload, short circuit, or ground fault.

15.2 Clearing Faults

To protect against electric shock from dangerous voltages on metal parts of electrical equipment, and to prevent a fire from an overload, ground fault or short circuit, the fault must quickly be removed by the opening of the circuit's overcurrent protection device.

Remove Dangerous Touch Voltage

To remove dangerous touch voltage on metal parts from a ground fault, the fault-current path must have sufficiently low impedance to allow the fault current to quickly rise to facilitate the opening of the branch-circuit overcurrent protection device.

15.3 Overcurrent Protection Device Types

The most common types of overcurrent protection are fuses and circuit breakers.

15.4 Fuse

Construction

A typical fuse consists of an element electrically connected to the end blades, called the ferrules. The conductive element provides a path for current through the fuse. The element is enclosed in a tube and surrounded by a non-conductive filler material.

Overload Protection

When a sustained overload occurs, the heat melts a portion of the element, stopping the flow of current.

Short-Circuit and Ground-Fault Protection

When a short circuit occurs, several element segments melt at the same time, removing the load from the source very quickly.

15.5 Circuit Breaker Trip Elements

Electromagnetic circuit breakers open on the principle of thermo and electromagnetism.

Thermal Trip Element

In normal operation, the thermal sensing element (bimetal) will cause the circuit breaker to open when a predetermined calibration temperature is reached.

Magnetic Trip Element

The magnetic time-delay circuit breaker operates on the solenoid principle where a movable core held with a spring, in a tube, is moved by the magnetic field caused by a short circuit or ground fault.

15.6 Circuit Breaker Types

Inverse-Time

Inverse-time breakers operate on the principle that as the current increases, the time it takes for the devices to open decreases.

Adjustable-Trip

Adjustable-trip breakers permit the magnetic trip setting to be adjusted to coordinate the operation of the circuit breakers with other overcurrent protection devices.

Instantaneous-Trip

Instantaneous-trip breakers operate on the principle of electromagnetism only and are used for very large motors. Instantaneous-trip circuit breakers have no intentional time delay and are sensitive to current inrush, and to vibration and shock.

15.7 Available Short-Circuit Current

Available short-circuit current (SCA) is the current in amperes that is available at a given point in the electrical system. The available short-circuit current is different at each point of the electrical system. It is highest at the utility transformer and lowest at the branch-circuit load.

Factors that impact the available short-circuit current include the system voltage, transformer kVA rating and its impedance, conductor material, conductor size, and its length.

15.8 Interrupting Rating

Overcurrent protection devices such as circuit breakers and fuses are intended to interrupt the circuit, and they shall have an ampere interrupting rating (AIR) sufficient for the available short-circuit current.

DANGER: ***If the circuit overcurrent protection device is not rated to interrupt the current at the available fault values at its listed voltage rating, it could explode while attempting to clear the fault. Naturally this can cause serious injury or death, as well as property damage.***

15.9 Short-Circuit Current Rating

Electrical equipment shall have a short-circuit current rating that permits the circuit overcurrent protection device to clear a short circuit or ground fault without extensive damage to the electrical components of the circuit.

15.10 Current Limiting Protection

When a fuse operates in its current limiting range, it will clear a short circuit in less than half a cycle. This type of fuse substantially limits the instantaneous peak let-through current.

If the available short-circuit current exceeds the equipment/conductor short-circuit current rating, then the thermal and magnetic forces can cause the equipment circuit conductors, as well as grounding conductors, to vaporize.

PART B—GROUND-FAULT CIRCUIT INTERRUPTERS

15.11 How a GFCI Works

A GFCI protection device operates on the principle of monitoring the imbalance of current between the circuit's ungrounded and grounded (neutral) conductors. If the difference between the current leaving and returning through the current transformer of the GFCI protection device exceeds 5 mA (± 1 mA), the solid-state circuitry opens the switching contacts and de-energizes the circuit.

15.12 Neutral-to-Case Detection

Another function of a GFCI device is the detection of downstream neutral-to-case connections. This feature can give the appearance of a "defective" GFCI device because it trips when the circuit is energized, even with no loads on or connected.

15.13 Line-to-Neutral Shock Hazard

Severe electric shock or death can occur if a person touches the ungrounded and grounded (neutral) conductors at the same time, even if the circuit is GFCI protected.

15.14 GFCI Fails—Circuit Remains Energized

Typically, when a GFCI protection device fails, the switching contacts remain closed and the device will continue to provide power without GFCI protection!

15.15 GFCI Test Button

Press the test feature of the GFCI protection device to ensure that it turns the power off to the connected load. Do not assume that a GFCI protection device is operational unless you properly test it!

PART C—ARC-FAULT CIRCUIT INTERRUPTER

15.16 Arcing Definition

Arcing is defined as a luminous discharge of electricity across an insulating medium. Electric arcs operate at temperatures between 5,000 and 15,000°F and expel small particles of very hot molten materials.

15.17 Series Versus Parallel Arc

Series Arc

A series arc can occur when the conductor in series with the load is unintentionally broken. A series arc-fault current is load limited; the arc's current cannot be greater than the load current the conductor serves.

Parallel Arc

Short-Circuit Parallel Arc. A short-circuit arc might occur if the wire's insulation is damaged by an excessively or incorrectly driven staple in nonmetallic sheath cable. The current flow in a short-circuit type arc is limited by the system impedance and the impedance of the arcing fault itself.

Ground-Fault Parallel Arc. A ground-fault type parallel arc fault can only occur when a ground path is present. This type of arcing fault can be quickly cleared by either a GFCI or AFCI circuit protective device.

15.18 AFCI and the NEC

To help reduce the hazard of electrical fires from a parallel arcing fault in the branch-circuit wiring, the *NEC* requires a listed AFCI protection device to be installed to protect the branch-circuit wiring for dwelling unit bedrooms.

15.19 AFCI—How They Operate

An AFCI protection device provides protection from an arcing fault by recognizing the characteristics unique to an arcing fault and by functioning to de-energize the circuit when a parallel arc fault is detected.

PART D—GROUND-FAULT PROTECTION OF EQUIPMENT

15.20 Ground-Fault Protection of Equipment Definition

Ground-fault protection of equipment is a system intended to provide protection of equipment from damaging ground-fault currents by opening all ungrounded conductors of the faulted circuit.

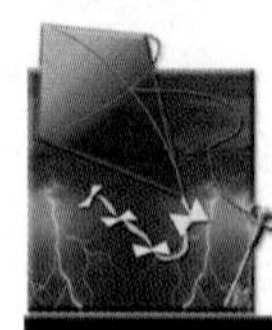

Unit 15 Conclusion

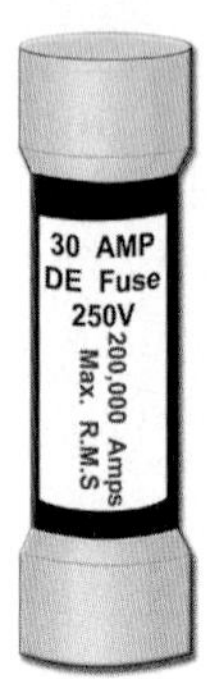

You've now gained an understanding of circuit protection devices and some basics about selecting them. You know the purpose of grounding in the proper functioning of ground-fault protection devices. You also know the hazards of energized parts and the hazards that can arise from improper grounding schemes, high-resistance ground paths, and ground faults.

Words to Live By: *When confronted with a Goliath-sized problem, which way do you respond: "He's too big to hit," or like David, "He's too big to miss"?*

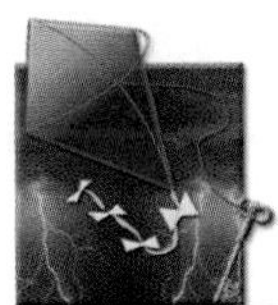

Unit 15 Practice Questions

PART A—OVERCURRENT PROTECTION DEVICES

15.1 Overcurrent Protection

1. The purpose of overcurrent protection is to protect the conductors and equipment against excessive or dangerous temperatures because of overcurrent. Overcurrent is current in excess of the rated current of equipment or conductors. It may result from a(n) _____.

   (a) overload (b) short circuit (c) ground fault (d) all of these

2. A(n)_____ is the operation of equipment or conductors in excess of their rated ampacity.

   (a) overload (b) short circuit (c) ground fault (d) all of these

3. A short circuit is the electrical connection between any two conductors of the electrical system _____ conductor.

   (a) line-to-line (b) line-to-neutral (c) line-to-ground (d) a and b

15.2 Clearing Faults

4. To protect against electric shock or to prevent a fire, a dangerous _____ must quickly be removed by opening the circuit's overcurrent protection device.

   (a) overload (b) short circuit (c) ground fault (d) all of these

5. The opening time for a protection device is inversely proportional to the magnitude of the current. The greater the current value, the less time it takes for the protection device to open.

   (a) True (b) False

6. Inverse-time breakers operate on the principle that as the current decreases, the time it takes for the device to open decreases.

   (a) True (b) False

7. To remove dangerous touch voltage on metal parts from a(n) _____, the fault-current path must have low impedance to allow the fault current to quickly rise to facilitate the opening of the protection device.

   (a) overload (b) short circuit (c) ground fault (d) all of these

15.4 Fuse

8. A fuse consists of an element electrically connected to the end blades, which is enclosed in a tube and surrounded by a _____ filler material.

   (a) conductive (b) foam (c) light (d) nonconductive

9. As current flows through the element of a fuse, it generates heat. When a sustained overload occurs, the heat melts _____, stopping the flow of current.

   (a) several elements
   (b) all of the elements
   (c) a portion of the element
   (d) none of these

10. When a short circuit or ground fault occurs, _____ melt at the same time, removing the load from the source very quickly.

    (a) several elements
    (b) all of the elements
    (c) a portion of the element
    (d) none of these

15.5 Circuit Breaker Trip Elements

11. The _____ sensing element causes the circuit breaker to open when a predetermined calibration temperature is reached.

    (a) magnetic (b) electronic (c) thermo (d) none of these

12. The magnetic time-delay circuit breaker operates on the solenoid principle where a movable core, held with a spring, is moved by the magnetic field of a(n) _____.

    (a) overload (b) short circuit (c) ground fault (d) b or c

15.6 Circuit Breaker Types

13. _____ breakers operate on the principle that as the current increases, the time it takes for the device to open decreases.

    (a) Inverse-time (b) Adjustable-trip (c) Instantaneous-trip (d) all of these

14. _____ breakers permit the thermo trip setting to be adjusted to coordinate the circuit breaker's operation with other protection devices.

    (a) Inverse-time (b) Adjustable-trip (c) Instantaneous-trip (d) all of these

15. _____ breakers operate on the principle of electromagnetism only and are used for very large motors.

    (a) Inverse-time (b) Adjustable-trip (c) Instantaneous-trip (d) all of these

15.7 Available Short-Circuit Current

16. Available short-circuit current is the current in amperes that is available at a given point in the electrical system.

(a) True (b) False

17. The available short-circuit current is different at each point of the electrical system; it is highest at the _____.

(a) branch circuit (b) feeder (c) service (d) utility transformer

18. Factors that impact the available short-circuit current include transformer _____.

(a) voltage (b) kVA rating (c) impedance (d) all of these

19. Factors that impact the available short-circuit current include circuit conductor _____.

(a) material (b) size (c) length (d) all of these

15.8 Interrupting Rating

20. Circuit breakers and fuses are intended to interrupt the circuit, and they shall have an ampere interrupting rating (AIR) sufficient for the available short-circuit current.

(a) True (b) False

21. Unless marked otherwise, circuit breakers have a 5,000 AIC rating and fuses have a 10,000 AIC rating.

(a) True (b) False

22. If the protection device is not rated to interrupt the current at the available fault values at its listed voltage rating, it could explode while attempting to clear the fault.

(a) True (b) False

15.9 Short-Circuit Current Rating

23. Equipment must have a(n) _____ current rating that permits the protection device to clear a short circuit or ground fault without extensive damage to the components of the circuit.

(a) overload (b) short circuit (c) ground fault (d) b or c

15.10 Current Limiting Protection

24. A thermal-magnetic circuit breaker typically clears fault current in less than 3 to 5 cycles when subjected to a(n) _____.

(a) overload (b) short circuit (c) ground fault (d) b or c

25. When equipment does not have a withstand rating sufficient for the available fault current, the equipment can be protected by the use of _____.

(a) one-time fuses
(b) dual-element fuses
(c) instantaneous-type circuit breakers
(d) current-limiting fuses

PART B—GROUND-FAULT CIRCUIT INTERRUPTERS

15.11 How a GFCI Works

26. A GFCI is designed to protect persons against electric shock. It operates on the principle of monitoring the imbalance of current between the circuit's _____ conductor.

(a) ungrounded (b) grounded (c) equipment (d) a and b

27. If the difference between the current leaving and returning through the current transformer of the GFCI protection device exceeds _____, the solid-state circuitry de-energizes the circuit.

(a) 1 mA (b) 3 mA (c) 5 mA (d) 10 mA

15.12 Neutral-to-Case Detection

28. A GFCI protection device contains an internal monitor that prevents the device from being turned on if there is a neutral-to-case connection downstream of the device, but this only occurs if there is a load on the circuit.

(a) True (b) False

15.13 Line-to-Neutral Shock Hazard

29. Severe electric shock or death can occur if a person touches the ungrounded and the grounded (neutral) conductors at the same time, even if the circuit is GFCI protected.

(a) True (b) False

15.14 GFCI Fails—Circuit Remains Energized

30. Typically, when a GFCI protection device fails, the switching contacts remain closed and the device will continue to provide power without GFCI protection.

(a) True (b) False

15.15 GFCI Test Button

31. According to a NEMA report, 11 percent of the GFCI breakers protecting indoor receptacles failed, and _____ protecting outdoor receptacles failed.

(a) 10% (b) 15% (c) 20% (d) 25%

PART C—ARC-FAULT CIRCUIT INTERRUPTER

15.16 Arcing Definition

32. Arcing is defined as a luminous discharge of electricity across an insulating medium. Electric arcs operate at temperatures between _____ and expel small particles of very hot molten materials.

(a) 1,000 and 5,000°F (b) 2,000 and 10,000°F
(c) 5,000 and 15,000°F (d) 10,000 and 25,000°F

15.17 Series Versus Parallel Arc

33. Unsafe arcing faults can occur in one of two ways, as series arcing faults or as parallel arcing faults. The most dangerous is the parallel arcing fault.

(a) True (b) False

34. A series arc can occur when the conductor in series with the load is unintentionally broken. A series arc-fault current is load limited.

(a) True (b) False

35. The current in a short-circuit type arc is limited by the system impedance and the impedance of the arcing fault itself. Typically, at a receptacle, fault current will be above 75A, but not likely above _____.

(a) 100A (b) 220A (c) 330A (d) 450A

36. A ground-fault type parallel arc can only occur when a ground path is present. This type of arcing fault can be quickly cleared by a(n) _____ circuit protective device.

(a) GFCI (b) AFCI (c) a or b (d) none of these

15.18 AFCI and the NEC

37. To help reduce the hazard of electrical fires from a parallel arcing fault, the *NEC* requires a listed AFCI protection device to protect _____ wiring in dwelling unit bedrooms.

    (a) branch-circuit (b) feeder (c) service (d) all of these

15.19 AFCI—How They Operate

38. An AFCI protection device provides protection from an arcing fault by recognizing the characteristics unique to a parallel arcing fault and by functioning to de-energize the circuit when an arc fault is detected.

    (a) True (b) False

PART D—GROUND-FAULT PROTECTION OF EQUIPMENT

15.20 Ground-Fault Protection of Equipment Definition

39. A ground-fault protection of equipment device is intended to provide protection of equipment from damaging ground-fault currents by opening all ungrounded conductors of the faulted circuit. This device will also protect persons.

    (a) True (b) False

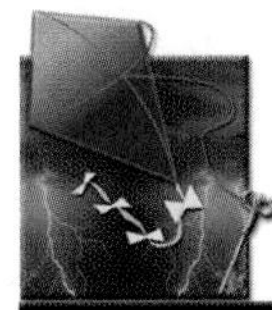

Chapter 4 Final Exam

Unit 14—The Electrical System

14.1 Current Flow

1. Electrons leaving a power supply are always trying to return to the same power supply; they are not trying to go into the earth.

   (a) True (b) False

14.4 Premises Neutral Current Path

2. To prevent fires and electric shock, the *NEC* specifies that neutral current can flow on metal parts of the electrical system.

   (a) True (b) False

14.5 Premises Ground-Fault Current Path

3. Metal parts of premises wiring must be bonded to a low-impedance path designed so that the circuit protection device will quickly open and clear a ground fault.

   (a) True (b) False

4. Because of the earth's high resistance to current flow, it cannot be used for the purpose of clearing a line-to-case ground fault for _____ wiring.

   (a) utility (b) premises (c) a or b (d) none of these

14.7 Conductor Voltage Drop

5. The voltage drop over a conductor is directly proportional to the _____ of the conductor.

   (a) area (b) circular mils (c) length (d) none of these

14.8 Conductor Power Loss

6. Conductor power losses are directly proportional to the length of the conductor and the square of the current. If the current is doubled, the power loss will be increased by _____.

   (a) 100% (b) 200% (c) 300% (d) 400%

14.9 Reducing Voltage Drop and Power Loss

7. The most effective way to reduce conductor voltage drop and power loss is to lower the current flowing through the conductors. This is accomplished by _____ the transmission voltage.

   (a) reducing (b) applying (c) increasing (d) none of these

Unit 15—Protection Devices

PART A—OVERCURRENT PROTECTION DEVICES

15.1 Overcurrent Protection

8. The purpose of overcurrent protection is to protect the conductors and equipment against excessive or dangerous temperatures because of overcurrent. Overcurrent is current in excess of the rated current of equipment or conductors. It may result from a(n) _____.

   (a) overload (b) short circuit (c) ground fault (d) all of these

9. A(n)_____ is the operation of equipment or conductors in excess of their rated ampacity.

   (a) overload (b) short circuit (c) ground fault (d) all of these

15.2 Clearing Faults

10. To protect against electric shock or to prevent a fire, dangerous _____ must quickly be removed by opening the circuit's overcurrent protection device.

    (a) overload (b) short circuit (c) ground fault (d) all of these

11. The opening time for a protection device is inversely proportional to the magnitude of the current. The greater the current value, the less time it takes for the protection device to open.

    (a) True (b) False

12. Inverse-time breakers operate on the principle that as the current decreases, the time it takes for the device to open decreases.

    (a) True (b) False

15.5 Circuit Breaker Trip Elements

13. The _____ sensing element causes the circuit breaker to open when a predetermined calibration temperature is reached.

    (a) magnetic (b) electronic (c) thermo (d) none of these

14. The magnetic time-delay circuit breaker operates on the solenoid principle where a movable core, held with a spring, is moved by the magnetic field of a(n) _____.

(a) overload (b) short circuit (c) ground fault (d) b or c

15.7 Available Short-Circuit Current

15. Available short-circuit current is the current in amperes that is available at a given point in the electrical system.

(a) True (b) False

16. The available short-circuit current is different at each point of the electrical system; it is highest at the _____.

(a) branch circuit (b) feeder (c) service (d) utility transformer

17. Factors that impact the available short-circuit current include transformer _____.

(a) voltage (b) kVA rating (c) impedance (d) all of these

18. Factors that impact the available short-circuit current include circuit conductor _____.

(a) material (b) size (c) length (d) all of these

15.8 Interrupting Rating

19. Circuit breakers and fuses are intended to interrupt the circuit, and they shall have an ampere interrupting rating (AIR) sufficient for the available short-circuit current.

(a) True (b) False

20. If the protection device is not rated to interrupt the current at the available fault values at its listed voltage rating, it could explode while attempting to clear the fault.

(a) True (b) False

15.9 Short-Circuit Current Rating

21. Equipment must have a(n) _____ current rating that permits the protection device to clear a short circuit or ground fault without extensive damage to the components of the circuit.

(a) overload (b) short circuit (c) ground fault (d) b or c

PART B—GROUND-FAULT CIRCUIT INTERRUPTERS

15.11 How a GFCI Works

22. A GFCI is designed to protect persons against electric shock. It operates on the principle of monitoring the imbalance of current between the circuit's _____ conductor.

(a) ungrounded (b) grounded (c) equipment (d) a and b

23. If the difference between the current leaving and returning through the current transformer of the GFCI protection device exceeds _____, the solid-state circuitry de-energizes the circuit.

(a) 1 mA (b) 3 mA (c) 5 mA (d) 10 mA

15.12 Neutral-to-Case Detection

24. A GFCI protection device contains an internal monitor that prevents the device from being turned on if there is a neutral-to-case connection downstream of the device, but this only occurs if there is a load on the circuit.

(a) True (b) False

15.13 Line-to-Neutral Shock Hazard

25. Severe electric shock or death can occur if a person touches the ungrounded and the grounded (neutral) conductors at the same time, even if the circuit is GFCI protected.

(a) True (b) False

15.14 GFCI Fails—Circuit Remains Energized

26. Typically, when a GFCI protection device fails, the switching contacts remain closed and the device will continue to provide power without GFCI protection.

(a) True (b) False

PART C—ARC-FAULT CIRCUIT INTERRUPTER

15.16 Arcing Definition

27. Arcing is defined as a luminous discharge of electricity across an insulating medium. Electric arcs operate at temperatures between _____ and expel small particles of very hot molten materials.

(a) 1,000 and 5,000°F (b) 2,000 and 10,000°F
(c) 5,000 and 15,000°F (d) 10,000 and 25,000°F

15.17 Series Versus Parallel Arc

28. Unsafe arcing faults can occur in one of two ways, as series arcing faults or as parallel arcing faults. The most dangerous is the parallel arcing fault.

(a) True (b) False

29. A series arc can occur when the conductor in series with the load is unintentionally broken. A series arc-fault current is load limited.

(a) True (b) False

30. The current in a short-circuit type arc is limited by the system impedance and the impedance of the arcing fault itself. Typically, at a receptacle, fault current will be above 75A, but not likely above _____.

(a) 100A (b) 220A (c) 330A (d) 450A

31. A ground-fault type parallel arc can only occur when a ground path is present. This type of arcing fault can be quickly cleared by a(n) _____ circuit protective device.

(a) GFCI (b) AFCI (c) a or b (d) none of these

15.18 AFCI and the NEC

32. To help reduce the hazard of electrical fires from a parallel arcing fault, the *NEC* requires a listed AFCI protection device to protect _____ wiring in dwelling unit bedrooms.

(a) branch-circuit (b) feeder (c) service (d) all of these

15.19 AFCI—How They Operate

33. An AFCI protection device provides protection from an arcing fault by recognizing the characteristics unique to a parallel arcing fault and by functioning to de-energize the circuit when an arc fault is detected.

(a) True (b) False

PART D—GROUND-FAULT PROTECTION OF EQUIPMENT

15.20 Ground-Fault Protection of Equipment Definition

34. A ground-fault protection of equipment device is intended to provide protection of equipment from damaging ground-fault currents by opening all ungrounded conductors of the faulted circuit. This device will also protect persons.

(a) True (b) False

Chapter 5
Alternating Current

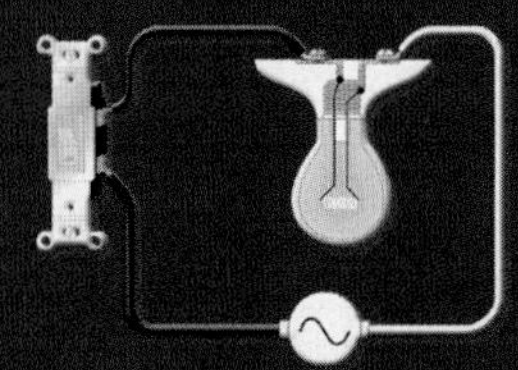

Unit 16 – Alternating Current

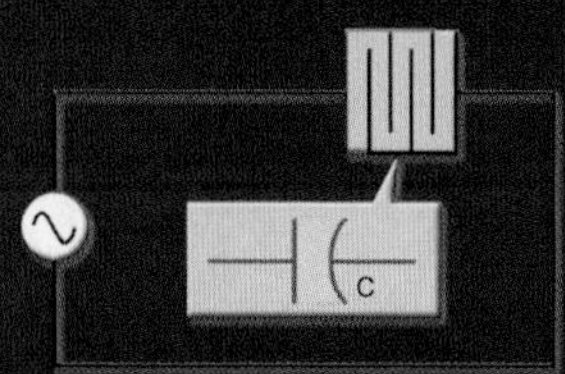

Unit 17 – Capacitance

Unit 18 – Induction

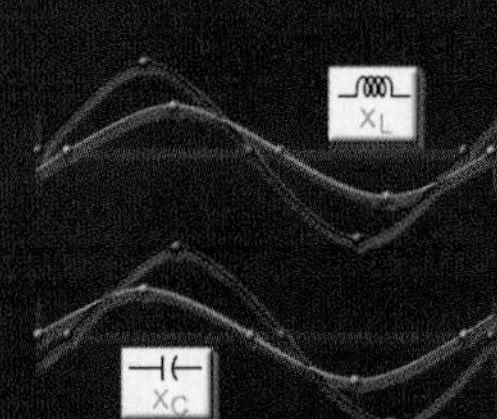

Unit 19 – Power Factor and Efficiency

Notes

UNIT

16 Alternating Current

Introduction

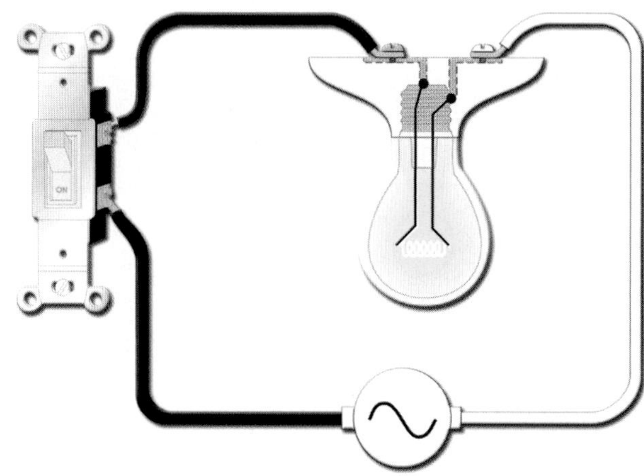

Because ac current is inexpensive to transmit compared to dc current, ac has become the dominant form of electricity in our modern infrastructure. In the early days of commercially available electric power, dc was dominant. But, economics won out. Applying ac safely or effectively, however, requires an understanding of certain concepts that border on the complex. All of those concepts build on what you have already learned.

16.1 Current Flow

In order for current to flow in a circuit, the power supply must apply sufficient electromotive force to cause the electrons to move. The movement of the electrons themselves does not produce any useful work; it's the effects that the moving electrons have on the loads they flow through that are important. The effects of electron movement are the same regardless of the direction of the current flow. Figure 16–1

16.2 Why Alternating Current is Used

Alternating current is primarily used because it can be transmitted inexpensively due to the ease of transforming to high-transmission voltage and then transforming this voltage back to low distribution voltage. In addition, alternating current is used when direct current is not suitable for the application.

Direct-Current Use. There are other applications however, particularly inside electronic equipment, where only direct current can perform the desired function. This is accomplished by rectifying ac to dc to power these electronic loads. Figure 16–2

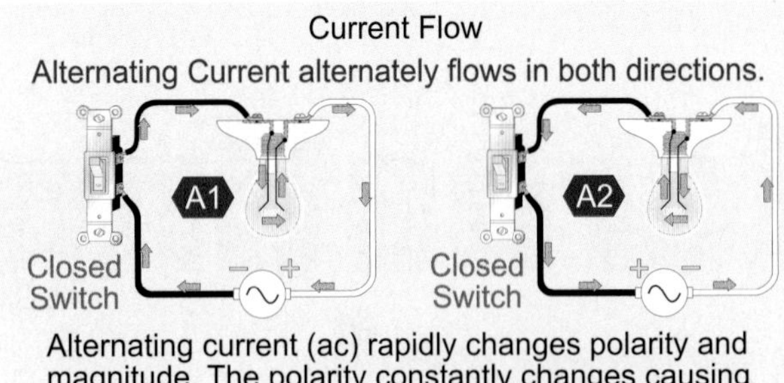

Current Flow
Alternating Current alternately flows in both directions.
A1
A2
Closed Switch
Closed Switch
Alternating current (ac) rapidly changes polarity and magnitude. The polarity constantly changes causing the current to alternately flow in both directions.

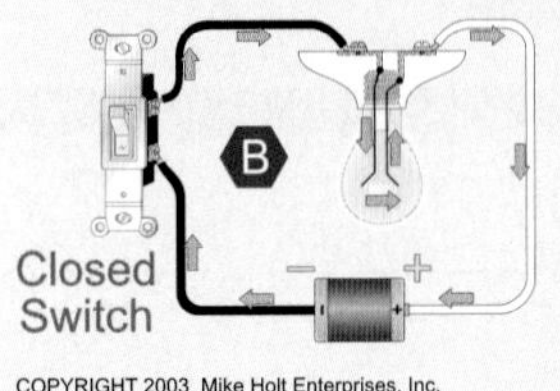

B
Closed Switch
Direct Current Flows in One Direction
Direct current (dc) flows from the negative terminal of the power source to the positive terminal of the power source. The polarity of the voltage always remains the same.

Figure 16–1

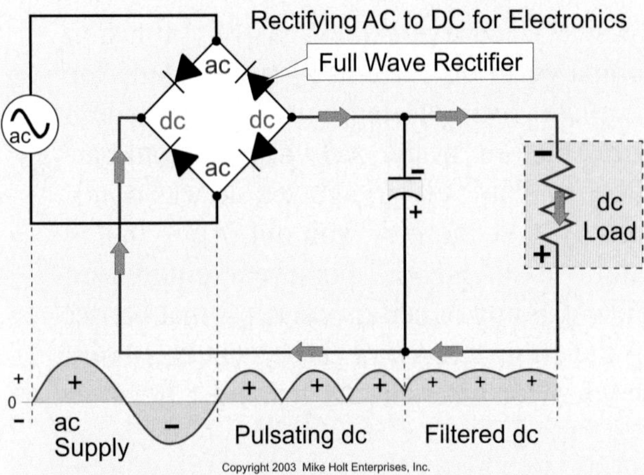

Figure 16–2

16.3 How Alternating Current is Produced

In 1831, Michael Faraday discovered that electricity could be produced from a source other than a battery. Faraday knew that electricity produced magnetism, and he wondered why magnetism couldn't produce electricity. Faraday discovered that when he moved a magnet inside a coil of wire, he got a pulse of electricity. When he pulled the magnet out, he got another pulse. He also got the same reaction when he moved the coil toward and away from the magnet.

Faraday's experiments revealed that when a magnetic field moves through a coil of wire, the lines of force of the magnetic field cause the electrons in the wire to flow in a specific direction. When the magnetic field moves in the opposite direction, electrons in the wire flow in the opposite direction. Electrons will flow only when there is motion of the conductors relative to the magnetic field. **Figure 16–3**

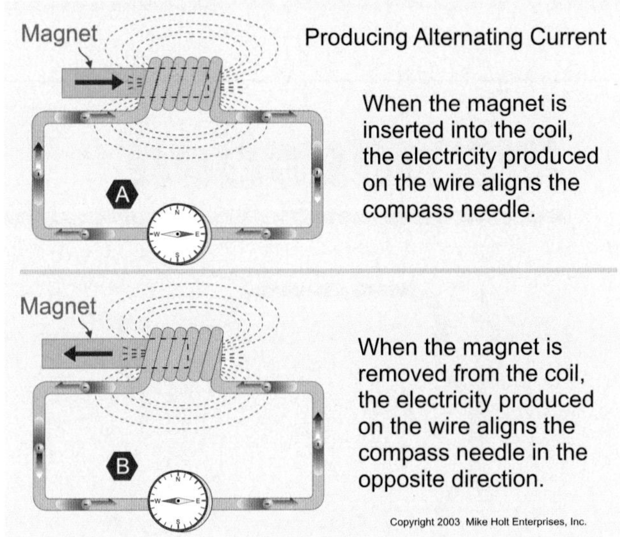

Magnet
Producing Alternating Current
When the magnet is inserted into the coil, the electricity produced on the wire aligns the compass needle.
A
Magnet
When the magnet is removed from the coil, the electricity produced on the wire aligns the compass needle in the opposite direction.
B
Copyright 2003 Mike Holt Enterprises, Inc.

Figure 16–3

16.4 AC Generator

A simple ac generator consists of a loop of wire rotating between the lines of force between the opposite poles of a magnet. The halves of each conductor loop travel through the magnetic lines of force in opposite directions, causing the electrons within the conductor to move in a given direction. The magnitude of the voltage produced is dependent upon the number of turns of wire, the strength of the magnetic field, and the speed at which the coil rotates. **Figure 16–4**

> **AUTHOR'S COMMENT:** The rotating conductor loop is called a rotor or armature. Slip or collector rings and carbon brushes are used to connect the output voltage from the generator to an external circuit.

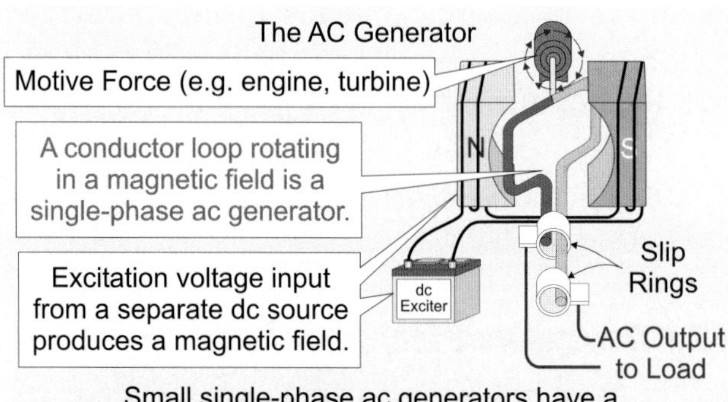

Figure 16–4

In generators that produce large quantities of electricity, the conductor coils are stationary and the magnetic field revolves within the coils. The magnetic field is produced by an electromagnet, instead of a permanent magnet. Use of electromagnets permit the strength of the magnetic field, and thus the lines of force, to be modified, thereby controlling the output voltage. Figure 16–5

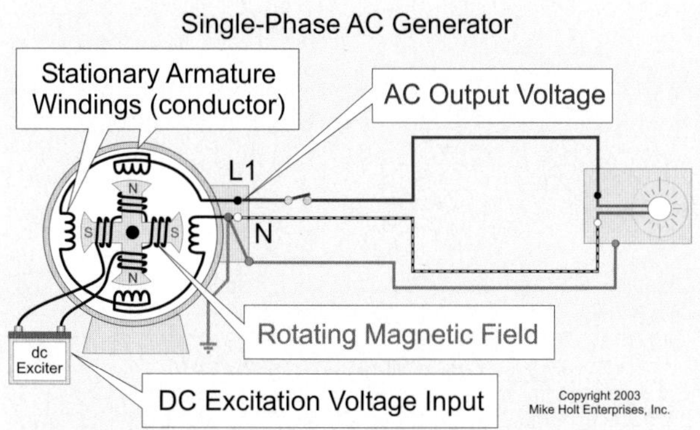

Figure 16–5

16.5 Waveform

A waveform image is used to display the level and direction of current and voltage.

Direct-Current Waveform

A direct-current waveform displays the direction (polarity) and magnitude of the current or voltage. Figure 16–6A and Figure 16–6B

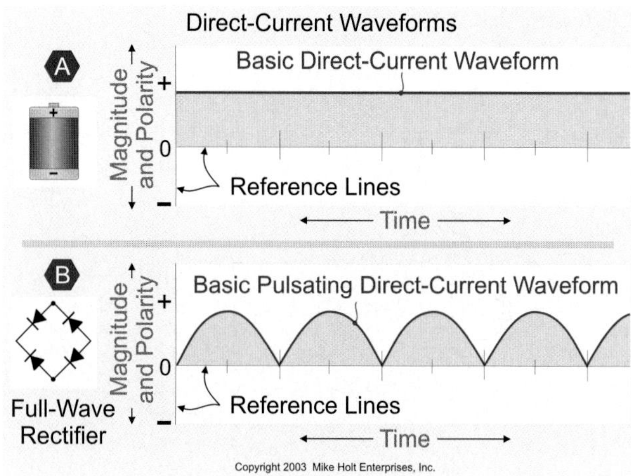

Figure 16–6

Alternating-Current Waveform

The waveform for alternating-current circuits displays the level and direction of the current and voltage for every instant of time for one full revolution of the rotor. Figure 16–7

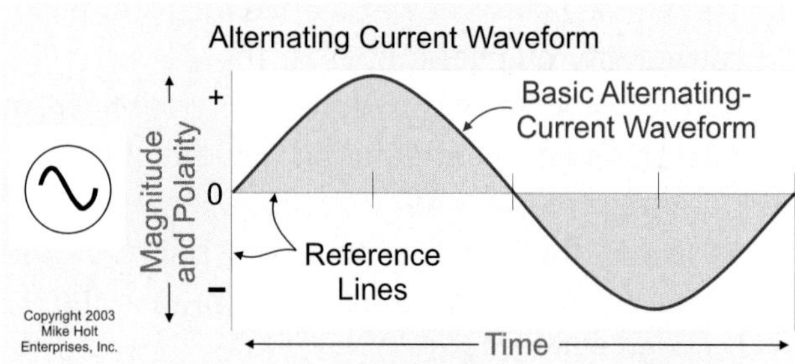

Figure 16–7

16.6 Sine Wave

Sinusoidal Waveform

The waveform for alternating-current circuits is symmetrical with positive above and negative below the zero reference level. For most alternating-current circuits, the waveform is called a sine wave.

Figure 16–8A shows the relationship of the waveform and the rotor.

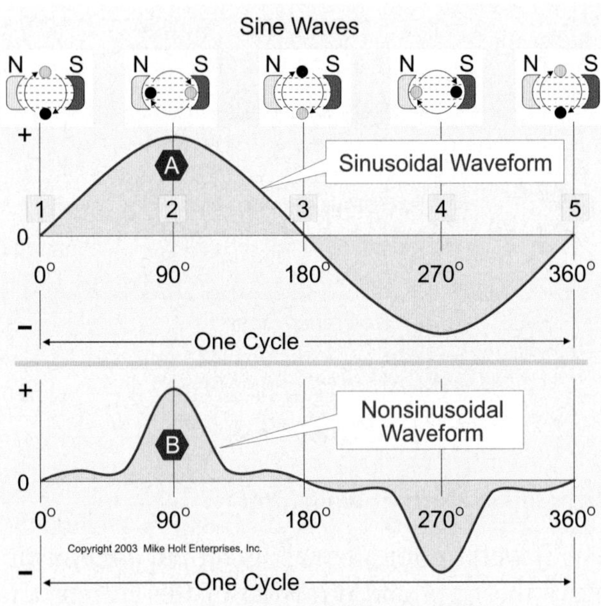

Figure 16–8

(1) The voltage starts at zero, when the rotor is not cutting any magnetic lines of force.
(2) As the rotor turns, the voltage increases from zero to a maximum value in one direction.
(3) It then decreases until it reaches zero.
(4) At zero, the voltage reverses polarity and increases until it reaches a maximum value at this opposite polarity.
(5) It decreases until it reaches zero again.

Nonsinusoidal Waveform

Figure 16–8B shows another ac waveform, but this one is nonsinusoidal. A nonsinusoidal waveform is created when nonlinear loads distort the sine wave. Examples of nonlinear loads include computer power supplies and electronic ballasts for fluorescent lighting fixtures.

AUTHOR'S COMMENT: This topic is beyond the scope of this textbook.

16.7 Nonsymmetrical Waveform

The combination of alternating-current and direct-current waveforms results in a nonsymmetrical waveform. **Figure 16–9**

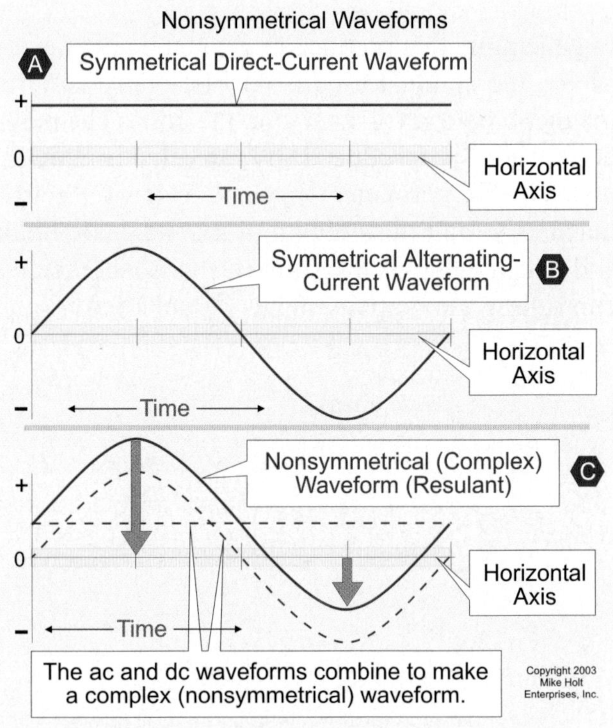

Figure 16–9

16.8 Frequency

The number of times the rotor turns in one second is called the frequency. Frequency is expressed as Hertz (Hz) or cycles per second, in honor of Heinrich Hertz. Most electrical power generated in the United States has a frequency of 60 Hz, **Figure 16–10**, whereas many other parts of the world use 50 Hz, and others use different power frequencies ranging from a low of 25 Hz to a high of 125 Hz.

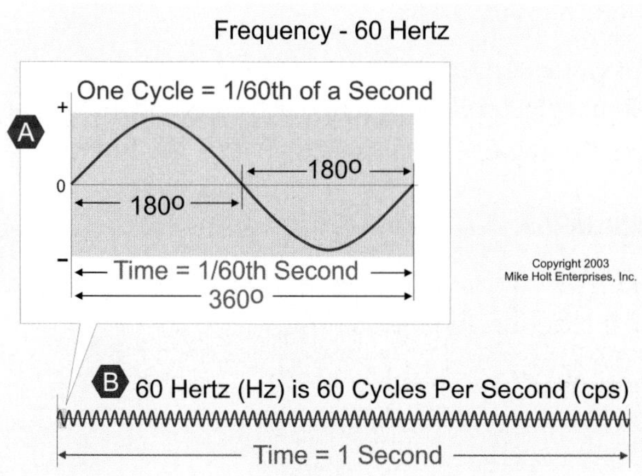

Figure 16–10

High-frequency electrical power, of 415 Hz, is often used for large computer systems and 400 Hz is used for airplane lighting. High-frequency power is often derived from motor-generator sets or other converters that operate at 60 Hz.

16.9 Phase

Phase is a term used to indicate the time or degree relationship between two waveforms, such as voltage-to-current or voltage-to-voltage. When two waveforms are in step with each other, they are said to be in-phase. In a purely resistive ac circuit, the current and voltage are in-phase. This means that, at every instant, the current is exactly in step with the applied voltage. They both reach their zero and peak values at the same time. **Figure 16–11**

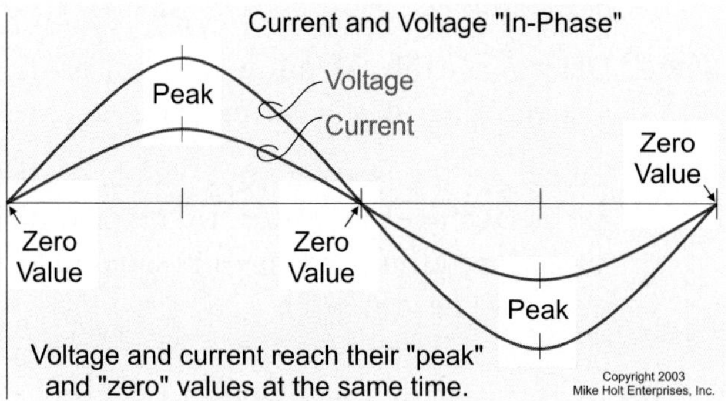

Figure 16–11

16.10 Degrees

Phase differences are often expressed in degrees; one full waveform is equal to 360 degrees. For example, a three-phase generator has each of its windings out-of-phase with each other by 120 degrees. **Figure 16–12**

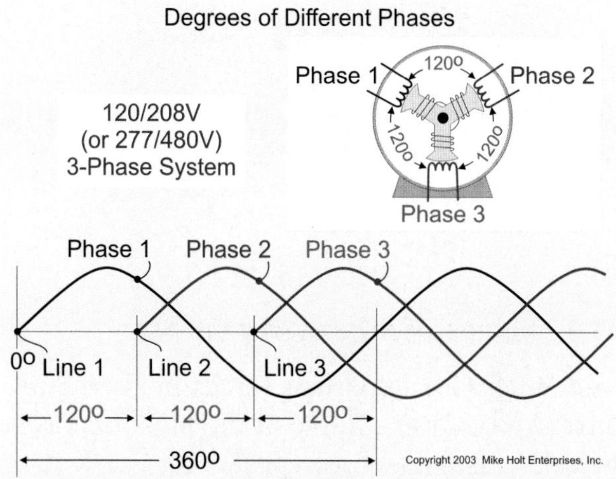

Figure 16–12

16.11 Lead or Lag

When describing the relationship between voltage and current, the reference waveform is always voltage—thus, a "lagging" waveform means that the voltage lags behind the current; a "leading" waveform means that the voltage leads the current.

Leading

It is easy to get confused as to which waveform leads and which one lags behind. The best way to remember this is to look at which waveform finishes its cycle first. In **Figure 16–13A**, the voltage waveform finishes its waveform cycle before the current waveform (designated by E_2 in **Figure 16–13**), so the voltage waveform "leads" the current waveform.

Lagging

In **Figure 16–13B**, the voltage waveform finishes its waveform cycle after the current waveform (designated by I_2 in **Figure 16–13**), in this case the voltage "lags" the current.

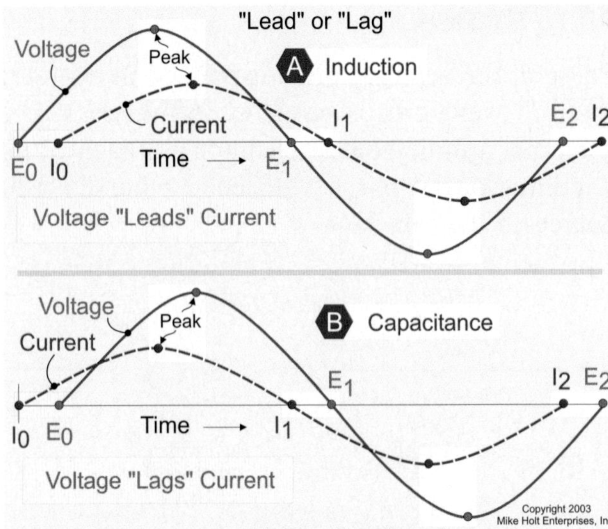

Figure 16–13

16.12 Values of Alternating Current

There are many important values in alternating-current waveforms. Some of the most important include instantaneous, peak, and effective. **Figure 16–14**

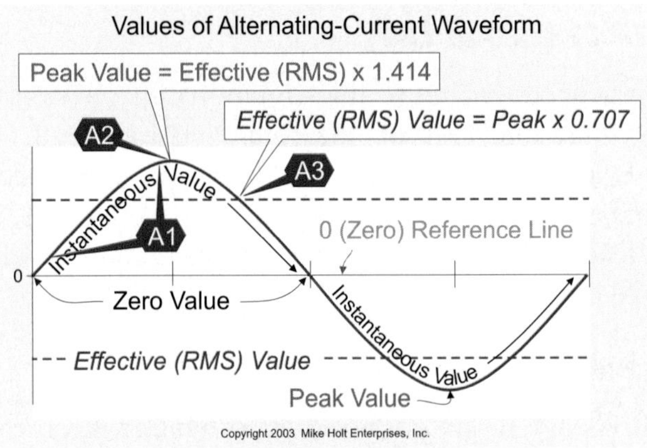

Figure 16–14

Instantaneous Value

The value at a moment of time. Depending upon the instant selected, it can range anywhere from zero, to peak, to negative peak value. **Figure 16–14A1**

Peak Value

The maximum value the current or voltage waveform reaches. **Figure 16–14A2**

For a pure Sine wave:

$$\text{Peak Value} = \frac{\text{Effective Value}}{0.707}$$

Peak Value = Effective Value x 1.414

Effective Value = Peak Value x 0.707

Effective Value

Effective ac voltage or effective ac current is the equivalent value of dc voltage or dc current that would produce the same amount of heat in a resistor. **Figure 16–14A3**

For a pure sine wave:

Effective Value = RMS Value

RMS Value

Root-Mean-Square (RMS) describes the steps (in reverse) necessary to determine the effective voltage or current value. **Figure 16–14A3**

Step 1 Square the instant waveform values; this turns all of the negative portions into positive portions.

Step 2 Determine the Mean (average) of the instant values of the waveform.

Step 3 Calculate the square root value of the mean average in order to reverse the numerical effects of having squared the instant values (Step 1).

AUTHOR'S COMMENT: Actually it should be SMR, not RMS!

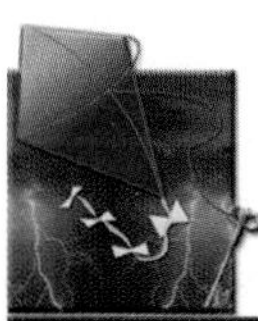

Unit 16 Summary

16.1 Current Flow

In order for current to flow, a circuit must be a closed loop and the power supply must apply sufficient pressure to cause the electrons to move. The effects of electron movement are the same regardless of the direction of the current flow.

16.2 Why Alternating Current is Used

Alternating current is primarily used because it can be transmitted inexpensively due to the ease of transforming to high-transmission voltages and then transforming this voltage back to lower distribution voltages.

16.3 How Alternating Current is Produced

Faraday's experiments revealed that when a magnetic field moves through a coil of wire, the lines of force of the magnetic field cause the electrons in the wire to flow in a specific direction. When the magnetic field moves in the opposite direction, electrons in the wire flow in the opposite direction. Electrons flow only when there is motion of the conductors relative to the magnetic field.

16.4 AC Generator

A simple ac generator consists of a loop of wire rotating between the lines of force between the opposite poles of a magnet. The halves of each conductor loop travel through the magnetic lines of force in opposite directions, causing the electrons within the conductor to move in a given direction. The magnitude of the voltage produced is dependent upon the number of turns of wire, the strength of the magnetic field, and the speed at which the coil rotates.

In generators that produce large quantities of electricity, the conductor coils are stationary and the magnetic field revolves within the coils. Use of electromagnets permits the strength of the magnetic field, and thus the lines of force, to be modified, thereby controlling the output voltage.

16.5 Waveform

Direct-Current Waveform

A direct-current waveform displays the direction (polarity) and magnitude of the current or voltage.

Alternating-Current Waveform

The waveform for alternating-current circuits displays the level and direction of the current and voltage for every instant of time for one full revolution of the rotor.

16.6 Sine Wave

Sinusoidal Waveform

The waveform for alternating-current circuits is symmetrical with positive above and negative below the zero reference level. For most alternating-current circuits, the waveform is called a sine wave.

Nonsinusoidal Waveform

A nonsinusoidal waveform is created by what are called nonlinear loads being supplied by the circuit; these could distort the sine wave.

16.7 Nonsymmetrical Waveform

The combination of alternating current and direct-current waveforms results in a nonsymmetrical waveform.

16.8 Frequency

The number of times the rotor turns in one second is called the frequency. Frequency is expressed as Hertz (Hz) or cycles per second.

16.9 Phase

Phase is a term used to indicate the time or degree relationship between two waveforms, such as voltage-to-current or voltage-to-voltage. When two waveforms are in step with each other, they are said to be in-phase.

This means that, at every instant, the current is exactly in step with the applied voltage. They both reach their zero and peak values at the same time.

16.10 Degrees

Phase differences are often expressed in degrees; one full waveform is equal to 360 degrees. Generators that are out-of-phase, conceptually, by 120 degrees (one-third cycle), produce three-phase power.

16.11 Lead or Lag

When describing the relationship between voltage and current, the reference waveform is always voltage—thus, a "lagging" waveform means that the voltage lags behind the current; a "leading" waveform means that the voltage leads the current.

16.12 Values of Alternating Current

Instantaneous Value

The value at a moment of time. Depending upon the instant selected, it can range anywhere from zero, to peak, to negative peak value.

Peak Value

The maximum value the current or voltage waveform reaches. For a pure Sine wave:

$$\text{Peak Value} = \frac{\text{Effective Value}}{0.707}$$

$$\text{Peak Value} = \text{Effective Value} \times 1.414$$

$$\text{Effective Value} = \text{Peak Value} \times 0.707$$

Effective Value

For a pure sine wave:

$$\text{Effective Value} = \text{RMS Value}$$

RMS Value

Root-Mean-Square (RMS) describes the steps (in reverse) necessary to determine the effective voltage or current value.

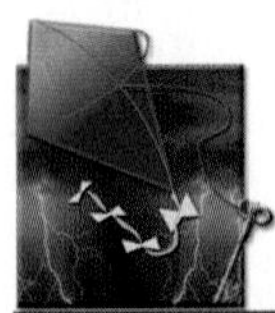

Unit 16 Conclusion

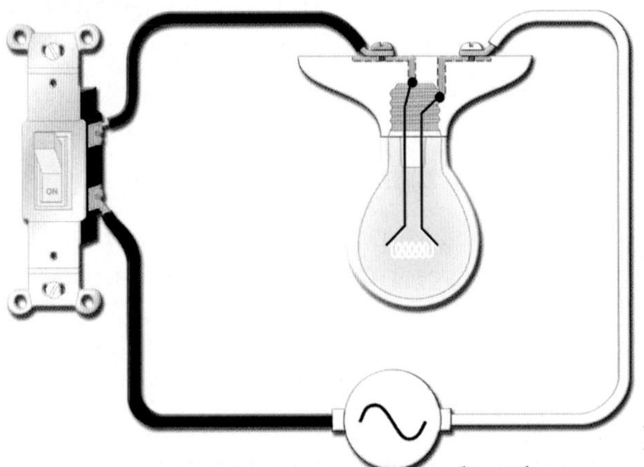

You now have a solid understanding of the basic concepts of alternating current. You know where it comes from and why it's used, plus you understand the various properties that characterize the current in a given circuit or system. The concepts of frequency, phase, and waveform are all critical to the field of power quality.

Your knowledge of what lead and lag mean will help you understand power factor. Remember that three-phase alternating current has three waveforms that, when conditions are perfect, have sinusoidal shapes and are 120 degrees out-of-phase with each other.

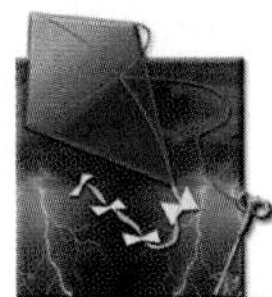

Unit 16 Practice Questions

16.1 Current Flow

1. The movement of electrons themselves does not produce any useful work; it's the effects that the moving electrons have on the loads they flow through that are important.

   (a) True (b) False

16.2 Why Alternating Current is Used

2. Alternating current is primarily used because it can be transmitted inexpensively.

   (a) True (b) False

16.3 How Alternating Current is Produced

3. Faraday discovered that the lines of force of the magnetic field cause the electrons in the wire to flow in a specific direction. When the magnetic field moves in the opposite direction, electrons flow in the opposite direction.

   (a) True (b) False

16.4 AC Generator

4. A simple ac generator consists of a loop of wire rotating between the lines of force between the opposite poles of a magnet.

   (a) True (b) False

5. In ac generators that produce large quantities of electricity, the conductor coils are stationary and the magnetic field revolves within the coils.

   (a) True (b) False

6. Output voltage of a generator is dependent upon the _____.

   (a) number of turns of wire (b) strength of the magnetic field
   (c) speed at which the coil rotates (d) all of these

16.5 Waveform

7. A waveform image is used to display the level and direction of current, but not voltage.

   (a) True (b) False

8. The waveform for ac circuits displays the level and direction of the current and voltage for every instant of time for one full revolution of the rotor.

(a) True (b) False

16.6 Sine Wave

9. The _____ wave is a waveform that is symmetrical with positive above and negative below the zero reference level.

(a) nonsinusoidal (b) nonsymmetrical (c) sine (d) any of these

10. A nonsinusoidal waveform is created when _____ loads distort the voltage and current sine wave.

(a) linear (b) resistive (c) inductive (d) nonlinear

16.7 Nonsymmetrical Waveform

11. The combination of alternating-current and direct-current waveforms results in a _____ waveform.

(a) nonsinusoidal (b) nonsymmetrical (c) sine (d) any of these

16.8 Frequency

12. The number of complete waveforms in one second is called the frequency. Frequency is expressed as _____ or cycles per second.

(a) degrees (b) sine wave (c) phase (d) Hertz

16.9 Phase

13. Phase is a term used to indicate the time or degree relationship between two waveforms, such as voltage-to-current or voltage-to-voltage.

(a) True (b) False

14. In a purely resistive ac circuit, the current and voltage are _____. This means that they both reach their zero and peak values at the same time.

(a) in-phase (b) out-of-phase (c) a or b (d) none of these

16.10 Degrees

15. Phase differences are expressed in degrees; one full waveform is equal to _____.

(a) 90º (b) 120º (c) 180º (d) 360º

16. A 3Ø generator has each of its windings out-of-phase with each other by _____.

(a) 90º (b) 120º (c) 180º (d) 360º

17. Phase differences are expressed in _____.

(a) sine waves (b) phases (c) Hertz (d) degrees

16.11 Lead or Lag

18. When describing the relationship between voltage and current, the reference waveform is always _____.

(a) current (b) resistance (c) voltage (d) none of these

19. If the voltage waveform finishes before the current waveform, the voltage is said to _____ the current waveform.

(a) lead (b) lag (c) be in-phase with (d) none of these

20. When the current waveform finishes before the voltage waveform, the voltage _____ the current waveform.

(a) leads (b) lags (c) is in-phase with (d) none of these

16.12 Values of Alternating Current

21. _____ is the value of the voltage or current at a moment of time.

(a) Peak (b) Root-mean-square (c) Effective (d) Instantaneous

22. The peak value is equal to the effective value _____.

(a) times 0.707 (b) times 1.41 (c) divided by 1.41 (d) none of these

23. _____ is the maximum value that ac current or voltage reaches, both for positive and negative polarity.

(a) Peak (b) Root-mean-square (c) Instantaneous (d) none of these

24. The effective value is equal to the peak value _____.

(a) times 0.707 (b) times 1.41 (c) divided by 1.41 (d) none of these

25. Effective voltage or current value is the ac voltage or current that produces the same amount of heat in a resistor that would be produced by the same amount of dc voltage or current.

(a) True (b) False

26. _____ describes the steps necessary to determine the effective voltage or current value.

(a) Peak (b) Root-mean-square (c) Instantaneous (d) none of these

UNIT 17 Capacitance

Introduction

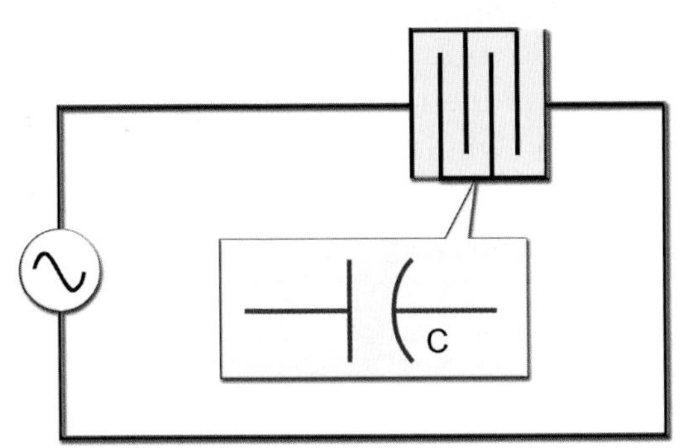

Capacitance is the property of an electrical circuit that enables it to store electrical energy by means of an electric field and to release that energy at a later time. Capacitance exists whenever an insulating material (dielectric) separates two conductors that have a difference of potential between them. Devices that intentionally introduce capacitance into circuits are called capacitors and are sometimes referred to as condensers. Figure 17–1

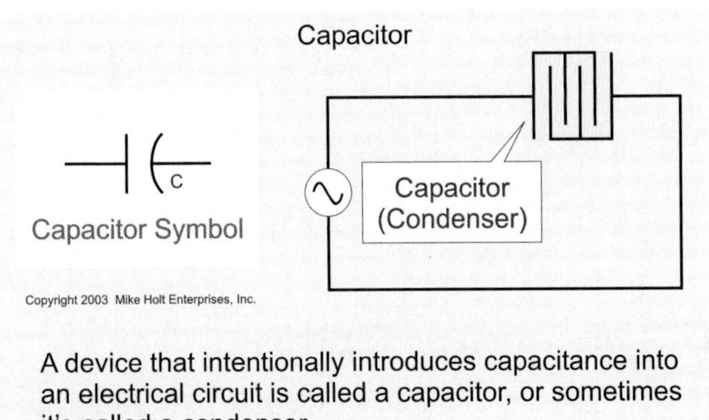

A device that intentionally introduces capacitance into an electrical circuit is called a capacitor, or sometimes it's called a condenser.

Figure 17–1

Capacitor Current Flow

Current does not flow through a capacitor. In an ac circuit, the electrons in the circuit move back and forth to alternately charge the capacitor, first in one direction, and then in the other. A capacitor permits current to flow because of its ability to store energy and then discharge the energy as the ac current flows in the opposite direction.

AUTHOR'S COMMENT: If a "full-wave rectifier" converts the ac voltage to filtered dc voltage, the capacitor will be continuously charged. Figure 17–2

17.1 Charged Capacitor

When a capacitor has a potential difference between the conductors (plates), the capacitor is charged. One plate has an excess of free electrons and the other plate has a lack of them. The plate with the excess electrons has an overall negative

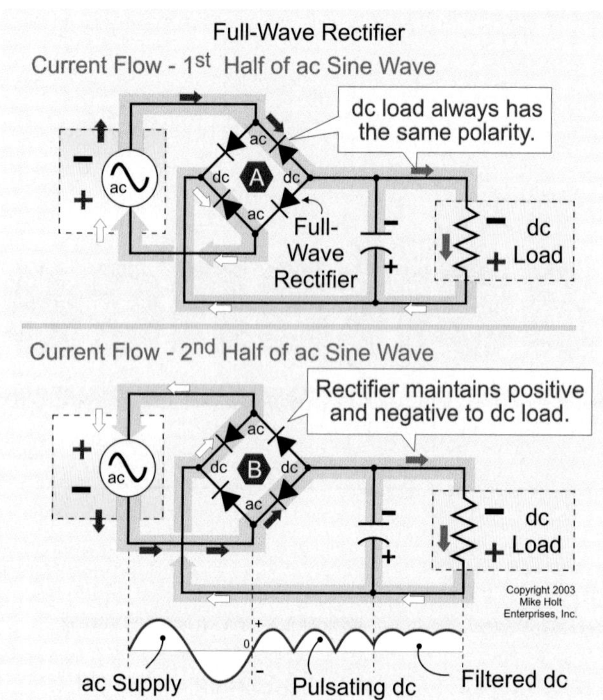

Figure 17–2

charge (-), while the plate from which electrons were removed has an overall positive charge (+). A difference of potential or voltage exists between the plates. Figure 17–3

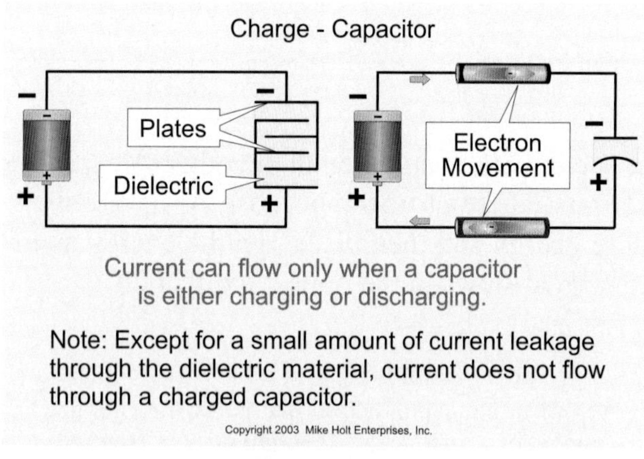

Charge - Capacitor
Plates
Dielectric
Electron Movement
Current can flow only when a capacitor is either charging or discharging.
Note: Except for a small amount of current leakage through the dielectric material, current does not flow through a charged capacitor.
Copyright 2003 Mike Holt Enterprises, Inc.

Figure 17–3

17.2 Electrical Field

Though the electrons cannot flow, the force that attracts them still exists; this force is called the electrical field. The electrical field can be thought of as lines of electrical force that exist between the capacitor plates. Figure 17–4

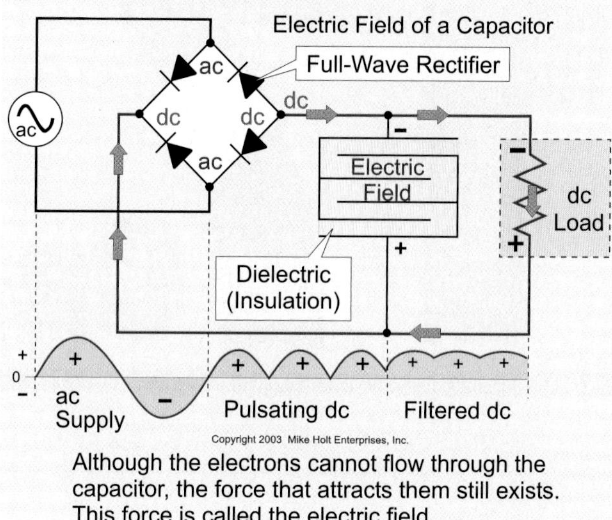

Figure 17–4

The more the capacitor is charged, the stronger the electrical field. If the capacitor is overcharged, the electrons from the negative plate could be pulled through the insulation to the positive plate. If this happens, the capacitor is said to have broken down (shorted). Figure 17–5

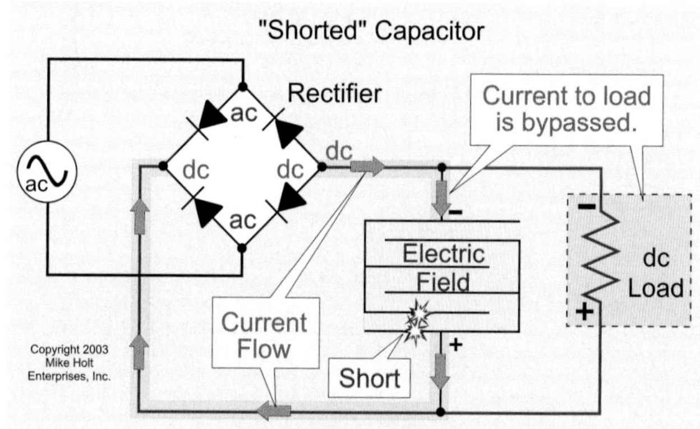

Figure 17–5

17.3 Discharging a Capacitor

To discharge a capacitor, all that is required is a conducting path connected across the terminals of the capacitor. The free electrons on the negative plate will then flow through the external circuit to the positive plate.

CAUTION: *Great care should be taken when working on a circuit that contains capacitors (such as those found in variable speed drives). Even when power is removed from the circuit, the capacitors can store large amounts of energy for a long period of time, and can discharge and arc if inadvertently shorted or grounded out.*

17.4 Determining Capacitance

Factors that determine the capacitance of a capacitor are the surface area of the plates, the distance between the plates, and the insulating material or dielectric between the plates.

Plate Distance

Capacitance is inversely proportional to the distance between the capacitor plates. The closer the plates of the capacitor, the greater the capacitance and, conversely, the greater the distance between the plates, the lower the capacitance. **Figure 17–6**

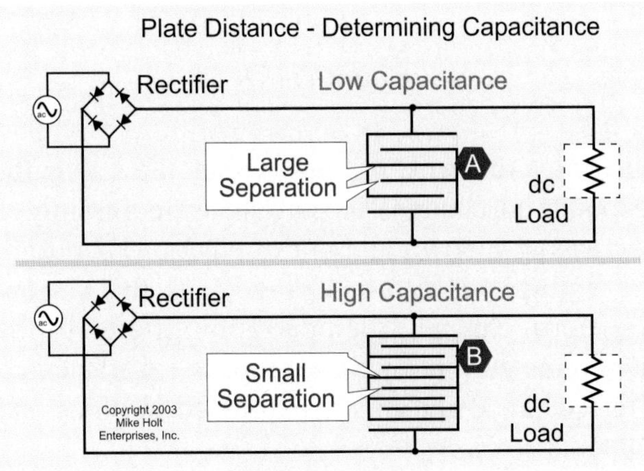

Figure 17–6

Surface Area

Capacitance is directly proportional to the surface area. The greater the surface area of the plates, the greater the capacitance. **Figure 17–7**

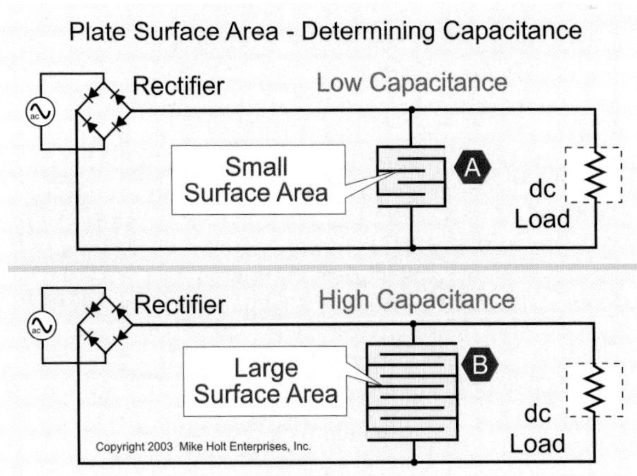

Figure 17–7

Dielectric Strength

Dielectric strength indicates the maximum voltage that can be applied across the dielectric safely. **Figure 17–8**

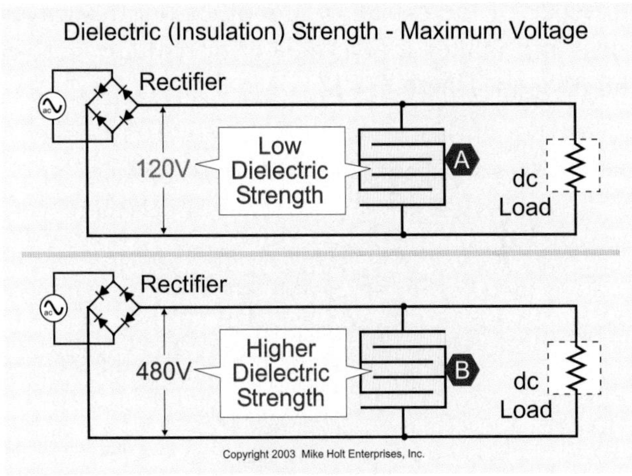

Figure 17–8

17.5 Uses of Capacitors

One use of capacitors is to start single-phase ac motors and to prevent arcing across the contacts of electric switches. A capacitor connected across the switch contacts provides a path for current flow until the switch is fully open and the danger of arcing has passed. **Figure 17–9**

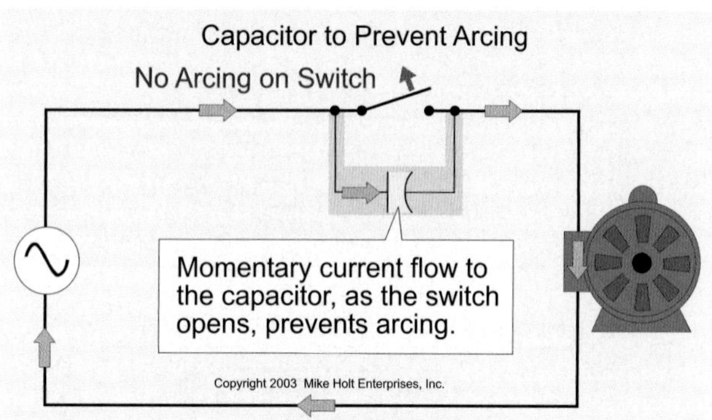

Figure 17–9

Electronic Power Supplies

One other very important use of capacitors is to smooth out pulsating dc waveforms, such as those which would be present through the dc load if the capacitor was not present. The full-wave bridge rectifier would transform the ac waveform from the source into a pulsating dc waveform—the presence of the capacitor smoothes out the waveform and makes a near-steady dc voltage across the dc load. Figure 17–10

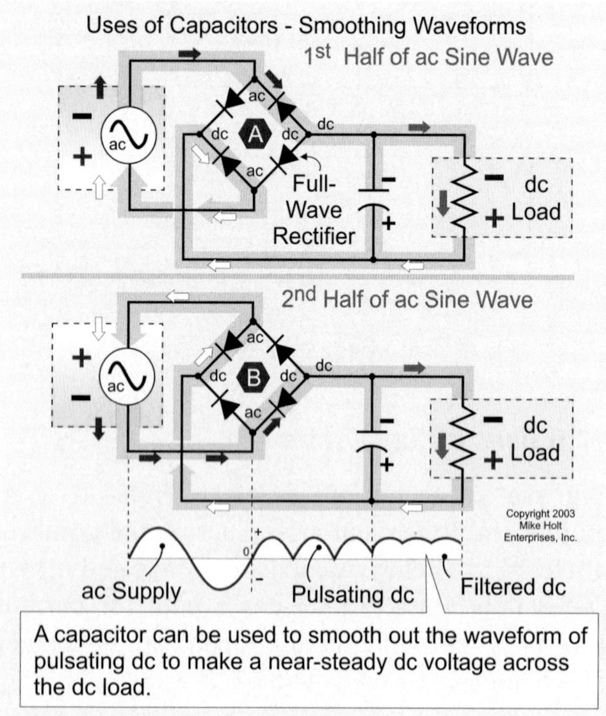

A capacitor can be used to smooth out the waveform of pulsating dc to make a near-steady dc voltage across the dc load.

Figure 17–10

17.6 Phase Relationship

A capacitor can be thought of as a device that resists changes in voltage. It supplies charge or accepts charge to this end. Because a capacitor introduces reactance to the circuit, it shifts the current waveform out-of-phase to the voltage waveform. Capacitive reactance causes the voltage waveform to lag the current waveform. Figure 17–11

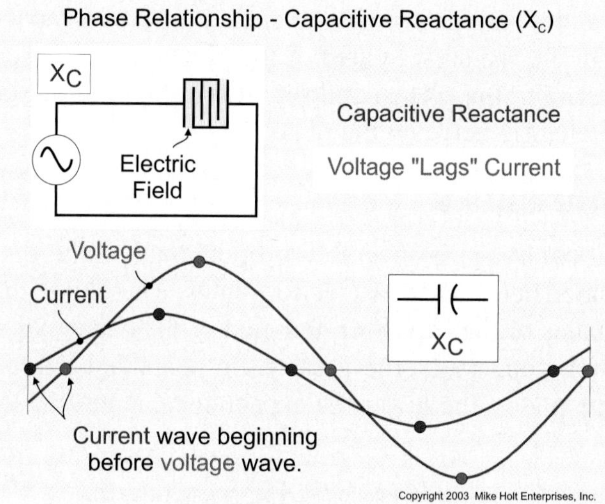

Figure 17–11

One way to think of this is that the capacitor responds to changes in current by increasing or decreasing its own amount of charge. Therefore, the voltage waveform change lags the current waveform change. The opposition offered to the flow of ac current by a capacitor is called capacitive reactance and this is expressed in ohms and abbreviated X_C.

Capacitive reactance can be calculated by the equation:

$$X_C = \frac{1}{(2 \times \pi \times F \times C)}$$

Where π is equal to 3.14, "F" is the frequency in hertz, "C" is the capacitance in farads, and X_C is expressed in ohms.

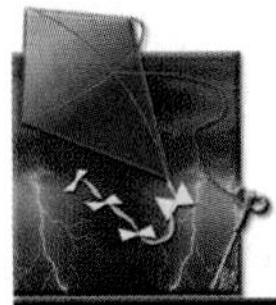

Unit 17 Summary

Introduction

Capacitance exists whenever an insulating material separates two conductors that have a difference of potential between them. Devices that intentionally introduce capacitance into circuits are called capacitors or condensers.

Capacitor Current Flow

If a "full-wave rectifier" converts the ac voltage to a capacitor, the capacitor will be continuously charged.

17.1 Charged Capacitor

When a capacitor has a potential difference between the conductors (plates), the capacitor is charged. One plate has an excess of free electrons and the other plate has a lack of them. The plate with the excess electrons has an overall negative charge (-), while the plate from which electrons were removed has an overall positive charge (+).

17.2 Electrical Field

Though the electrons cannot flow, the force that attracts them still exists; this force is called the electrical field.

The more the capacitor is charged, the stronger the electrical field. If the capacitor is overcharged, the electrons from the negative plate could be pulled through the insulation to the positive plate. If this happens, the capacitor is said to have broken down (shorted).

17.3 Discharging a Capacitor

To discharge a capacitor, all that is required is a conducting path connected across the terminals of the capacitor. The free electrons on the negative plate will then flow through the external circuit to the positive plate.

> **CAUTION:** *Even when power is removed from the circuit, the capacitors can store large amounts of energy for a long period of time, and can discharge and arc if inadvertently shorted or grounded out.*

17.4 Determining Capacitance

Plate Distance

The closer the plates, the greater the capacitance and, conversely, the greater the distance between the plates, the smaller the capacitance.

Surface Area

Capacitance is directly proportional to the surface area. The greater the surface area of the plates, the greater the capacitance.

Dielectric Strength

Dielectric strength indicates the maximum voltage that can be applied across the dielectric safely.

17.5 Uses of Capacitors

An important use of capacitors is to start single-phase ac motors and to smooth out pulsating dc waveforms, such as those which would be present through the dc load if the capacitor was not present. The full-wave bridge rectifier would transform the ac waveform from the source into a pulsating dc waveform—the presence of the capacitor smoothes out the waveform and makes a near-steady dc voltage across the dc load.

17.6 Phase Relationship

A capacitor resists changes in current. Because a capacitor introduces reactance to the circuit, it causes the voltage waveform to lag the current waveform.

One way to think of this is that the capacitor responds to changes in current by increasing or decreasing its own amount of charge. Therefore, the voltage waveform lags the current waveform. The opposition offered to the flow of ac current by a capacitor is called capacitive reactance and is expressed in ohms and abbreviated X_C.

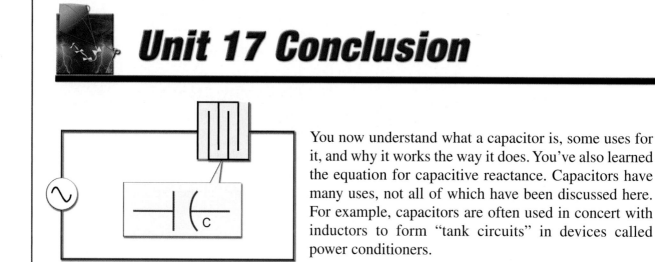

Unit 17 Conclusion

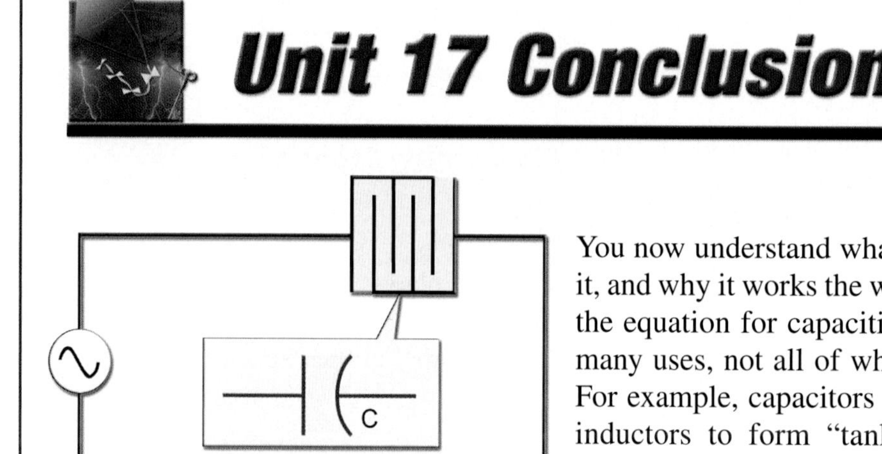

You now understand what a capacitor is, some uses for it, and why it works the way it does. You've also learned the equation for capacitive reactance. Capacitors have many uses, not all of which have been discussed here. For example, capacitors are often used in concert with inductors to form "tank circuits" in devices called power conditioners.

Words to Live By: ***The best way to be successful is to follow the advice you give others.***

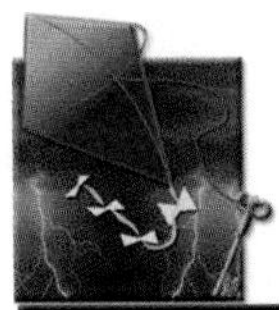

Unit 17 Practice Questions

Introduction

1. _____ is a property of an electrical circuit that enables it to store electrical energy by means of an electric field and to release this energy at a later time.

   (a) Capacitance (b) Induction (c) Self-induction (d) none of these

2. A half-wave rectifier can be used to convert ac voltage into dc voltage to continuously charge a capacitor.

   (a) True (b) False

17.1 Charged Capacitor

3. When a capacitor has a potential difference between the plates, it is said to be _____. One plate has an excess of free electrons, and the other plate has a lack of them.

   (a) induced (b) charged (c) discharged (d) shorted

17.2 Electrical Field

4. If the capacitor is overcharged, the electrons from the negative plate could be pulled through the insulation to the positive plate. The capacitor is said to have _____.

   (a) charged (b) discharged (c) induced (d) shorted

17.3 Discharging a Capacitor

5. To discharge a capacitor, all that is required is a(n) _____ path between the terminals of the capacitor. The free electrons on the negative plate will then flow through the external circuit to the positive plate.

   (a) conductive (b) insulating (c) resistive (d) semiconductor

6. Even when power is removed from the circuit, capacitors store large amounts of energy for a long period of time. They can discharge and arc if inadvertently shorted or grounded out.

   (a) True (b) False

17.4 Determining Capacitance

7. Factors that determine the capacitance of a capacitor are _____.

(a) surface area of the plates
(b) distance between the plates
(c) dielectric between the plates
(d) all of these

17.5 Uses of Capacitors

8. Capacitors are used to start single-phase ac motors and to prevent arcing across the contacts of electric switches.

(a) True
(b) False

17.6 Phase Relationship

9. A capacitor can be thought of as a device that resists changes in current. Because a capacitor introduces reactance to the circuit, it shifts the current waveform to _____.

(a) lead the applied voltage by 90 degrees
(b) lag the applied voltage by 90 degrees
(c) lead the applied voltage by 180 degrees
(d) lag the applied voltage by 180 degrees

10. The opposition offered to the flow of ac current by a capacitor is called capacitive reactance, which is expressed in ohms and abbreviated _____.

(a) X_C
(b) X_L
(c) Z
(d) none of these

UNIT 18 Induction

Introduction

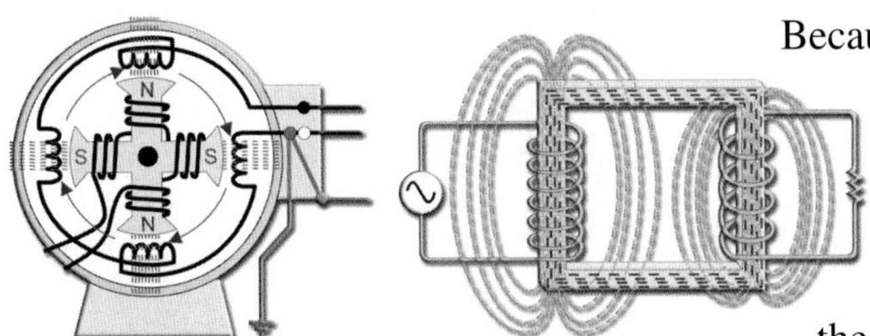

Because electrons spin, they have their own magnetic fields. When electrons move, the magnetic fields of the individual electrons combine to produce an overall magnetic field. The overall magnetic field extends outside the conductor. The greater the current flow, the greater the overall magnetic field. The direction of the overall magnetic field around the conductor follows the left-hand rule, based on the electron current flow theory.

The movement of electrons caused by an external magnetic field is called induced current, and the associated potential that is established is called induced voltage. In order to induce voltage, all that is required is a conductor and an external magnetic field with relative motion between the two. This is the basis of the generator and transformer. **Figure 18–1**

Inductance is the property of an electrical circuit that enables it to store electrical energy by means of an electromagnetic field and to release this energy at a later time.

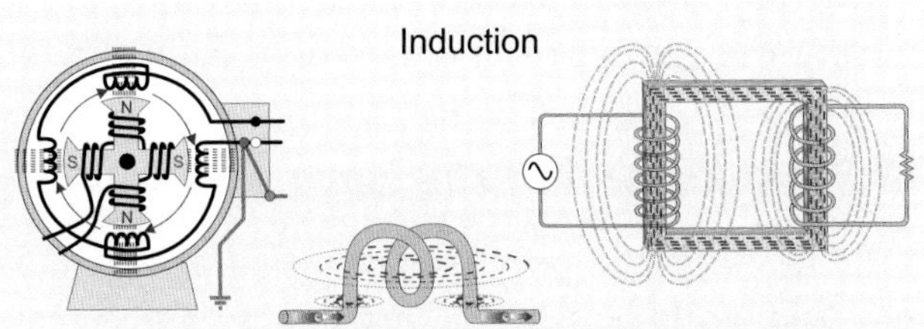

Figure 18–1

18.1 Self-Induction

As the ac current through a conductor increases, an expanding electromagnetic field is created through the conductor. The expanding magnetic flux lines cut through the conductor itself (which, in effect, is in motion relative to the field), thus inducing a voltage within the conductor.

When the current within the conductor decreases, the electromagnetic field collapses, and again the magnetic flux lines through the conductor cut through the conductor itself. The voltage induced within the conductor caused by its own expanding and collapsing magnetic field is known as self-induced voltage. **Figure 18–2**

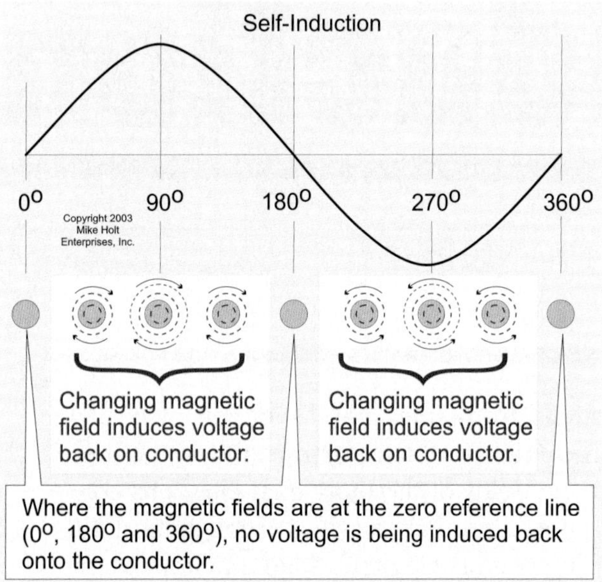

Figure 18–2

18.2 Induced Voltage and Applied Current

The induced voltage in a conductor carrying alternating current always opposes the change in current flowing through the conductor. The induced voltage, that opposes the current flow, is called "counter-electromotive force" (CEMF), or back-EMF.

The waveform of the induced voltage in the conductor (CEMF) is 90 degrees out-of-phase with the circuit current and it is 180 degrees out-of-phase with the applied voltage waveform. CEMF either opposes or aids the conductor current flow. **Figure 18–3**

Opposes Current Flow

When alternating current increases, the polarity of the induced voltage (CEMF) within the conductor opposes the conductor's current and tries to prevent the current from increasing. **Figure 18–4A**

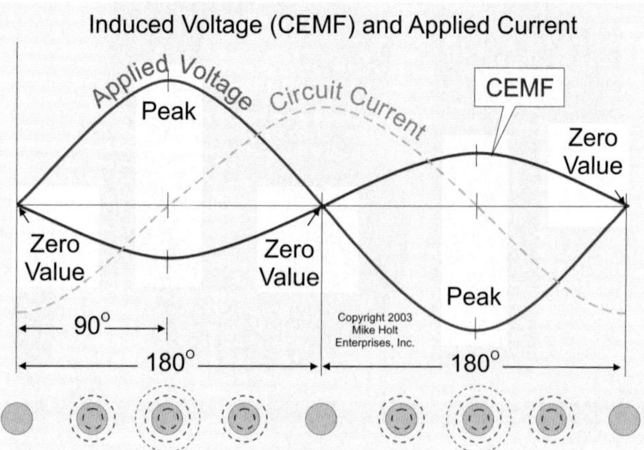

Figure 18–3

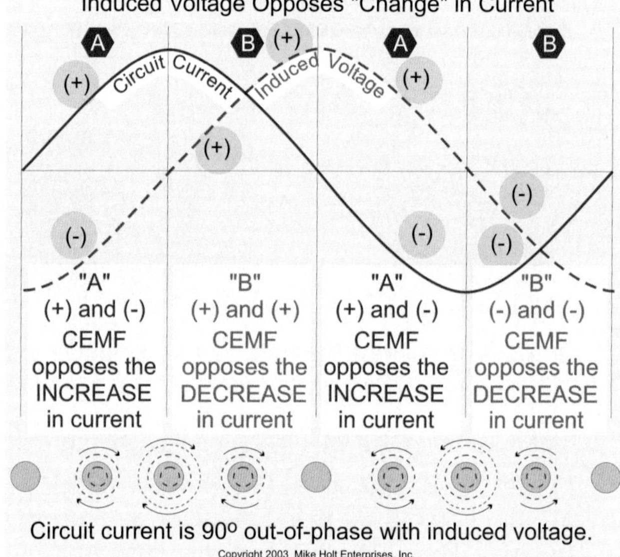

Figure 18–4

Aids the Current Flow

When the alternating current decreases, the polarity of the induced voltage within the conductor aids the conductor's current and tries to prevent the current from decreasing. **Figure 18–4B**

18.3 Conductor AC Resistance

In dc circuits, the only property that affects current and voltage flow is resistance. Conductor resistance is a physical property of the conductor. It is directly proportional to the conductor's length and inversely proportional to the conductor's cross-sectional area. This means that if the conductor's length is doubled, the total resistance is doubled; if the conductor's diameter is reduced, the resistance increases. **Figure 18–5**

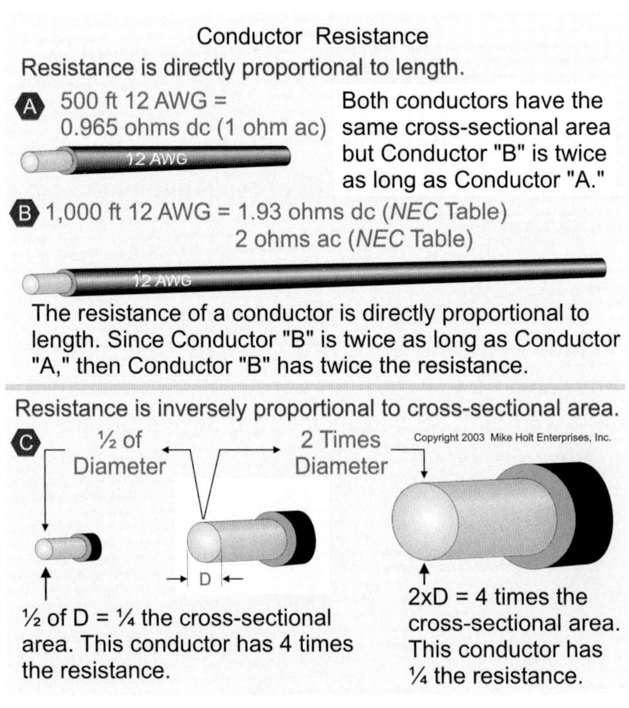

Conductor Resistance
Resistance is directly proportional to length.
A 500 ft 12 AWG = 0.965 ohms dc (1 ohm ac)
Both conductors have the same cross-sectional area but Conductor "B" is twice as long as Conductor "A."
12 AWG
B 1,000 ft 12 AWG = 1.93 ohms dc (NEC Table) 2 ohms ac (NEC Table)
12 AWG
The resistance of a conductor is directly proportional to length. Since Conductor "B" is twice as long as Conductor "A," then Conductor "B" has twice the resistance.
Resistance is inversely proportional to cross-sectional area.
C ½ of Diameter
2 Times Diameter
Copyright 2003 Mike Holt Enterprises, Inc.
D
½ of D = ¼ the cross-sectional area. This conductor has 4 times the resistance.
2xD = 4 times the cross-sectional area. This conductor has ¼ the resistance.

Figure 18–5

For ac circuits, the ac resistance of a conductor must factor the effects of eddy currents and skin effect (inductive reactance), in addition to resistance.

Eddy Currents

Eddy currents are small independent currents that are produced as a result of the expanding and collapsing magnetic field from an ac circuit. Eddy currents flow erratically through a conductor, consume power, and increase the opposition of current flow. **Figure 18–6**

Skin Effect

The expanding and collapsing magnetic field from an ac circuit induces a voltage in the conductors that repels the flowing electrons toward the surface of the conductor. This has the effect of decreasing the effective conductor cross-sectional area because more current (electrons) flows near the conductor surface than at the center. The decreased conductor cross-sectional area causes an increased opposition to current flow. **Figure 18–7**

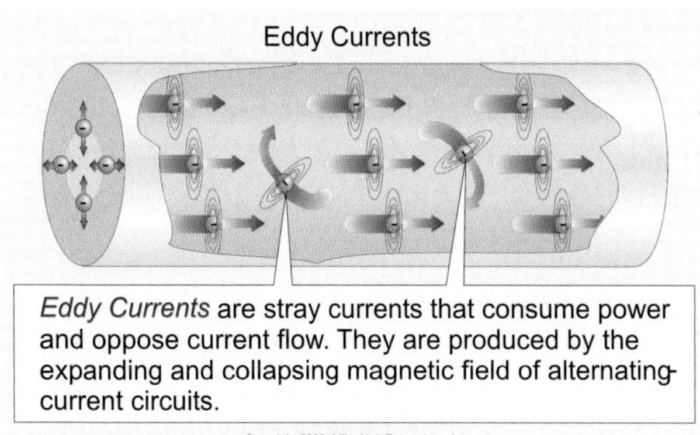

Eddy Currents
Eddy Currents are stray currents that consume power and oppose current flow. They are produced by the expanding and collapsing magnetic field of alternating-current circuits.
Copyright 2003 Mike Holt Enterprises, Inc.

Figure 18–6

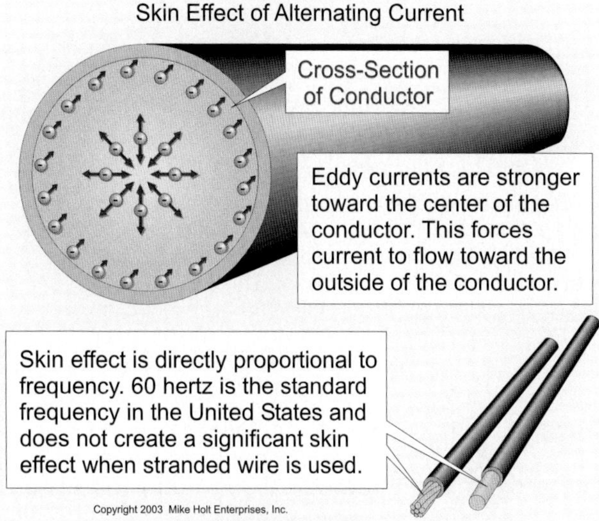

Skin Effect of Alternating Current
Cross-Section of Conductor
Eddy currents are stronger toward the center of the conductor. This forces current to flow toward the outside of the conductor.
Skin effect is directly proportional to frequency. 60 hertz is the standard frequency in the United States and does not create a significant skin effect when stranded wire is used.
Copyright 2003 Mike Holt Enterprises, Inc.

Figure 18–7

18.4 Impedance

The total opposition to current flow (resistance and reactance) in ac circuits is called Impedance and it is measured in ohms. The abbreviation for the term Impedance is the letter "Z."

> **AUTHOR'S COMMENT:** I have no idea why the letter "Z" stands for impedance.

18.5 Conductor Shape

The physical shape of a conductor affects the amount of self-induced voltage within the conductor itself. When a conductor is coiled into adjacent loops (helically wound), it is called a winding. The expanding and collapsing magnetic flux lines of ac current flowing through the conductor loops interact and add together to create a strong overall magnetic field. As the combined flux lines expand and collapse they cut additional conductor loops, creating greater self-inductance in each conductor loop. **Figure 18–8**

The amount of the self-induced voltage created within the winding is directly proportional to the current flow, the winding (conductor length and the number of turns), and the frequency at which the expanding and collapsing magnetic fields cut through the conductors of the winding.

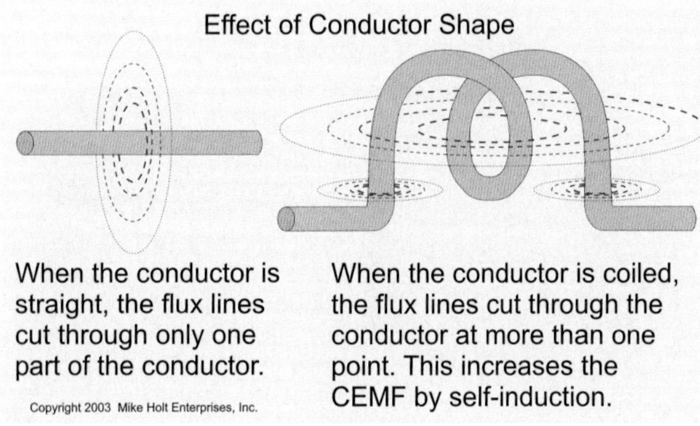

Figure 18–8

Current

The greater the winding current, and the greater the alternating magnetic field, the greater the CEMF within the winding.

Winding

The greater the number of winding conductor loops (turns) and the closer the windings, the greater the CEMF produced within the winding. **Figure 18–9**

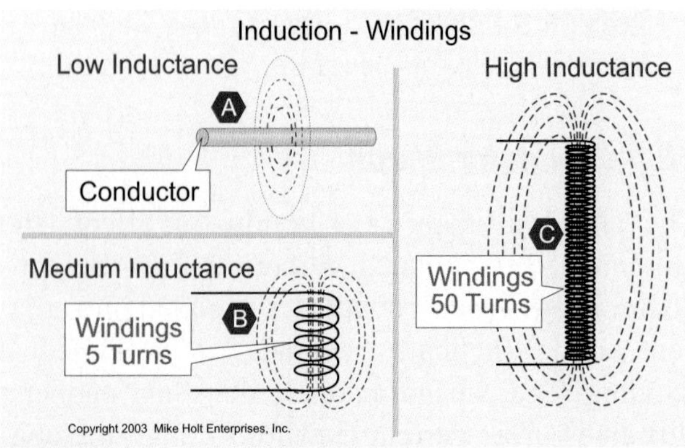

Figure 18–9

Frequency

Self-induced voltage is dependent upon the frequency at which the magnetic field expands or collapses. Therefore, the greater the frequency, the greater the CEMF induced within the winding.

18.6 Magnetic Cores

The core material also affects self-inductance in a winding (coil).

Core Material

Because an iron core provides an easy path for magnetic flux, windings with soft iron cores produce a greater self-inductance than windings with an air core. **Figure 18–10**

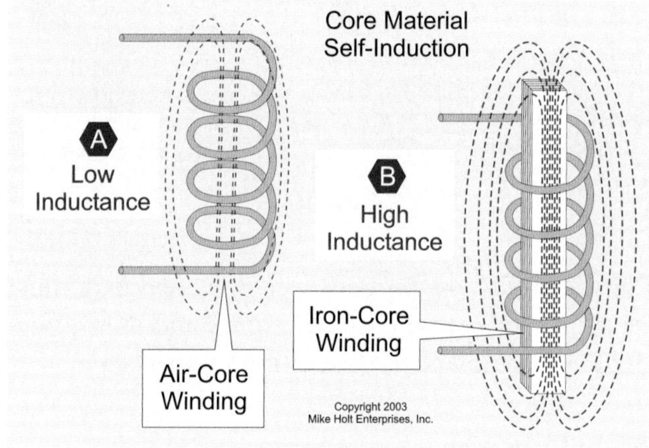

Figure 18–10

Core Length

Longer cores result in fewer flux lines; this results in reduced self-inductance. If the core length is doubled, the CEMF will be decreased by 50 percent. **Figure 18–11**

Core Area

Self-inductance (CEMF) is directly proportional to the cross-sectional area of the core, and inversely proportional to its length. This means that if the core area is doubled, the CEMF will be increased 200 percent. **Figure 18–12**

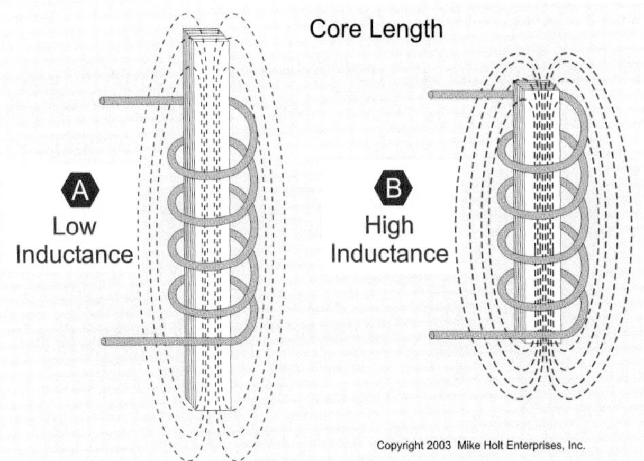

Figure 18–11

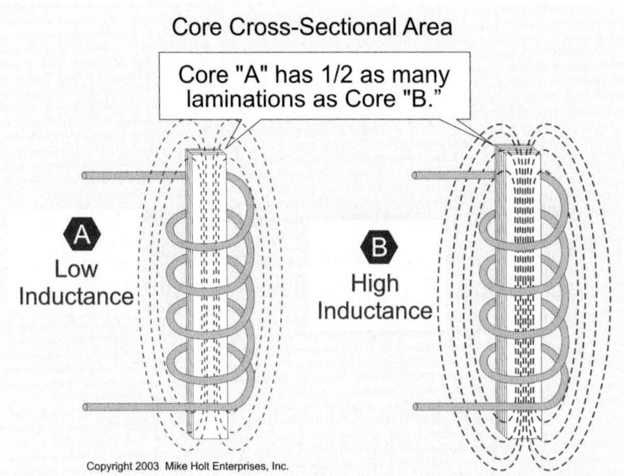

Figure 18–12

18.7 Self-Induced and Applied Voltage

A self-induced voltage waveform is 180 degrees out-of-phase with the applied voltage waveform. When the applied voltage increases or decreases, the polarity of the self-induced voltage is opposite that of the applied voltage. When the applied voltage is at its maximum in one direction, the induced voltage is at its maximum in the opposite direction. Figure 18–13

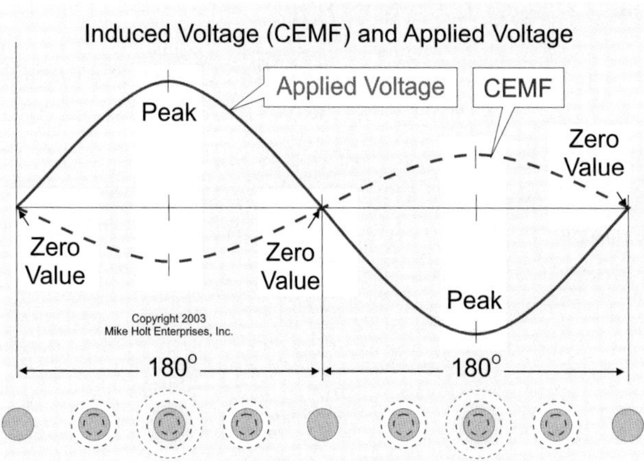

Figure 18–13

18.8 Current Flow

Alternating-current flow in a conductor is limited by the conductor's resistance and self-induced voltage (CEMF). Self-induced voltage (CEMF) acts to oppose the change in current flowing in the conductor. This property is called "inductive reactance" and it is measured in ohms.

Inductive Reactance

Inductive reactance is abbreviated X_L and can be calculated by the equation $X_L = 2 \times \pi \times F \times L$, where "F" is frequency with units of hertz, and "L" is inductance with units of Henrys.

AUTHOR'S COMMENT: Just remember that ac current flow contains an additional element that opposes the flow of electrons, besides conductor resistance.

18.9 Phase Relationship

In a purely inductive circuit, the CEMF waveform is 90 degrees out-of-phase with the circuit current waveform and 180 degrees out-of-phase with the applied voltage waveform. As a result, the applied voltage waveform leads the current waveform by 90 degrees. **Figure 18–14**

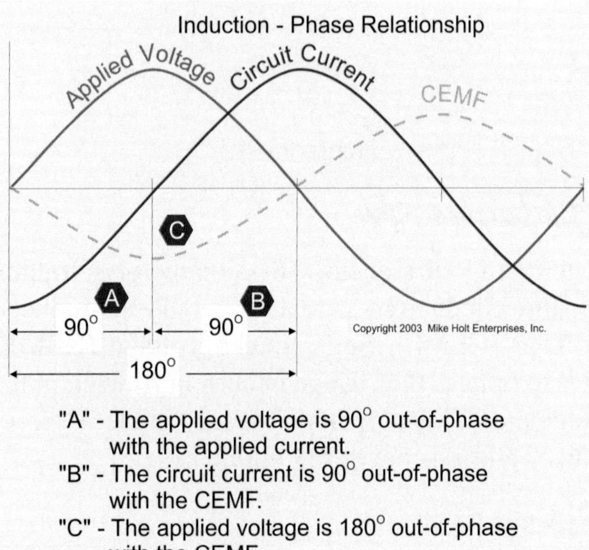

Figure 18–14

AUTHOR'S COMMENT: Just remember that an ac circuit contains inductive reactance because the voltage and current are "not in-phase with each other."

18.10 Uses of Induction

The major use of induction is in transformers, motors, and generators. **Figure 18–15**

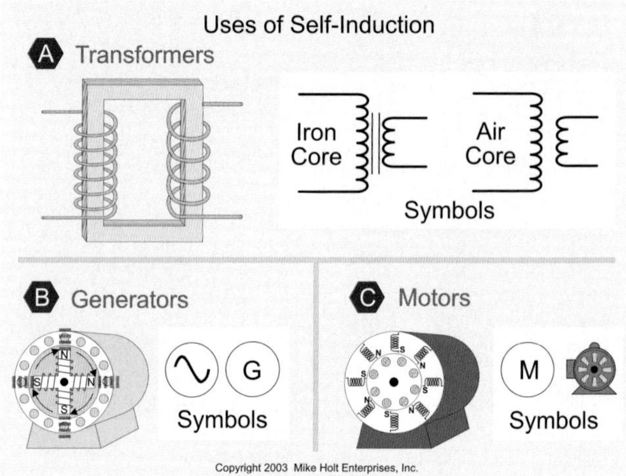

Figure 18–15

AUTHOR'S COMMENT: Inductors are also used to increase the impedance in high-impedance grounding systems. This topic is beyond the scope of this textbook. **Figure 18–16**

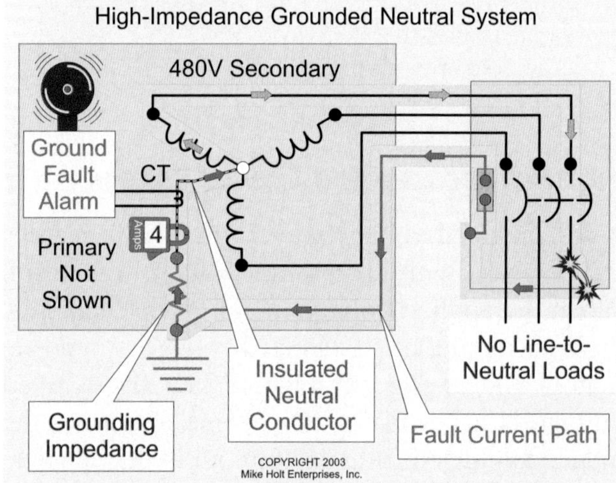

Figure 18–16

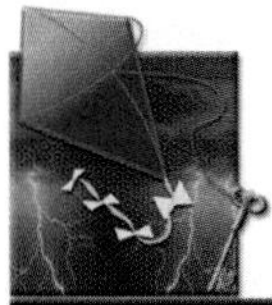

Unit 18 Summary

Introduction

When electrons move, the magnetic fields of the individual electrons combine to produce an overall magnetic field that extends outside the conductor. The direction of the overall magnetic field around the conductor follows the left-hand rule, based on the electron current flow theory.

The movement of electrons caused by an external magnetic field is called induced current, and the associated potential that is established is called induced voltage. In order to induce voltage, all that is required is a conductor and an external magnetic field with relative motion between the two.

18.1 Self-Induction

As the current through a conductor increases, an expanding electromagnetic field is created through the conductor. The voltage induced within the conductor caused by its own expanding and collapsing magnetic field is known as self-induced voltage.

18.2 Induced Voltage and Applied Current

The induced voltage in a conductor carrying alternating current always opposes the change in current flowing through the conductor. The induced voltage that opposes the change in current flow is called "counter-electromotive force" (CEMF), or back-EMF.

When alternating current increases, the polarity of the induced voltage (CEMF) within the conductor opposes the conductor's current and tries to prevent the current from increasing. When the alternating current decreases, the polarity of the induced voltage aids the conductor's current and tries to prevent the current from decreasing.

18.3 Conductor AC Resistance

In dc circuits, the only property that affects current and voltage flow is resistance. The ac resistance of a conductor must factor the effects of eddy currents and skin effect, as well as resistance.

Eddy Currents

Eddy currents are small independent currents that are produced as a result of the expanding and collapsing magnetic field from an ac circuit. Eddy currents flow erratically through a conductor, consume power, and increase the opposition of current flow.

Skin Effect

The expanding and collapsing magnetic field from an ac circuit induces a voltage in the conductors that repels the flowing electrons toward the surface of the conductor. This has the effect of decreasing the effective conductor cross-sectional area.

18.4 Impedance

The opposition to current flow in ac circuits is called Impedance (Z) and it is measured in ohms.

18.5 Conductor Shape

The physical shape of a conductor affects the amount of self-induced voltage within the conductor itself. The expanding and collapsing magnetic flux lines of ac current flowing through the conductor loops interact and add together to create a strong overall magnetic field. As the combined flux lines expand and collapse they cut additional conductor loops, creating greater self-inductance in each conductor loop.

Current

The greater the current and the number of conductor loops (turns), the closer the windings, and the greater the frequency at which the magnetic field expands or collapses, the greater the counter-electromotive force.

18.6 Magnetic Cores

Because an iron core provides an easy path for magnetic flux, iron cores within the windings produce a greater self-inductance than air-core windings. The larger the cross-sectional area of the core, the more the conductivity of the flux lines, and the greater the self-inductance.

18.7 Self-Induced and Applied Voltage

Self-induced voltage is always 180 degrees out-of-phase with the applied voltage. When the applied voltage increases or decreases, the polarity of the self-induced voltage (CEMF) is opposite that of the applied voltage. When the applied voltage is at its maximum in one direction, the induced voltage is at its maximum in the opposite direction.

18.8 Current Flow

Alternating-current flow in a conductor is limited by the conductor's resistance and self-induced voltage (CEMF). Self-induced voltage (CEMF) acts to oppose the current flowing in the conductor. This property is called inductive reactance and it is measured in ohms.

18.9 Phase Relationship

In a purely inductive circuit, the CEMF is 90 degrees out-of-phase with the current and 180 degrees out-of-phase with the applied voltage. As a result, the applied voltage leads the current by 90 degrees.

18.10 Uses of Induction

The major use of induction is in transformers, motors, and generators.

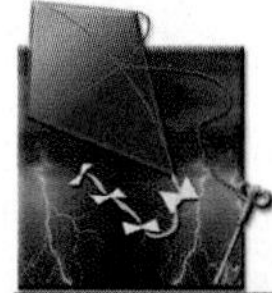

Unit 18 Conclusion

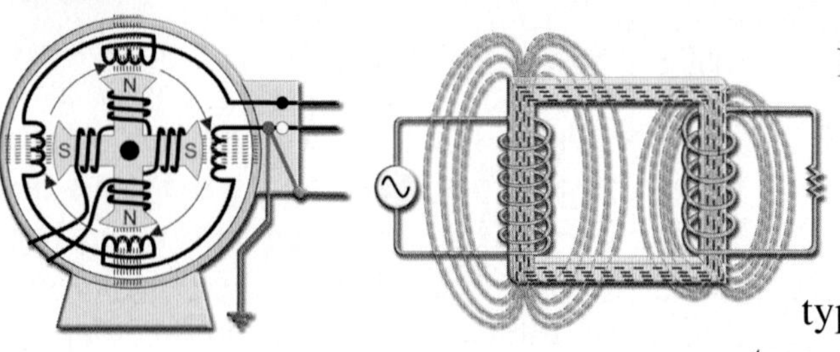

Induction, like capacitance and impedance, is one of the fundamental properties of electrical circuits. Now that you understand inductance, you are ready to learn the basic theory behind three important types of inductive devices—motors, generators, and transformers.

Words to Live By: *Too many people quit looking for work when they find a job.*

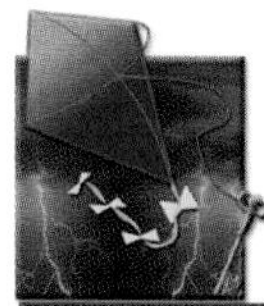

Unit 18 Practice Questions

Introduction

1. When electrons move, the magnetic fields of the individual electrons combine to produce an overall magnetic field. The greater the current flow, the greater the overall magnetic field around the conductor.

   (a) True (b) False

2. The direction of the overall magnetic field around the conductor follows the _____ rule, based on the electron current flow theory.

   (a) left-hand (b) right-hand (c) law of attraction (d) none of these

3. The movement of electrons caused by an external magnetic field is called _____ current, and the associated potential that is established is called _____ voltage.

   (a) circuit (b) applied (c) induced (d) none of these

4. In order to induce voltage, all that is required is relative motion between a conductor and a _____ field. This is the basis of the generator and transformer.

   (a) voltage (b) current (c) magnetic (d) none of these

18.1 Self-Induction

5. As the ac current through a conductor increases, an expanding and collapsing electromagnetic field through the conductor induces a voltage within the conductor. This is known as _____ voltage.

   (a) applied (b) circuit (c) self-induced (d) none of these

18.2 Induced Voltage and Applied Current

6. The induced voltage in a conductor carrying alternating current opposes the change in current flowing through the conductor. The induced voltage that opposes the current flow is called _____.

   (a) CEMF (b) counter-electromotive force
   (c) back-EMF (d) all of these

7. The waveform of the CEMF is _____ out-of-phase with the applied voltage.

   (a) 90° (b) 120° (c) 180° (d) 360°

8. When alternating current increases, the polarity of the CEMF within the conductor tries to prevent the current from increasing.

   (a) True (b) False

9. When the alternating current decreases, the polarity of the induced voltage within the conductor tries to prevent the current from decreasing.

   (a) True (b) False

18.3 Conductor AC Resistance

10. In dc circuits, the only property that affects current and voltage flow is _____.

   (a) impedance (b) reactance (c) resistance (d) none of these

11. Conductor resistance is directly proportional to the conductor's length and cross-sectional area.

   (a) True (b) False

12. For ac circuits, the ac _____ of a conductor must be taken into consideration.

   (a) eddy currents (b) skin effect (c) resistance (d) all of these

13. Eddy currents are small independent currents induced within the conductor because of direct current.

   (a) True (b) False

14. The expanding and collapsing magnetic field within the conductor induces a voltage in the conductors (CEMF) that repels the flowing electrons toward the surface of the conductor. This is called _____.

   (a) eddy currents (b) induced voltage (c) impedance (d) skin effect

18.4 Impedance

15. The total opposition to current flow in ac circuits is called _____ and it is measured in ohms.

   (a) resistance (b) reactance (c) impedance (d) skin effect

16. The abbreviation for impedance is _____.

   (a) X_L (b) X_C (c) Z (d) none of these

18.5 Conductor Shape

17. The magnitude of self-induced voltage within a winding is directly proportional to the current flow, the winding, and the frequency at which magnetic fields cut through the winding.

(a) True (b) False

18.6 Magnetic Cores

18. Because an iron core provides an easy path for magnetic flux, windings with soft iron cores produce a greater self-inductance than windings with air cores.

(a) True (b) False

18.7 Self-Induced and Applied Voltage

19. Self-induced voltage is 180º out-of-phase with the _____. When the applied voltage is at its maximum in one direction, the induced voltage is at its maximum in the opposite direction.

(a) applied current (b) applied voltage (c) induced voltage (d) induced current

18.8 Current Flow

20. Self-induced voltage opposes the change in current flowing in the conductor. This is called inductive reactance and it is abbreviated _____.

(a) X_L (b) X_C (c) Z (d) none of these

18.9 Phase Relationship

21. The CEMF waveform is _____ out-of-phase with the applied voltage waveform.

(a) 90º (b) 120º (c) 180º (d) 360º

22. The current waveform lags the applied voltage waveform by _____.

(a) 90º (b) 120º (c) 180º (d) 360º

18.10 Uses of Induction

23. The most common use of induction is for _____.

(a) motors (b) transformers (c) generators (d) all of these

Notes

Power Factor and Efficiency

Introduction

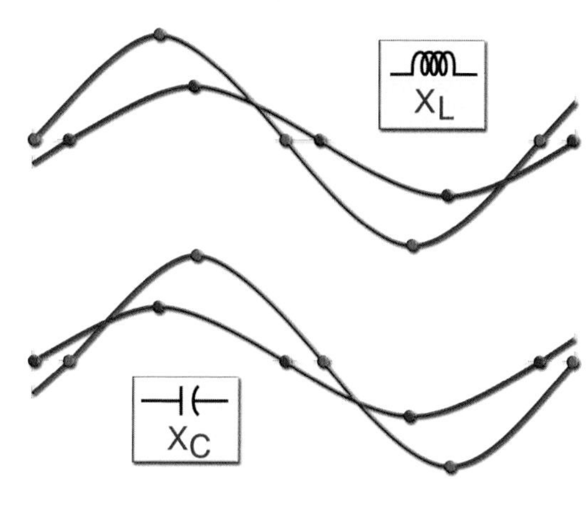

In previous units, you learned that one waveform can lead or lag another. You learned about voltage and current waveforms and how they relate to each other. Here, you'll learn about apparent power. You'll also see how power factor is a way of looking at the relationship between effective power and apparent power. One way we correct power factor is by using energy storage devices.

Inductors and Capacitors

Inductors and capacitors are energy storage devices in ac and dc circuits. The energy is stored in the electromagnetic field of an inductor and the electric field of a capacitor. **Figure 19–1**

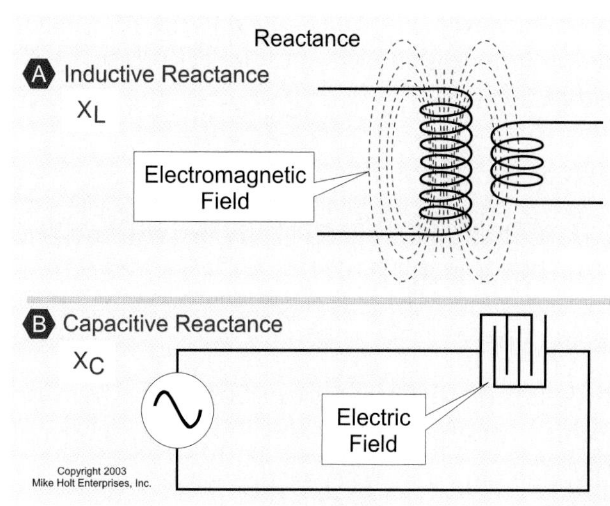

Figure 19–1

PART A—POWER FACTOR

19.1 Apparent Power (Volt-Ampere)

If you measure voltage and current in an inductive or capacitive circuit, and then multiply them together, you will obtain the apparent power supplied to the circuit by the source. Apparent power is expressed in volt-amperes (VA). Circuits and equipment must be sized to the circuit VA load. Apparent Power = Volts x Amperes

Example

What is the apparent power in VA of a 1 hp, 115V motor that has a full-load current rating of 16A? **Figure 19–2**

(a) 2,400 VA (b) 1,320 VA
(c) 1,840 VA (d) 1,920 VA

• Answer: (c) 1,840 VA

VA = E x I
VA = 115V x 16A = 1,840 VA

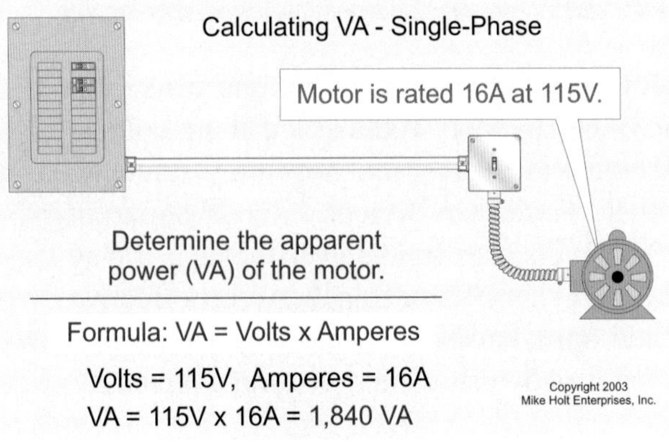

Calculating VA - Single-Phase
Motor is rated 16A at 115V.
Determine the apparent power (VA) of the motor.
Formula: VA = Volts x Amperes
Volts = 115V, Amperes = 16A
VA = 115V x 16A = 1,840 VA
Copyright 2003 Mike Holt Enterprises, Inc.

Figure 19–2

19.2 True Power (Watts)

True power is the energy consumed, expressed in the unit watts. Utility companies charge based on the total power consumed for one month, measured in units called kilowatt hours (kWh or 1,000 watts x 1 hour).

Example

A 100W bulb, burning for 10 hours will use one kWh: 100W x 10 hrs = kWh

Direct Current

To determine the true power consumed by a dc circuit, multiply the volts by the amperes (W = E x I).

Alternating Current

In an ac circuit, true power (W) is determined by multiplying the circuit volts (E), by the amperes (I), times the power factor (W = E x I x PF).

19.3 Power Factor

AC inductive or capacitive reactive loads cause the voltage and current sine waves to be out-of-phase with each other. Power factor is a measurement of how far the current waveform is out-of-phase with the voltage waveform. Power factor is equal to the ratio of circuit resistance to circuit impedance (capacitance reactance, inductive reactance and resistance), and is expressed as a percentage. **Figure 19–3**

Power factor is defined as a ratio of true power (watts) to apparent power (VA).

$$PF = \frac{\text{True Power (Watts)}}{\text{Apparent Power (VA)}}$$

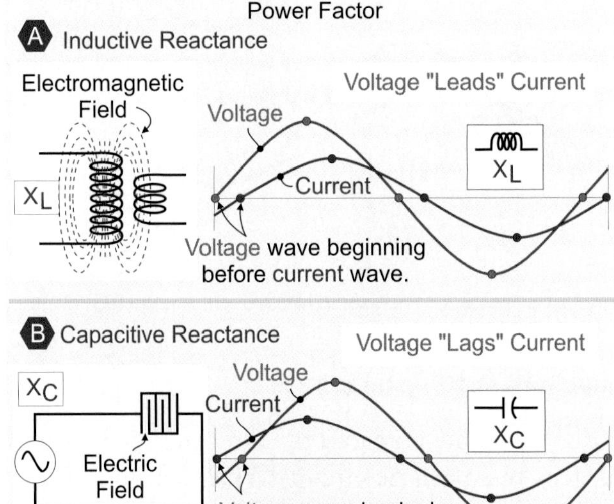

Figure 19–3

19.4 Unity Power Factor

When an ac circuit supplies power to a purely resistive load, such as incandescent lighting, heating elements, etc., the circuit voltage and current will be in-phase with each other.

Because the voltage and current reach their zero and peak values at the same time, there is no leading or lagging of the voltage to the current. Therefore, the power factor of the load is 100 percent, and this condition is called "unity power factor." Figure 19–4

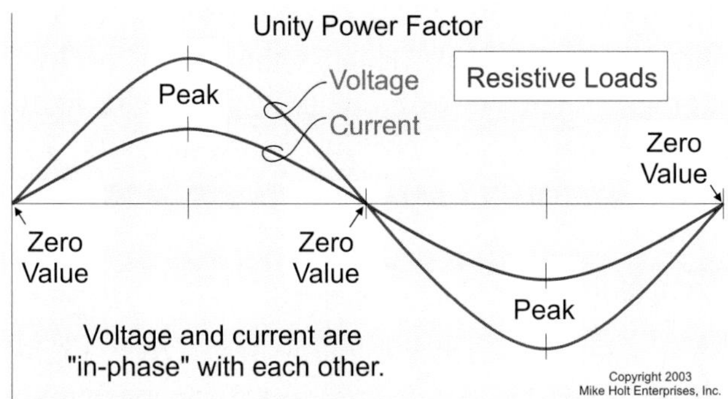

Figure 19–4

19.5 Power Factor Formulas

The relationship between True Power (watts), Apparent Power (VA), and Power Factor can be shown as:

$$\text{Power Factor (PF)} = \frac{\text{True Power (W)}}{\text{Apparent Power (VA)}}$$

$$\text{Apparent Power (VA)} = \frac{\text{True Power (W)}}{\text{Power Factor (PF)}}$$

True Power = Apparent Power x Power Factor

Power Factor Example

Assuming 100 percent efficiency, what is the power factor for each ballast rated 0.75A at 120V for a 2 x 4 fixture containing four 40W lamps (two lamps per ballast)? Figure 19–5

(a) 69% (b) 75%
(c) 89% (d) 95%

- Answer: (c) 89%

PF = W/VA

$$PF = \frac{80W}{(0.75A \times 120V)}$$

$$PF = \frac{80W}{90\ VA}$$

PF = 0.888 or 89%

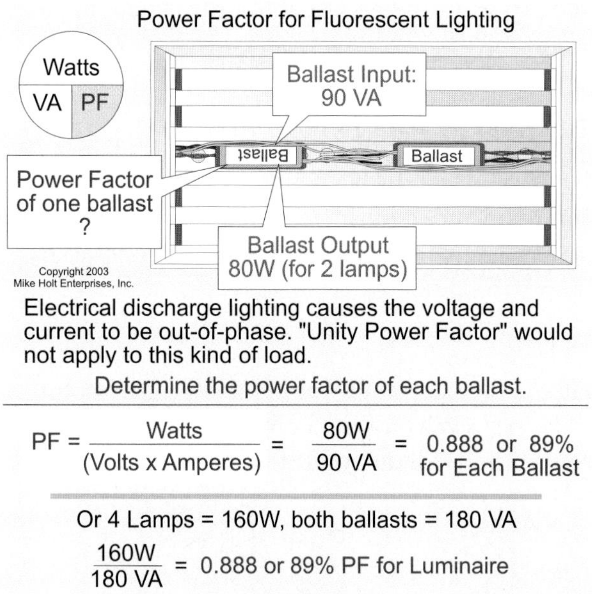

Power Factor for Fluorescent Lighting

Watts
VA PF
Ballast Input: 90 VA
Ballast
Ballast
Power Factor of one ballast ?
Ballast Output 80W (for 2 lamps)
Copyright 2003 Mike Holt Enterprises, Inc.

Electrical discharge lighting causes the voltage and current to be out-of-phase. "Unity Power Factor" would not apply to this kind of load.

Determine the power factor of each ballast.

$$PF = \frac{\text{Watts}}{\text{(Volts x Amperes)}} = \frac{80W}{90\ VA} = 0.888 \text{ or } 89\% \text{ for Each Ballast}$$

Or 4 Lamps = 160W, both ballasts = 180 VA

$$\frac{160W}{180\ VA} = 0.888 \text{ or } 89\% \text{ PF for Luminaire}$$

Figure 19–5

Apparent Power (VA) Example

What is the apparent power in VA of a fluorescent ballast that has a power factor of 89% when connected to two 40W lamps?

(a) 70W (b) 80 VA
(c) 90 VA (d) 100W

- Answer: (c) 90 VA

Apparent power is expressed in VA; therefore, neither (a) nor (d) can be the answer.

VA = W/PF
VA = 80W/0.89 PF
VA = 89.9 VA

True Power (Watts) Example

What is the true power of a 16A load rated 120V, with a power factor of 85 percent?

(a) 2,400W (b) 1,920W
(c) 1,632W (d) none of these

- Answer: (c) 1,632W

True power (watts) is equal to volts times amperes times power factor.

Watts = VA x PF
Watts = (120V x 16A) x 0.85 PF
Watts = 1,632W

True power is always equal to or less than apparent power.

19.6 Cost of True Power

The cost of electrical power is based on the true power consumed during a month, multiplied by the cost per kWh (1,000W for a period of one hour).

Example:

What is the cost of power consumed per month (at $0.09 per kWh) for a 25 ohm ground rod having a ground-fault voltage of 120V? **Figure 19–6**

(a) $10 (b) $25
(c) $37 (d) $55

• Answer: (c) $37

Step 1 Power per hour = E^2/R

E = 120V
R = 25Ω

$$P = \frac{120V^2}{25\Omega}$$

P = 576W

Step 2 Power consumed per day:
567W x 24 = 13,824W or 13.824 kWh

Step 3 Power consumed in 30 days:
13.824 kWh x 30 = 415 kWh

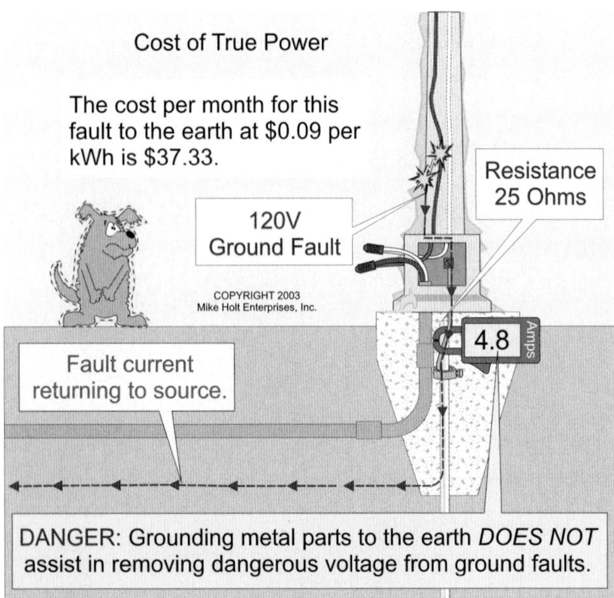

Figure 19–6

Step 4 Cost of power at $0.09 per kWh:
415 kWh x $0.09 = $37.33

19.7 Effects of Power Factor

The apparent power (VA) is used for sizing circuits and equipment. Because the VA of the load is greater than the watts of the load, fewer loads can be placed per circuit. More circuits and panels, and larger transformers might be required.

Example A

What size transformer is required for forty-eight, 150W incandescent luminaires (noncontinuous load)? **Figure 19–7A**

(a) 3 kVA (b) 5 kVA
(c) 7.5 kVA (d) 10 kVA

• Answer: (c) 7.5 kVA

$$kW = \frac{(48 \text{ Fixtures x } 150W)}{1,000}$$

$$kW = \frac{7,200W}{1,000}$$

kW = 7.2 kW

AUTHOR'S COMMENT: Transformers are always sized based on kVA, not kW.

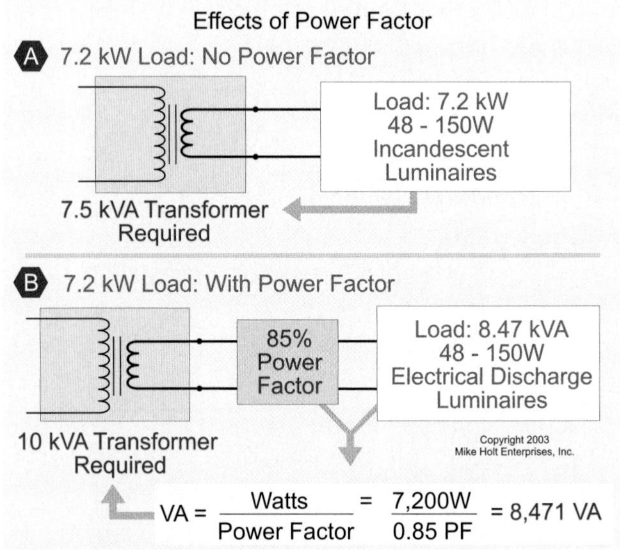

Figure 19–7

Example B

What size transformer is required for forty-eight, 150W electric discharge luminaires that have a power factor of 85 percent (noncontinuous load)? **Figure 19–7B**

(a) 3 kVA (b) 5 kVA
(c) 7.5 kVA (d) 10 kVA

• Answer: (d) 10 kVA

Transformers are sized for apparent power (kVA), not true power.

kW = (48 x 150W) / 1,000

$$\text{kW} = \frac{7{,}200\text{W}}{1{,}000}$$

kW = 7.2 kW

$$\text{Apparent Power} = \frac{\text{kW}}{\text{PF}}$$

$$\text{Apparent Power} = \frac{7.2 \text{ kW}}{0.85\text{PF}}$$

Apparent Power = 8.47 kVA

Example C

How many 20A, 120V circuits are required for forty-eight, 150W luminaires (noncontinuous load)? **Figure 19–8A**

(a) 2 circuits (b) 3 circuits
(c) 4 circuits (d) 5 circuits

• Answer: (b) 3 circuits

Each circuit has a capacity of:

120V x 20A = 2,400 VA

Each circuit can have:

$$\frac{2400\text{W}}{150\text{W}} = 16 \text{ luminaires}$$

The number of circuits required is:

$$\frac{48 \text{ luminaires}}{16 \text{ luminaires per circuit}} = 3 \text{ circuits}$$

Effects of Power Factor on Inductive Lighting

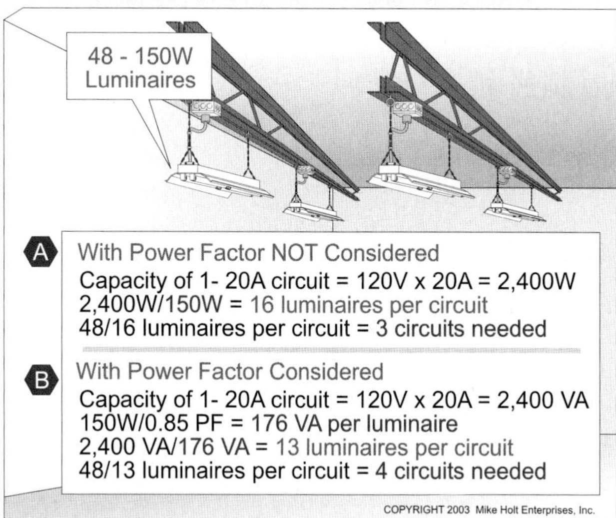

48 - 150W Luminaires
A
With Power Factor NOT Considered
Capacity of 1- 20A circuit = 120V x 20A = 2,400W
2,400W/150W = 16 luminaires per circuit
48/16 luminaires per circuit = 3 circuits needed
B
With Power Factor Considered
Capacity of 1- 20A circuit = 120V x 20A = 2,400 VA
150W/0.85 PF = 176 VA per luminaire
2,400 VA/176 VA = 13 luminaires per circuit
48/13 luminaires per circuit = 4 circuits needed
COPYRIGHT 2003 Mike Holt Enterprises, Inc.

Figure 19–8

Example D

How many 20A, 120V circuits are required for forty-eight, 150W luminaires (noncontinuous load) that have a power factor of 85 percent? **Figure 19–8B**

(a) 4 (b) 6
(c) 8 (d) 12

• Answer: (a) 4

Circuits are loaded according to VA, not watts!

VA of each luminaire is:

$$\text{VA} = \frac{\text{Watts}}{\text{PF}}$$

$$\text{VA} = \frac{150\text{W}}{0.85}$$

VA = 176 VA

Each circuit has a capacity of:
120V x 20A = 2,400 VA

Each circuit can have:

$$\frac{2{,}400\text{VA}}{176\text{VA}} = 13 \text{ luminaires}$$

The number of circuits required is:

$$\frac{48 \text{ luminaires}}{13 \text{ luminaires per circuit}} = 4 \text{ circuits}$$

AUTHOR'S COMMENT: If the building had 480 luminaires, we would need 40 circuits instead of 30 and the transformer would need to be rated at least 100 kVA, instead of 75 kVA.

PART B—EFFICIENCY

19.8 Efficiency

Electricity is used because of its convenience in transferring energy to operate lighting, heating, controls, motors, etc. In the transfer of energy, there will be power losses in the conductors, the power supply, and the load itself. The degree of power loss in watts (waste) is indicated by the term "Efficiency."

Efficiency describes how much input energy is used for its intended useful purpose, expressed as a ratio of output true power to input true power. Naturally, the output power can never be greater than the input power. **Figure 19–9**

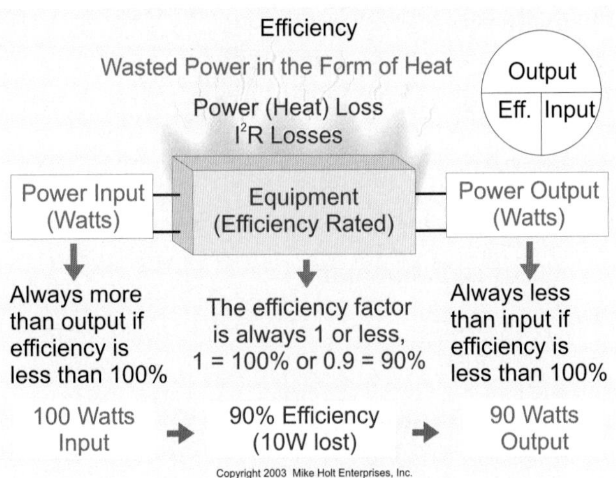

Figure 19–9

If equipment is rated at 100 percent efficiency (there are none), this would mean that 100 percent of the input energy is consumed for its intended useful purpose.

When equipment is rated at 90 percent efficiency, this means that only 90 percent of the input power is used for its intended useful purpose. Another way of saying this is that 10 percent of the input power is wasted.

When energy is not used for its intended purpose, this condition is called power loss. Conductor resistance, mechanical friction, as well as many other factors can contribute to increased power losses, or reduced efficiency rating.

19.9 Efficiency Formulas

The formulas that are often used with efficiency calculations include:

$$\text{Efficiency} = \frac{\text{Output Watts}}{\text{Input Watts}}$$

$$\text{Input Watts} = \frac{\text{Output Watts}}{\text{Efficiency}}$$

$$\text{Output Watts} = \text{Input Watts} \times \text{Efficiency}$$

Efficiency Example

If the output of a load is 640W and the input is 800W, what is the efficiency of the equipment? **Figure 19–10**

(a) 60% (b) 70%
(c) 80% (d) 100%

• Answer: (c) 80%

Efficiency is always less than 100%.

$$\text{Efficiency} = \frac{\text{Output Watts}}{\text{Input Watts}}$$

$$\text{Efficiency} = \frac{640\text{W}}{800\text{W}}$$

$$\text{Efficiency} = 0.8 \text{ or } 80\%$$

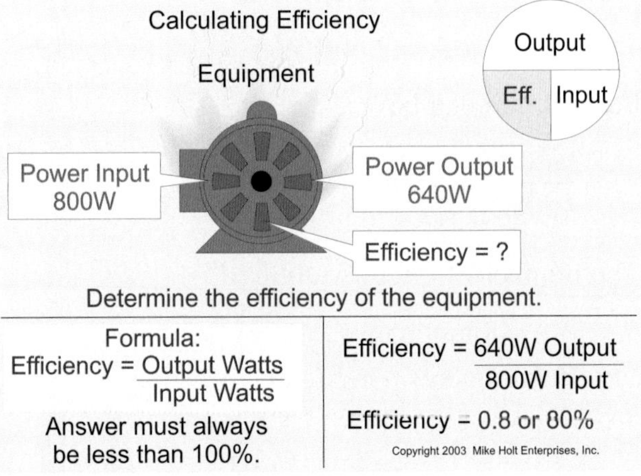

Figure 19–10

Efficiency Example B

If the output of a 5 hp dc motor is 3,730W (746W x 5) and the input is 4,800W (40A at 120V), what is the efficiency of the motor? **Figure 19–11**

(a) 60% (b) 78%
(c) 80% (d) 100%

• Answer: (b) 78%

$$\text{Efficiency} = \frac{\text{Output Watts}}{\text{Input Watts}}$$

$$\text{Efficiency} = \frac{3{,}730\text{W}}{4{,}800\text{W}}$$

Efficiency = 0.777 or 77.7%

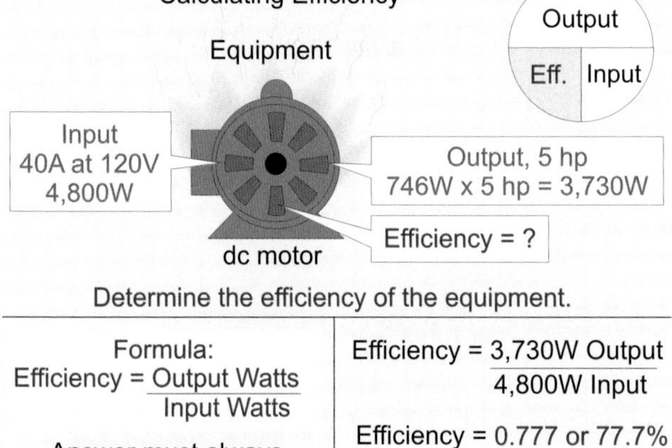

Figure 19–11

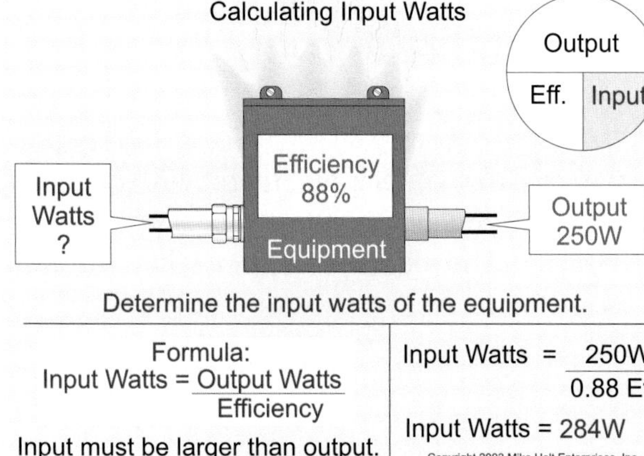

Figure 19–12

Input Example

If the output is 250W and the equipment is 88 percent efficient, what is the input power rating in watts? **Figure 19–12**

(a) 200W (b) 250W
(c) 285W (d) 325W

• Answer: (c) 285W

Input is always greater than the output.

$$\text{Input} = \frac{\text{Output Watts}}{\text{Input Watts}}$$

$$\text{Input} = \frac{250\text{W}}{0.88\ \text{Eff}}$$

Input = 284W

Output Example

If the input power to a load is 479W and the equipment is rated at 87.6 percent efficiency, what is the output power rating in watts? **Figure 19–13**

(a) 550W (b) 500W
(c) 420W (d) 350W

• Answer: (c) 420W

Output is always less than input.

Output Watts = Input Watts x Efficiency

Output Watts = 479W x 0.876 Eff

Output Watts = 419.6W

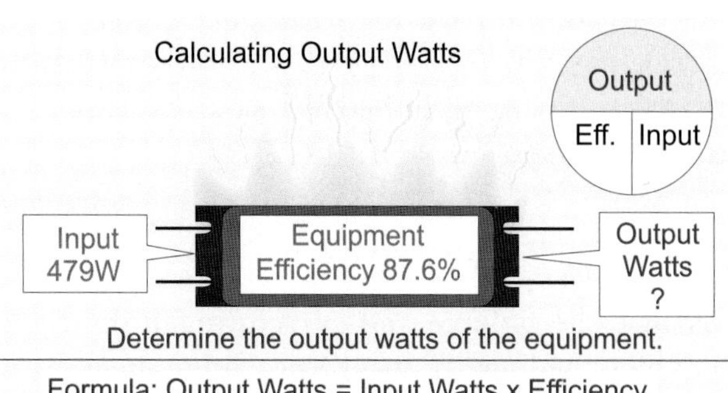

Figure 19–13

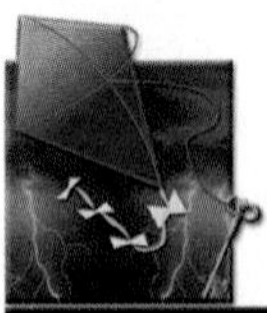

Unit 19 Summary

Introduction

Inductors and capacitors are energy storage devices. The energy is stored in the electromagnetic field of an inductor and the electric field of a capacitor.

PART A—POWER FACTOR

19.1 Apparent Power (Volt-Ampere)

If you measure voltage and current in an inductive or capacitive circuit, and then multiply them together, you will obtain the circuit's "apparent power," expressed in "volt-amperes."

19.2 True Power (Watts)

True power is the energy used (consumed), expressed in "watts." Utility companies charge on the power consumed. The true power of an ac circuit is volts, times the amperes, times the power factor multiplier. In dc circuits, true power is volts times amperes.

19.3 Power Factor

AC inductive or capacitive loads cause the voltage and current sine waves to be out-of-phase with each other. Power factor is the ratio of circuit resistance to circuit impedance and it is expressed as a percentage.

19.4 Unity Power Factor

Because the voltage and current reach their zero and peak values at the same time, there is no leading or lagging of the current to the voltage. Therefore the power factor of the load is 100 percent, and this condition is called "unity power factor."

19.5 Power Factor Formulas

The relationship between true power (watts), apparent power (VA), and power factor can be shown as:

$$\text{Power factor (PF)} = \frac{\text{True Power (W)}}{\text{Apparent Power (VA)}}$$

$$\text{Apparent Power (VA)} = \frac{\text{True Power (W)}}{\text{Power Factor (PF)}}$$

True Power = Apparent Power x Power Factor

19.6 Cost of True Power

The cost of electricity consumed (true power) is based on the unit of "watts," and is billed on the number of kilowatt-hours (kWh) times the cost per kWh.

19.7 Effects of Power Factor

VA (apparent power) is used for sizing circuits and equipment. Because the VA of the load is greater than the watts of the load, fewer loads can be placed per circuit. More circuits and panels, and larger transformers might be required.

PART B—EFFICIENCY

19.8 Efficiency

In the transfer of energy, there will be power losses in the conductors, the power supply, and the load itself. The degree of power loss in watts (waste) is indicated by the term "Efficiency."

Efficiency describes how much input energy is used for its intended useful purpose, expressed as a ratio of output power to input power.

When energy is not used for its intended purpose, this condition is called power loss. Conductor resistance, mechanical friction, as well as many other factors can contribute to increased power losses, or reduced efficiency rating.

19.9 Efficiency Formulas

The formulas that are often used with efficiency calculations include:

$$\text{Efficiency} = \frac{\text{Output Watts}}{\text{Input Watts}}$$

$$\text{Input Watts} = \frac{\text{Output Watts}}{\text{Efficiency}}$$

$$\text{Output Watts} = \text{Input Watts} \times \text{Efficiency}$$

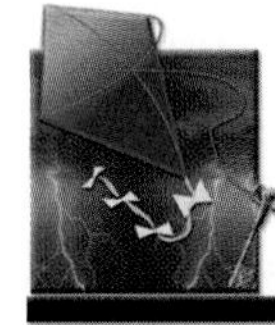

Unit 19 Conclusion

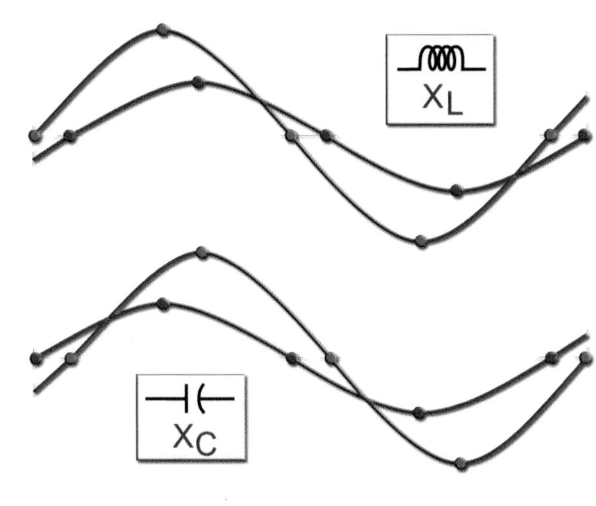

You know that no circuit is 100% efficient—all circuits and equipment have some power loss. The ability to calculate efficiency and power loss is now part of your skill set. While you don't normally have to use this skill, you may find it quite useful when troubleshooting or when deciding whether to replace old equipment.

You understand apparent power, true power, power factor, and unity power factor, and you know that it's possible to use capacitors to correct the power factor.

Words to Live By: *What counts is not the number of hours you put in, but how much you put in the hours.*

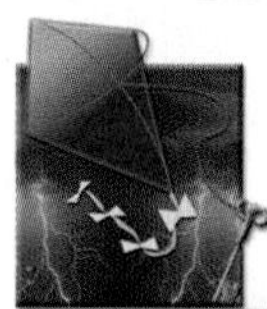

Unit 19 Practice Questions

Introduction

1. Inductors and capacitors are electrical devices that store energy in the electromagnetic field of an inductor and the electric field of a capacitor.

   (a) True (b) False

PART A—POWER FACTOR

19.1 Apparent Power (Volt-Ampere)

2. If you measure voltage and current in an inductive or capacitive circuit and then multiply them together, you obtain the circuit's _____.

   (a) true power (b) power factor (c) apparent power (d) none of these

19.2 True Power (Watts)

3. To determine the true power consumed by a dc circuit, multiply the volts by the amperes.

   (a) True (b) False

4. True power of an ac circuit equals the volts times the amperes.

   (a) True (b) False

19.3 Power Factor

5. AC inductive or capacitive reactive loads cause the voltage and current to be in-phase with each other.

   (a) True (b) False

6. Power factor is a measurement of how far the current is out-of-phase with the voltage.

   (a) True (b) False

19.4 Unity Power Factor

7. When an ac circuit supplies power to a purely _____ load, the circuit voltage and current will be in-phase with each other. This condition is called unity power factor.

   (a) capacitive (b) inductive (c) resistive (d) any of these

19.6 Cost of True Power

8. What does it cost per year (at 9 cents per kWh) for ten 150W recessed luminaires to operate if they are turned on for six hours per day?

   (a) $150 (b) $300 (c) $500 (d) $800

19.7 Effects of Power Factor

9. Because apparent power (VA) is greater than the true power (W), more loads can be placed on a circuit, and fewer circuits and panels, and smaller transformers might be required.

   (a) True (b) False

10. When sizing circuits or equipment, always size the circuit components and transformers according to the apparent power (VA), not the true power (W).

    (a) True (b) False

11. What is the true power of a 10A circuit operating at 120V with unity power factor?

    (a) 1,200 VA (b) 2,400 VA (c) 1,200W (d) 2,400W

12. What size transformer is required for a 100A, 240V, single-phase noncontinuous load (unity power factor)?

    (a) 15 kVA (b) 25 kVA (c) 37.5 kVA (d) 50 kVA

13. What size transformer is required for a 100A, 240V, single-phase (1Ø) noncontinuous load that has a power factor of 85 percent?

    (a) 15 kVA (b) 25 kVA (c) 37.5 kVA (d) 50 kVA

14. How many 20A, 120V circuits are required for forty-two, 300W incandescent luminaires (noncontinuous load)?

    (a) 3 circuits (b) 4 circuits (c) 5 circuits (d) 6 circuits

15. How many 20A, 120V circuits are required for forty-two, 300W luminaires (noncontinuous load) that have a power factor of 85 percent?

    (a) 5 circuits (b) 6 circuits (c) 7 circuits (d) 8 circuits

PART B—EFFICIENCY

19.8 Efficiency

16. In the transfer of electrical energy, there will be power losses in the conductors, the power supply, and the load itself.

    (a) True (b) False

17. Efficiency describes how much input energy is used for its intended purpose.

    (a) True (b) False

19.9 Efficiency Formulas

18. If the output is 1,320W and the input is 1,800W, what is the efficiency of the equipment?

    (a) 62% (b) 73% (c) 80% (d) 100%

19. If the input of a 1 hp dc motor is 1,128W and the output is 746W, what is the efficiency of the motor?

    (a) 66% (b) 74% (c) 87% (d) 100%

20. If the output is 1,600W and the equipment is 88 percent efficient, what are the input amperes at 120V?

    (a)10A (b) 15A (c) 20A (d) 25A

21. If a transformer is 97 percent efficient, for every 1 kW input, there will be _____ output.

    (a) 970W (b) 1,000W (c) 1,030W (d) 1,200W

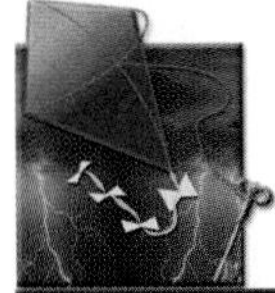

Chapter 5 Final Exam

Unit 16—Alternating Current

16.1 Current Flow

1. The movement of electrons themselves does not produce any useful work; it's the effects that the moving electrons have on the loads they flow through that are important.

   (a) True (b) False

16.6 Sine Wave

2. A nonsinusoidal waveform is created when _____ loads distort the voltage and current sine wave.

   (a) linear (b) resistive (c) inductive (d) nonlinear

16.9 Phase

3. In a purely resistive ac circuit, the current and voltage are _____. This means that they both reach their zero and peak value at the same time.

   (a) in-phase (b) out-of-phase (c) a or b (d) none of these

16.11 Lead or Lag

4. When describing the relationship between voltage and current, the reference waveform is always _____.

   (a) current (b) resistance (c) voltage (d) none of these

16.12 Values of Alternating Current

5. The peak value is equal to the effective value _____.

   (a) times 0.707 (b) times 1.41 (c) divided by 1.41 (d) none of these

6. The effective value is equal to the peak value _____.

   (a) times 0.707 (b) times 1.41 (c) divided by 1.41 (d) none of these

Unit 17—Capacitance

Introduction

7. A half-wave rectifier can be used to convert ac voltage into dc voltage to continuously charge a capacitor.

   (a) True (b) False

17.3 Discharging a Capacitor

8. Even when power is removed from the circuit, capacitors can store large amounts of energy for a long period of time. They can discharge and arc if inadvertently shorted or grounded out.

   (a) True (b) False

17.6 Phase Relationship

9. The opposition offered to the flow of ac current by a capacitor is called capacitive reactance, which is expressed in ohms and abbreviated _____.

   (a) X_C (b) X_L (c) Z (d) none of these

Unit 18—Induction

Introduction

10. The movement of electrons caused by an external magnetic field is called _____ current, and the associated potential that is established is called _____ voltage.

    (a) circuit (b) applied (c) induced (d) none of these

18.1 Self-Induction

11. As the ac current through a conductor increases, an expanding and collapsing electromagnetic field through the conductor induces a voltage within the conductor. This is known as _____ voltage.

    (a) applied (b) circuit (c) self-induced (d) none of these

18.2 Induced Voltage and Applied Current

12. The induced voltage in a conductor carrying alternating current opposes the change in current flowing through the conductor. The induced voltage that opposes the current flow is called _____.

    (a) CEMF (b) counter-electromotive force
    (c) back-EMF (d) all of these

13. The waveform of the CEMF is _____ out-of-phase with the applied voltage.

(a) 90° (b) 120° (c) 180° (d) 360°

14. When alternating current increases, the polarity of the CEMF within the conductor tries to prevent the current from increasing.

(a) True (b) False

18.3 Conductor AC Resistance

15. In dc circuits, the only property that affects voltage and current flow is _____.

(a) impedance (b) reactance (c) resistance (d) none of these

16. For ac circuits, the ac _____ of a conductor must be taken into consideration.

(a) eddy currents (b) skin effect (c) resistance (d) all of these

17. The expanding and collapsing magnetic field within the conductor induces a voltage in the conductors (CEMF) that repels the flowing electrons toward the surface of the conductor. This is called _____.

(a) eddy currents (b) induced voltage (c) impedance (d) skin effect

18.4 Impedance

18. The total opposition to current flow in ac circuits is called _____ and it is measured in ohms.

(a) resistance (b) reactance (c) impedance (d) skin effect

19. The abbreviation for impedance is _____.

(a) X_L (b) X_C (c) Z (d) none of these

18.5 Conductor Shape

20. The magnitude of self-induced voltage within a winding is directly proportional to the current flow, the winding, and the frequency at which magnetic fields cut through the winding.

(a) True (b) False

18.7 Self-Induced and Applied Voltage

21. Self-induced voltage is 180 degrees out-of-phase with the _____. When the applied voltage is at its maximum in one direction, the induced voltage is at its maximum in the opposite direction.

(a) applied current (b) applied voltage (c) induced voltage (d) induced current

18.8 Current Flow

22. Self-induced voltage opposes the change in current flowing in the conductor. This is called inductive reactance and it is abbreviated _____.

(a) X_L (b) X_C (c) Z (d) none of these

18.9 Phase Relationship

23. The CEMF waveform is _____ out-of-phase with the applied voltage waveform.

(a) 90º (b) 120º (c) 180º (d) 360º

Unit 19—Power Factor and Efficiency

19.1 Apparent Power (Volt-Ampere)

24. If you measure voltage and current in an inductive or capacitive circuit and then multiply them together, you obtain the circuit's _____.

(a) true power (b) power factor (c) apparent power (d) none of these

19.2 True Power (Watts)

25. True power of an ac circuit equals the volts times the amperes.

(a) True (b) False

19.3 Power Factor

26. AC inductive or capacitive reactive loads cause the voltage and current to be in-phase with each other.

(a) True (b) False

19.6 Cost of True Power

27. What does it cost per year (at 9 cents per kWh) for ten 150W recessed luminaires to operate if they are turned on for six hours per day?

(a) $150 (b) $300 (c) $500 (d) $800

19.7 Effects of Power Factor

28. Because apparent power (VA) is greater than the true power (W), more loads can be placed on a circuit, and fewer circuits and panels, and smaller transformers might be required.

(a) True (b) False

29. What size transformer is required for a 100A, 240V, 1Ø noncontinuous load (unity power factor)?

(a) 15 kVA (b) 25 kVA (c) 37.5 kVA (d) 50 kVA

30. What size transformer is required for a 100A, 240V, 1Ø noncontinuous load that has a power factor of 85 percent?

(a) 15 kVA (b) 25 kVA (c) 37.5 kVA (d) 50 kVA

31. How many 20A, 120V circuits are required for forty-two, 300W incandescent luminaires (noncontinuous load)?

(a) 3 circuits (b) 4 circuits (c) 5 circuits (d) 6 circuits

32. How many 20A, 120V circuits are required for forty-two, 300W luminaires (noncontinuous load) that have a power factor of 85 percent?

(a) 4 circuits (b) 5 circuits (c) 7 circuits (d) 8 circuits

19.8 Efficiency

33. Efficiency describes how much input energy is used for its intended purpose.

(a) True (b) False

19.9 Efficiency Formulas

34. If the output is 1,600W and the equipment is 88 percent efficient, what are the input amperes at 120V?

(a) 10A (b) 15A (c) 20A (d) 25A

Chapter 6
Motors, Generators and Transformers

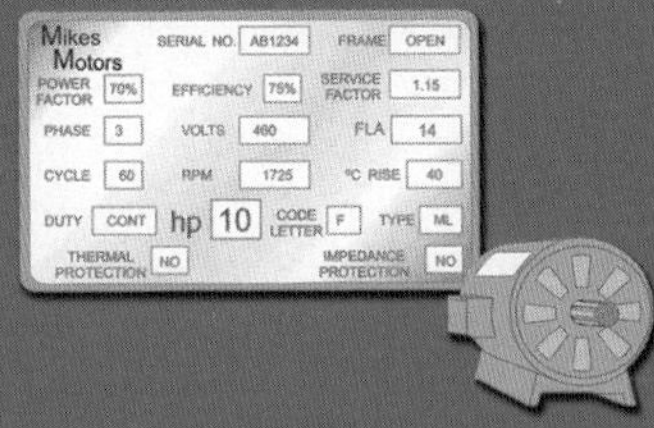

Unit 20 – Motors

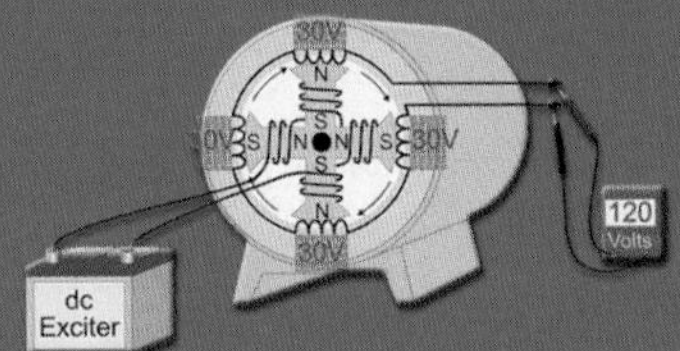

Unit 21 – Generators

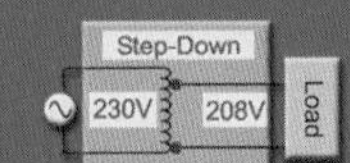

Unit 22 – Transformers

Notes

UNIT 20 Motors

Introduction

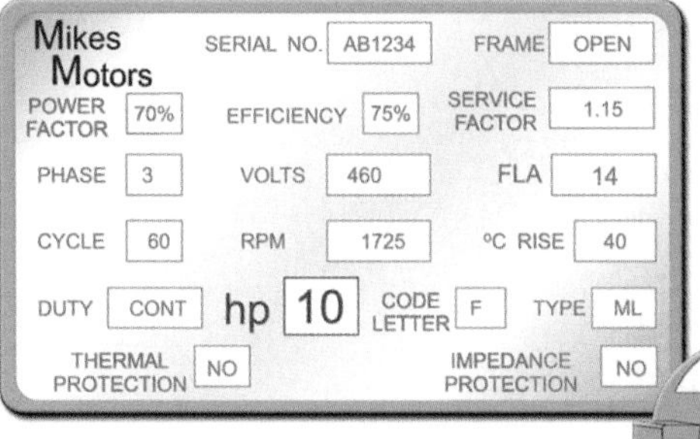

The electric motor is one of the most prevalent loads on the electrical system of commercial and industrial occupancies. Think of the sheer number of things that must move in some way. Every pump, fan, compressor, conveyor, or other device that moves material or objects, requires either a motor or an engine. A motor is a device that converts energy into motion; an engine is a device that burns fuel to release energy that it turns into motion. Computers contain many small motors (in the fans, DVDs, CD drives, hard drives, and other devices), as do automobiles (which have steadily been replacing vacuum-operated and fluid-operated motors with electrically-operated motors). Where there's motion, there's probably an electric motor.

An electrician typically works with various configurations of motors that are powered by 120V, 240V, or 480V supplies. A solid understanding of motor basics, motor calculations, motor circuits, and motor controls is essential for success as an electrician. The goal of this unit is to provide you with that basic understanding and prepare you for learning more about this important subject.

PART A—MOTOR BASICS

20.1 Motor Principles

A motor must have two opposing magnetic fields in order to rotate.

Stator

The stationary field winding of a motor is mounted on the stator, which is the part of the motor that does not turn. For permanent magnet motors, there is no field winding because the field is produced by permanent magnets.

Rotor

The rotating part of the motor is referred to as either the "rotor" or the "armature."

20.2 Dual-Voltage AC Motors

Dual-voltage ac motors are made with two field windings, each rated for the lower of two possible operating voltages. The field windings are connected in parallel for low-voltage operation and in series for high-voltage operation.

For example, a 460/230V dual-rated motor has its windings in series if connected to a 460V source, or the windings will be in parallel if connected to a 230V source. **Figure 20–1**

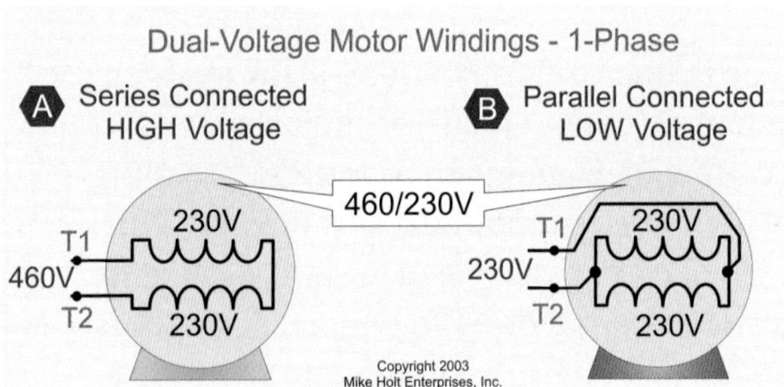

Figure 20–1

AUTHOR'S COMMENT: According to the *NEC*, voltages are described as either nominal voltage or rated voltage. Nominal voltage is in reference to the approximate expected utility voltage, for example a 120/240V system. However, because of circuit voltage drop, the actual voltage at the load will be less than 120V or 240V. Therefore the rated voltage of equipment would have a value less than the nominal system voltage. For example 115V/230V.

20.3 Motor Horsepower Rating

Motors are used to convert electrical energy into mechanical work. The output mechanical work of a motor is measured or rated in horsepower.

AUTHOR'S COMMENT: The conversion of mechanical work to electrical energy is measured in watts, where one horsepower = 746W.

CAUTION: *The 746W per horsepower is the electrical output value for each horsepower. This value is not the input electrical rating required to calculate the motor nameplate current rating.*

Horsepower Example

What size motor, in horsepower, is used to produce a 15 kW output? **Figure 20–2**

(a) 5 hp (b) 10 hp
(c) 20 hp (d) 30 hp

• Answer: (c) 20 hp

$$\text{Horsepower} = \frac{\text{Output Watts}}{746}$$

$$\text{Horsepower} = \frac{15{,}000\text{W}}{746\text{W}}$$

Horsepower = 20 hp

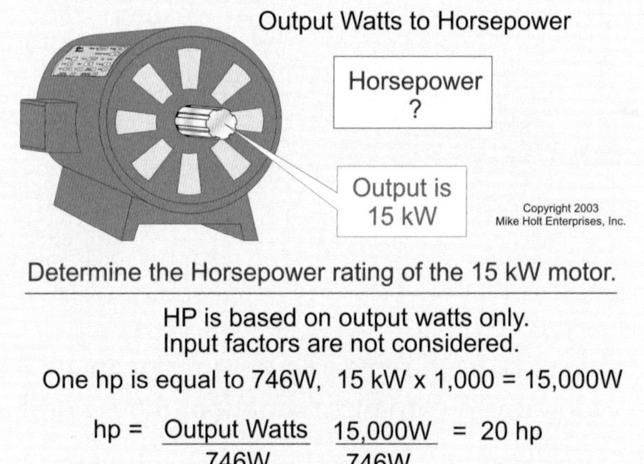

Output Watts to Horsepower
Horsepower ?
Output is 15 kW
Copyright 2003 Mike Holt Enterprises, Inc.
Determine the Horsepower rating of the 15 kW motor.
HP is based on output watts only.
Input factors are not considered.
One hp is equal to 746W, 15 kW x 1,000 = 15,000W
hp = Output Watts / 746W 15,000W / 746W = 20 hp

Figure 20–2

Output Watt Example

What is the output watts rating of a 10 hp, ac, 480V, 3Ø motor with an efficiency of 75 percent and power factor of 70 percent? **Figure 20–3**

(a) 5 kW (b) 7.5 kVA
(c) 7.5 kW (d) none of these

• Answer: (c) 7.5 kW

Output Watts = hp x 746W

Output Watts = 10 hp x 746W

Output Watts = 7,460W

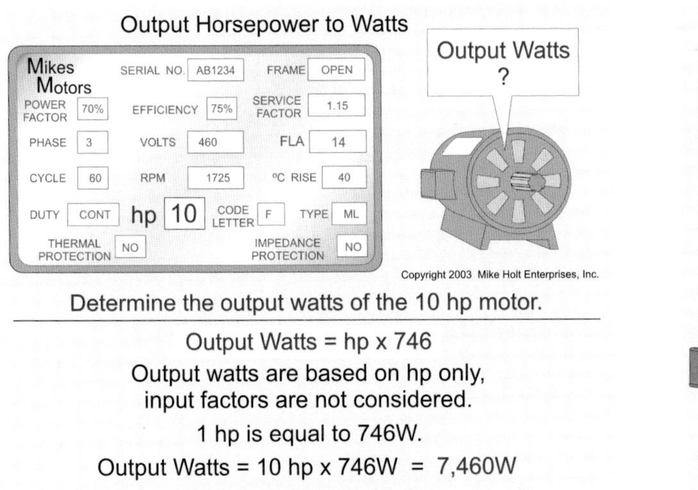

Figure 20–3

Efficiency, power factor, phases, and voltage have nothing to do with determining the output watts of a motor!

Calculating motor output watts can, however, help you understand how motor nameplate current numbers are developed.

20.4 Motor Current Ratings

Motor Full-Load Ampere (FLA) Rating

The motor nameplate full-load ampere rating is identified as FLA. The FLA rating is the current rating in amperes that the motor draws while carrying its rated horsepower load at its rated voltage. Figure 20–4

Actual Motor Current

The actual current drawn by the motor is dependent upon the load on the motor and the actual operating voltage at the motor terminals. That is, if the load increases, the current also increases and/or if the motor operates at a voltage below its nameplate rating, the operating current will increase.

> **CAUTION:** *To prevent damage to motor windings from excessive heat (because of excessive current), never place a load on the motor above its horsepower rating and/or be sure the voltage source matches the motor's voltage rating.*

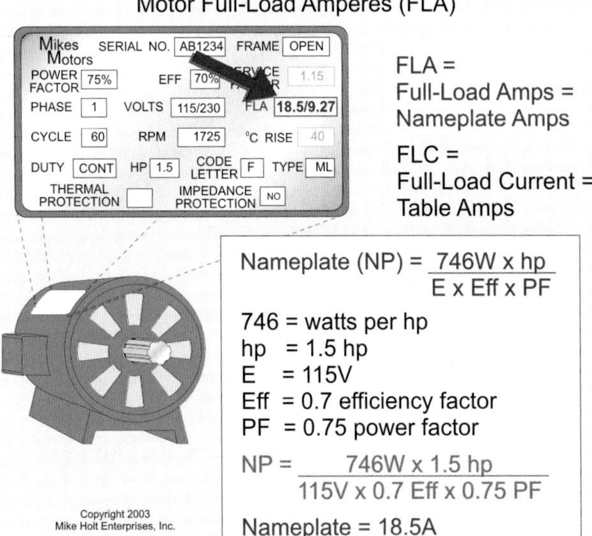

Figure 20–4

Motor Full-Load Current (FLC) Rating

The motor nameplate FLA rating is not to be used when sizing motor conductor size or circuit protection. According to the *NEC*, we must size these electrical components in accordance with the motor Full-Load Current (FLC) rating as listed in the *NEC* Tables. Figure 20–5

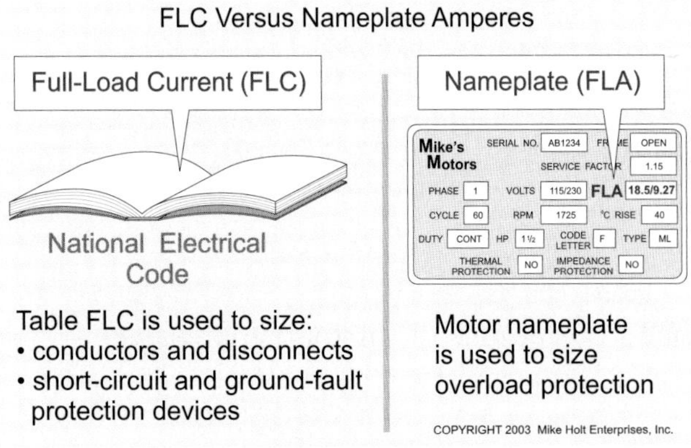

Figure 20–5

> **AUTHOR'S COMMENT:** This topic is beyond the scope of this textbook.

20.5 Calculating Motor FLA

The motor nameplate full-load ampere (FLA) rating can be determined by:

Single-Phase

$$FLA = \frac{\text{Motor hp x 746W}}{\text{E x Eff x PF}}$$

Three-Phase

$$FLA = \frac{\text{Motor hp x 746W}}{\text{E x } \sqrt{3} \text{ x Eff x PF}}$$

Single-Phase Motor FLA Example

What is the motor nameplate FLA rating for a 7.5 hp motor, 230V, 1Ø, having an efficiency of 93 percent and a power factor of 87 percent? **Figure 20–6**

(a) 16A (b) 24A
(c) 19A (d) 30A

• Answer: (d) 30A

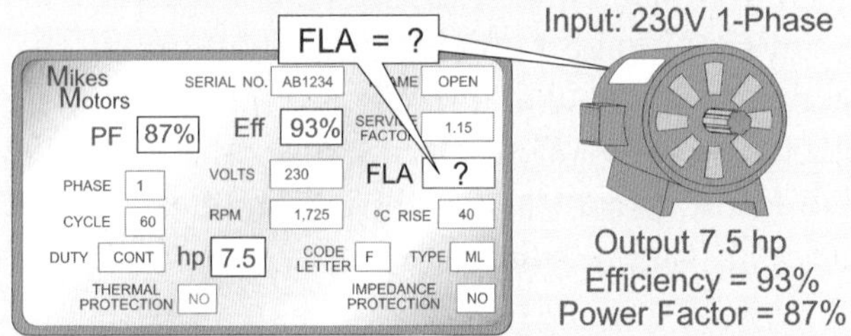

Figure 20–6

Step 1 Determine the motor output watts:
Output Watts = hp x 746W
Output Watts = 7.5 hp x 746W
Output Watts = 5,595W

Step 2 Determine the motor input watts:

$$\text{Input} = \frac{\text{Output}}{\text{Eff}}$$

$$\text{Input} = \frac{5{,}595W}{0.93 \text{ Eff}}$$

Input = 6,016W

Step 3 Determine the motor input VA:

$$VA = \frac{\text{Watts}}{PF}$$

$$VA = \frac{6{,}016W}{0.87 \text{ PF}}$$

VA = 6,915 VA

Step 4 Determine the motor amperes:

$$FLA = \frac{VA}{E}$$

$$FLA = \frac{6{,}915W}{230V}$$

FLA = 30A

OR

$$FLA = \frac{\text{hp} \times 746W}{\text{E x Eff x PF}}$$

$$FLA = \frac{\text{7.5 hp x 746W}}{\text{230V x 0.93 Eff x 0.87 PF}}$$

FLA = 30A

Three-Phase Motor FLA Example

What is the motor FLA rating for a 40 hp, 208V, 3Ø motor, having an efficiency rating of 80 percent and a power factor of 90 percent?

(a) 76A (b) 84A
(c) 99A (d) 115A

• Answer: (d) 115A

Step 1 Determine the motor output watts:

Output Watts = hp x 746W

Output Watts = 40 hp x 746W

Output Watts = 29,840W

Step 2 Determine the motor input watts:

$$\text{Input Watts} = \frac{\text{Output}}{\text{Eff}}$$

$$\text{Input Watts} = \frac{29{,}840W}{0.80 \text{ Eff}}$$

Input Watts = 37,300W

Step 3 Determine the motor input VA:

$$VA = \frac{Watts}{PF}$$

$$VA = \frac{37{,}300W}{0.90\ PF}$$

$$VA = 41{,}444\ VA$$

Step 4 Determine the motor amperes:

$$FLA = \frac{VA}{(E \times \sqrt{3})}$$

$$FLA = \frac{41{,}444\ VA}{(208V \times 1.732)}$$

$$FLA = 115A$$

OR

$$FLA = \frac{hp \times 746W}{E \times \sqrt{3} \times Eff \times PF}$$

$$FLA = \frac{40\ hp \times 746W}{208V \times 1.732 \times 0.8\ Eff \times 0.9\ PF}$$

$$FLA = 115A$$

20.6 Motor-Starting Current

When voltage is first applied to the field winding of an induction motor, only the conductor resistance opposes the flow of current through the motor winding. Because the conductor resistance is so low, the motor will have a very large inrush current (a minimum of six times the full-load ampere rating). Figure 20–7A

20.7 Motor-Running Current

However, once the rotor begins turning, the rotor-bars (winding) will be increasingly cut by the stationary magnetic field, resulting in an increasing counter-electromotive force. Figure 20–7B

We learned previously that the CEMF opposes the applied voltage, resulting in an increased opposition to current flow within the conductor. This is called inductive reactance. The increase in inductive reactance, because of self-induction, causes the impedance of the conductor winding to increase and this results in a reduction of current flow.

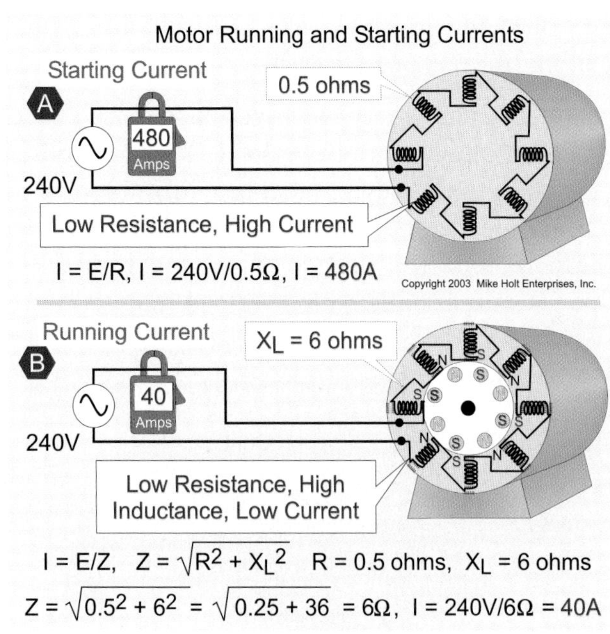

Figure 20–7

20.8 Motor Locked-Rotor Current (LRC)

If the rotating part of the motor winding (armature) becomes jammed so that it cannot rotate, no CEMF will be produced in the motor winding. This results in a decrease in conductor impedance to the point that it's effectively a short circuit. Result—the motor operates at locked-rotor current (LRC), which is about six times the running current value, and this will cause the motor winding to overheat to the point that it will be destroyed if the current is not quickly stopped.

AUTHOR'S COMMENT: The *National Electrical Code* requires most motors to be provided with overcurrent protection to prevent damage to the motor winding because of locked-rotor current.

20.9 Motor Overload Protection

Motors must be protected against excessive winding heat. Motors must not be overloaded, they must operate near their nameplate voltage, and measures must be taken to prevent the motor from jamming (LRC). If a motor is overloaded or if it operates at a voltage below its rating, the operating current can increase to a value above the motor full-load amperes (FLA) rating. The excessive operating current may damage the motor winding from excessive heat.

Figure 20–8 shows a type of overload device called a melting-alloy type of overload. There are other types of overload devices that provide motor overload protection, but they do it in different ways. These include the dashpot type and bimetallic type, as well as solid-state overload relays.

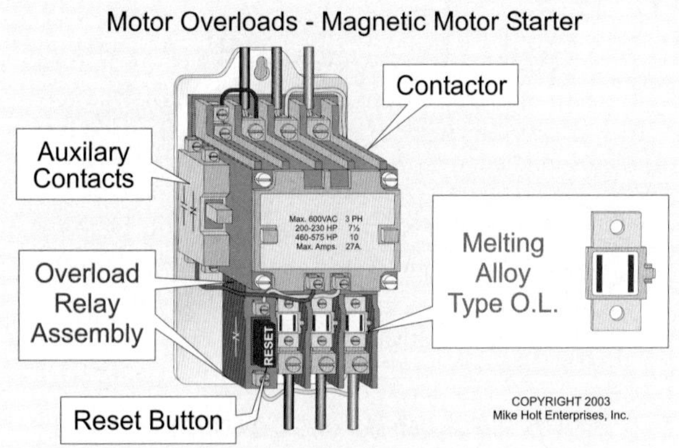

Figure 20–8

AUTHOR'S COMMENT: Motors are designed to operate with an inrush current of six to eight times the motor-rated FLA for short periods of time without damage to the motor windings. **Figure 20–9**

However, if a motor operates at LRC for a prolonged period of time, the motor insulation and lubrication can be destroyed by excessive heat. Most motors can operate at 600 percent of motor FLA satisfactorily for a period of less than one minute or 300 percent of the motor FLA for not more than three minutes.

NEC Requirement

To protect against excessive heat from an overload, the *National Electrical Code* requires standard overload protection devices to be sized at 115 to 125 percent of the motor FLA rating. **Figure 20–10**

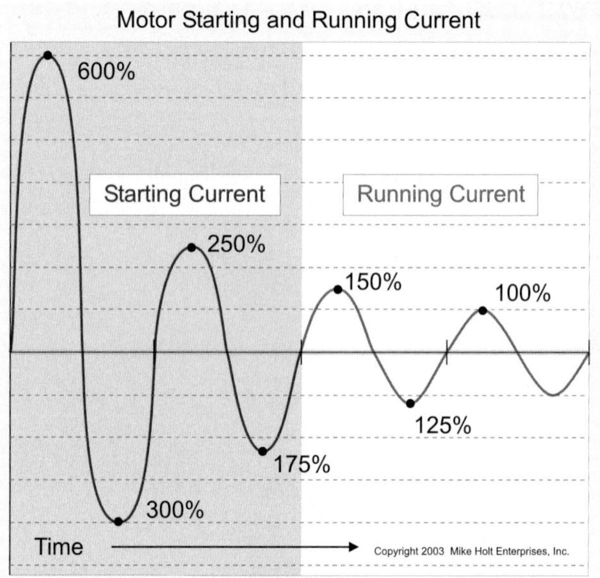

Figure 20–9

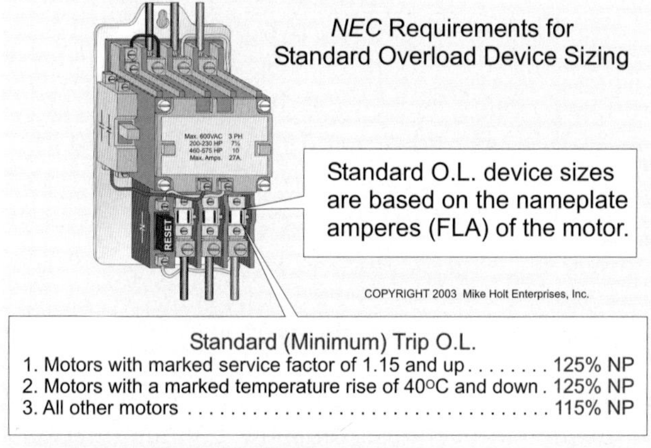

NEC Requirements for Standard Overload Device Sizing
Standard O.L. device sizes are based on the nameplate amperes (FLA) of the motor.
RESET
COPYRIGHT 2003 Mike Holt Enterprises, Inc.

Standard (Minimum) Trip O.L.
1. Motors with marked service factor of 1.15 and up . . . . 125% NP
2. Motors with a marked temperature rise of 40°C and down . 125% NP
3. All other motors . . . . 115% NP

Figure 20–10

PART B—DIRECT-CURRENT MOTORS

20.10 Direct-Current Motor Principles

DC motors use brushes (pieces of conductive carbon) with springs to hold them in contact with a commutator. A commutator is a ring around the rotor shaft that has segments with insulation between them.

A commutator is necessary for a dc motor because the maximum torque on the rotor is developed when the active rotor winding opposes the magnetic field of the stator. As the winding passes this point, less torque is developed. As the commutator

turns, the carbon brushes come into contact with the next set of rotor windings, which are in the proper position to oppose the stator field and keep the rotor moving. As the rotor turns, the brush-commutator set always supplies power to the rotor windings that are in the correct position to develop maximum torque.

20.11 Direct-Current Motor Types

Shunt-Wound DC Motor

One of the great advantages of the shunt-wound dc motor (whose armature and field are in parallel) is its ability to maintain a constant speed under load. If the speed of a dc motor begins to increase, the armature will cut through the electromagnetic field at an increasing rate. This results in a greater armature CEMF, which acts to cut down on the increased armature current, resulting in the motor slowing back down.

Placing a load on a dc motor causes the motor to slow down, which reduces the rate at which the armature is cut by the field flux lines. As a result, the armature CEMF decreases, resulting in an increase in the applied armature voltage and current. The increase in current results in an increase in motor speed. This gives shunt-wound dc motors a built-in system for regulating their own speed. For these reasons, computer disk drives and recording equipment use dc motors exclusively.

Series-Wound DC Motor

Series-wound dc motors (those in which the field winding and the armature winding are connected in series) have poor speed regulation, and slow down considerably when a load is applied. When unloaded, they often run at very high rpms. However, series dc motors have very good torque characteristics. One of the best examples of a series-wound dc motor is the starter motor on your automobile, which has very high torque to start the engine and is connected to a load so that it does not overspeed.

20.12 Reversing the Rotation of a DC Motor

To reverse the rotation of a dc motor, you must reverse either the stator field or the armature magnetic field. This is accomplished by reversing either the field or armature current. Because most dc motors have the field and armature windings fed from the same dc power supply, reversing the polarity of the power supply will change the field and armature simultaneously. This will result in the motor continuing to run in the same direction. Figure 20–11

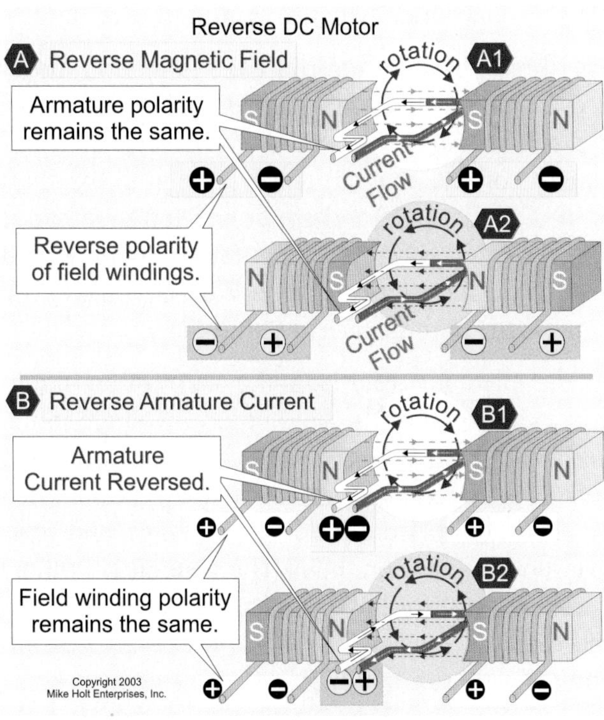

Figure 20–11

PART C—ALTERNATING-CURRENT MOTORS

20.13 AC Induction Motor

In the ac induction motor, the stator produces a rotating magnetic field.

The rotor is a series of coils (windings) that are connected in a closed loop. The rotating magnetic field of the stator induces (thus, induction motor) currents flowing in the rotor windings. These rotor currents generate a magnetic field in opposition to the magnetic field of the stator, thereby causing the rotor to turn. It is also for this reason that the rotor of an induction motor always turns with an rpm slightly less than the rpm of the stator's magnetic field.

20.14 Alternating-Current Motor Types

Squirrel-Cage Induction Motor

The most prevalent type of an ac motor is the induction motor, which uses no physical connection between its rotating member (the rotor), and the stationary member surrounding it (the stator).

The three-phase ac squirrel-cage induction motor is used in almost all major industrial applications. It is called a squirrel-cage motor because the rotor consists of bars that are either parallel to the shaft or at a slight angle and are connected together at the ends by shorting rings. These bars would resemble a hamster or squirrel cage if you were to remove the core material around them.

As the magnetic field from the stator of an induction motor rotates, the field induces voltage in the rotor bars as it cuts across them. Conditions for generator action exist—a conductor (rotor bars), a magnetic field (from the field winding), and relative motion between them. The generated voltage causes current to flow from bar to bar through the shorting rings. The conditions for motor action are now present—a conductor (each rotor bar) has current flowing through it in a magnetic field (from the stator field). This produces torque in the rotor causing it to turn.

Synchronous Motor

In a synchronous motor, the rotor is actually locked in step with the rotating stator field and is dragged along at the synchronous speed of the rotating magnetic field. Synchronous motors maintain their speed with a high degree of accuracy.

They are often found in large industrial facilities driving loads such as compressors, crushers, and large pumps. Sometimes they are operated unloaded, meaning that nothing is attached to their shafts. In this application, the synchronous motor is being operated "overexcited," meaning that a large amount of dc current is being fed into the rotor through the slip rings. The synchronous motor acts as though it were a large capacitor when it is in this condition and can be used for power factor correction.

Wound-Rotor Motor

Wound-rotor induction motors are used only in special applications because of their complexity. Wound-rotor induction motors only operate on three-phase ac power. They are similar to an induction motor; however, the rotor windings are connected in a wye configuration and the points of the wye are brought out through slip rings to an external controller. Resistors are usually inserted into the rotor winding circuit during start-up in order to reduce the inrush current. As the motor increases speed, the value of the resistance is changed to lower values. Ultimately, the rotor windings are shorted, thereby allowing the motor to achieve full speed.

The wound-rotor motor can also be used in applications that require some speed control. Today, however, it is much more customary to use a Variable Speed Drive coupled to an induction motor.

Universal Motor

Universal motors are fractional horsepower motors that operate equally well on ac and dc. They are used for vacuum cleaners, electric drills, mixers, and light household appliances. These motors have the inherent disadvantages associated with dc motors, which is the need for commutation. The problem with commutation is that as the motor operates, motor parts rub against each other and the motor wears itself out. Induction-type ac motors do not depend on commutation for operation.

20.15 Reversing the Rotation of an AC Motor

Swapping any two of the three line conductors can reverse a three-phase ac motor's rotation. Industry practice is to reverse Line 1 and Line 3. Figure 20–12

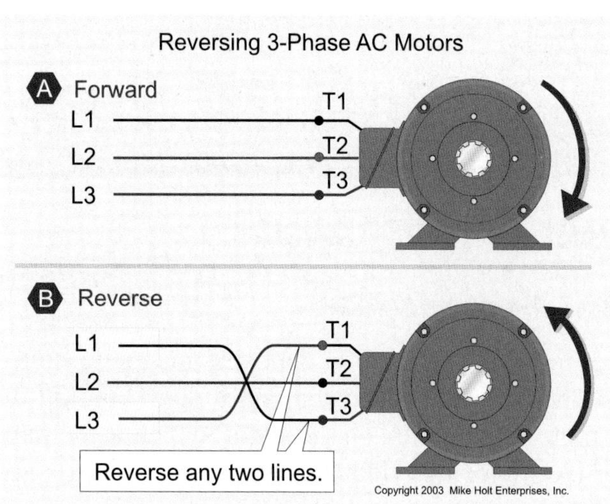

Figure 20–12

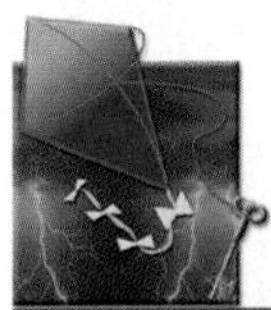

Unit 20 Summary

PART A—MOTOR BASICS

20.1 Motor Principles

A motor must have two opposing magnetic fields in order to rotate. The stationary field winding of a motor is mounted on the stator, which is the part of the motor that does not turn. The rotating part of the motor is referred to as either the "rotor" or the "armature."

20.2 Dual-Voltage AC Motors

Dual-voltage ac motors are made with two field windings, each rated for the lower of two possible operating voltages. The field windings are connected in parallel for low-voltage operation and in series for high-voltage operation.

20.3 Motor Horsepower Rating

Motors are used to convert electrical energy into mechanical work. The output mechanical work of a motor is measured or rated in horsepower. A good conversion to remember is 1 hp = 746W.

20.4 Motor Current Ratings

Motor Full-Load Ampere (FLA) Rating

The FLA rating is the current rating in amperes that the motor draws while carrying its rated horsepower load at its rated voltage.

Actual Motor Current

The actual current drawn by the motor is dependent upon the load on the motor and the actual operating voltage at the motor terminals.

Motor Full-Load Current Rating (FLC)

According to the *NEC*, we must size these electrical components in accordance with the motor Full-Load Current (FLC) rating as listed in the *NEC* Tables.

20.5 Calculating Motor FLA

The motor nameplate full-load ampere (FLA) rating can be determined by:

Single-Phase

$$FLA = \frac{\text{Motor hp x 746W}}{\text{E x Eff x PF}}$$

Three-Phase

$$FLA = \frac{\text{Motor hp x 746W}}{\text{E x } \sqrt{3} \text{ x Eff x PF}}$$

20.6 Motor-Starting Current

When voltage is first applied to the field winding of an induction motor, only the conductor resistance opposes the flow of current through the motor winding. Because the conductor resistance is so low, the motor will have a very large inrush current (a minimum of six times the full-load ampere rating).

20.7 Motor-Running Current

Once the motor begins turning, the rotor-bars (winding) will be increasingly cut by the stationary magnetic field, resulting in an increasing counter-electromotive force.

20.8 Motor Locked-Rotor Current (LRC)

If the rotating part of the motor winding (armature) is jammed so that it cannot rotate, no CEMF will be produced in the motor winding. The low impedance of this winding, without the aid of the CEMF, will cause the motor to operate at locked-rotor current. This results in a decrease in conductor impedance to the point that it's effectively

a short circuit. Result—the motor operates at locked-rotor current (LRC), which is at least six times the running current value, and this will cause the motor windings to overheat to the point that they will be destroyed if the current is not quickly stopped.

20.9 Motor Overload Protection

Motors must be protected against excessive winding heat. If a motor is overloaded, or if it operates at a voltage below its rating, the operating current can increase to a value above the motor full-load amperes (FLA) rating. The excessive operating current may damage the motor winding from excessive heat.

NEC Requirement

To protect against excessive heat from an overload, the *National Electrical Code* requires standard overload protection devices to be sized at 115 to 125 percent of the motor FLA rating.

PART B—DIRECT-CURRENT MOTORS

20.10 Direct-Current Motor Principles

DC motors use brushes (pieces of conductive carbon) with springs to hold them in contact with a commutator.

20.11 Direct-Current Types

Shunt-Wound DC Motor

One of the great advantages of the shunt-wound dc motor (whose armature and field are in parallel) is its ability to maintain a constant speed under load.

Series-Wound DC Motor

Series-wound dc motors (those in which the field winding and the armature winding are connected in series) have poor speed regulation, and slow down considerably when a load is applied. When unloaded, they often run at very high rpms. However, these dc motors have very good torque characteristics and are used as starter motors for engines.

20.12 Reversing the Rotation of a DC Motor

To reverse the rotation of a dc motor, you must reverse either the stator field or the armature magnetic field.

PART C—ALTERNATING-CURRENT MOTORS

20.13 AC Induction Motor

In the ac induction motor, the stator produces a rotating magnetic field.

20.14 Alternating-Current Motor Types

Squirrel-Cage Induction Motor

The most prevalent type of ac motor is the induction motor, which uses no physical connection between its rotating member (the rotor), and the stationary member surrounding it (the stator).

Synchronous Motor

In a synchronous motor, the rotor is actually locked in step with the rotating stator field and is dragged along at the synchronous speed of the rotating magnetic field. Synchronous motors maintain their speed with a high degree of accuracy.

Wound-Rotor Motor

Wound-rotor induction motors are used only in special applications because of their complexity. Wound-rotor induction motors only operate on three-phase ac power.

The wound-rotor motor can also be used in applications that require some speed control. Today, however, it is much more customary to use a Variable Speed Drive coupled to an induction motor.

Universal Motor

Universal motors are fractional horsepower motors that operate equally well on ac and dc. The problem with commutation is that as the motor operates, motor parts rub against each other and the motor wears itself out. Induction-type ac motors do not depend on commutation for operation.

20.15 Reversing the Rotation of an AC Motor

Swapping any two of the three line conductors can reverse a three-phase ac motor's rotation.

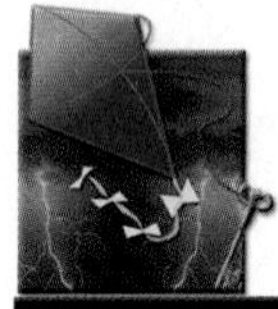

Unit 20 Conclusion

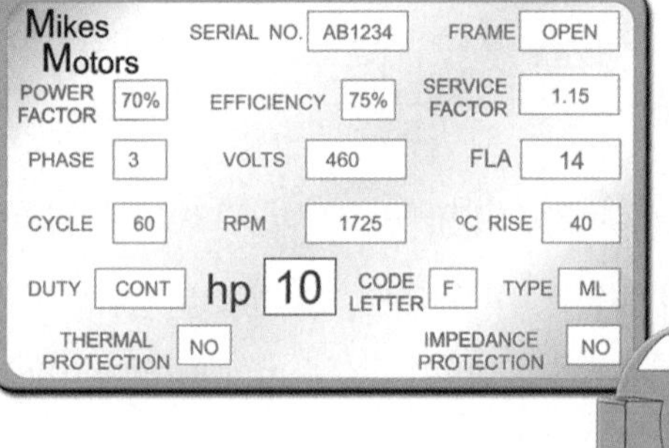

Article 430 of the *National Electrical Code* addresses motors, motor circuits, and motor controllers. It is the largest of all the *NEC* articles. Now that you have studied basic motor theory, motor calculations, motor circuits, and motor controls, you can see why this is so. Although you have learned much here, you would benefit from learning even more, especially if you are going to do much commercial or industrial work.

Words to Live By: *Laziness and poverty are cousins.*

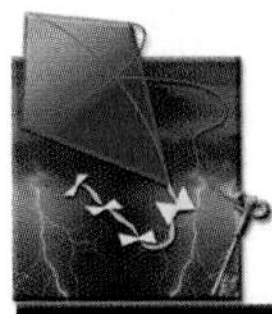

Unit 20 Practice Questions

PART A—MOTOR BASICS

20.1 Motor Principles

1. A motor must have two opposing magnetic fields in order to rotate. The stationary field winding is mounted on the stator, and the rotating part is referred to as the armature.

   (a) True (b) False

20.2 Dual-Voltage AC Motors

2. Dual-voltage ac motors are made with two field windings. The field windings are connected in _____ for low-voltage operation and in _____ for high-voltage operation.

   (a) series, parallel (b) parallel, series (c) series, series (d) parallel, parallel

3. For a dual-voltage 230/460V motor, the field windings are connected in parallel for _____ operation and in series for _____ operation.

   (a) 230V, 460V (b) 460V, 230V (c) 230V, 230V (d) 460V, 460V

20.3 Motor Horsepower Rating

4. Motors are used to convert electrical energy into mechanical work and the output mechanical work of a motor is rated in horsepower. 1 hp = _____.

   (a) 476W (b) 674W (c) 746W (d) 840W

5. What size motor, in horsepower, is required to produce 30 kW output?

   (a) 20 hp (b) 30 hp (c) 40 hp (d) 50 hp

6. What is the output of a 15 hp motor?

   (a) 11 kW (b) 15 kW (c) 22 kW (d) 31 kW

7. What is the approximate output of a 5 hp, 3Ø, 480V motor?

   (a) 3.75 kW (b) 4.75 kW (c) 6.75 kW (d) 7.75 kW

20.4 Motor Current Ratings

8. The nameplate motor FLA rating describes the motor current rating when it carries its rated horsepower load at its rated _____.

   (a) power (b) resistance (c) CEMF (d) voltage

9. The actual motor current is dependent upon the load on the motor and the operating voltage at the motor terminals.

   (a) True (b) False

10. The motor FLA rating is used when sizing motor conductor size or circuit protection.

    (a) True (b) False

20.5 Calculating Motor FLA

11. What is the nameplate FLA for a 5 hp, 230V, 1Ø motor, with 93 percent power factor and 87 percent efficiency?

    (a) 10A (b) 20A (c) 28A (d) 35A

12. What is the nameplate FLA of a 20 hp, 208V, 3Ø motor with 90 percent power factor and 80 percent efficiency?

    (a) 51A (b) 58A (c) 65A (d) 80A

20.6 Motor-Starting Current

13. When a motor starts, the current drawn is at least _____ times the motor FLA; this is known as motor locked-rotor amperes (LRA).

    (a) 1.25 (b) 0.8 (c) 3 (d) 6

20.7 Motor-Running Current

14. Once a motor begins turning, the rotor winding will be increasingly cut by the stationary magnetic field, resulting in an increasing counter-electromotive force.

    (a) True (b) False

20.8 Motor Locked-Rotor Current (LRC)

15. If the rotating part of the motor winding is jammed so that it cannot rotate, no CEMF will be produced in the motor winding. Result—the motor operates at _____ and the windings will be destroyed by excessive heat.

    (a) FLA (b) FLC (c) LRC (d) any of these

20.9 Motor Overload Protection

16. Motors must be protected against excessive winding heat by a properly sized overload protection device, based on the motor _____ current rating.

(a) FLA (b) FLC (c) LRC (d) any of these

PART B—DIRECT-CURRENT MOTORS

20.10 Direct-Current Motor Principles

17. DC motors use brushes with springs to hold them in contact with a(n) _____.

(a) rotor (b) stator (c) armature (d) commutator

20.11 Direct-Current Types

18. If the speed of a dc motor is increased, the armature will cut through the field at an increasing rate, resulting in a lower CEMF that acts to cut down on the increased armature current, which slows the motor back down.

(a) True (b) False

19. Placing a load on a dc motor causes the motor to slow down, which increases the rate at which the field flux lines are being cut by the armature. As a result, the armature CEMF increases resulting in an increase in the applied armature voltage and current. The increase in current results in increased motor speed.

(a) True (b) False

20.12 Reversing the Rotation of a DC Motor

20. To reverse the rotation of a dc motor, you must reverse the _____.

(a) stator field (b) rotor field (c) a and b (d) a or b

PART C—ALTERNATING-CURRENT MOTORS

20.13 AC Induction Motor

21. In the ac induction motor, the stator produces a rotating magnetic field that induces current in the rotor windings. The rotor current generates a magnetic field in opposition to the magnetic field of the stator, thereby causing the rotor to turn.

(a) True (b) False

20.14 Alternating-Current Motor Types

22. In a(n) _____ motor, the rotor is actually locked in step with the rotating stator field and is dragged along at the speed of the rotating magnetic field.

    (a) wound-rotor (b) induction (c) synchronous (d) squirrel-cage

23. _____ motors are fractional horsepower motors that operate equally well on ac and dc and are used for vacuum cleaners, electric drills, mixers, and light household appliances.

    (a) AC (b) Universal (c) Wound-rotor (d) Synchronous

20.15 Reversing the Rotation of an AC Motor

24. Swapping _____ of the line conductors can reverse a 3Ø ac motor's rotation.

    (a) one (b) two (c) three (d) none of these

UNIT

21 Generators

Introduction

At one time, most electricians didn't need to know about generators or generator theory. At most facilities, power came from the central utility, and unless you were working at a power generation plant you were unlikely to come across a generator. Places like glass plants or paper mills often generated their own electricity, but the typical maintenance and construction electrician almost never worked on these even if assigned to the plant. Data centers, few that there were, had their own power generation capabilities for backup situations.

Today, generators are moving from "the exception" status to "the rule" status. They are ubiquitous. Almost any facility with critical operations, or whose owners consider electrical downtime to be extremely expensive, has on-site power generation. Examples include hospitals, data centers (now quite numerous), warehouses, food handling operations, hotels, casinos, banks, many manufacturing operations, and trucking companies. Even some residential buildings, including single-family dwellings, have on-site power generation.

21.1 Direct-Current Generator

Direct-current generators require a magnetic field to induce voltage in the rotating armature to create current flow. Small dc generators often use a permanent magnet for the magnetic field winding instead of an electromagnet. If the magnetic field is created by an electromagnet, the electromagnetic field is called the field winding. **Figure 21–1**

AUTHOR'S COMMENT: The stronger the magnetic field, the greater the induced armature current or generator output.

Excitation Current

The current used for the field winding is called the excitation current and can be supplied from the dc generator output or by an external dc voltage source. When the generator supplies the excitation

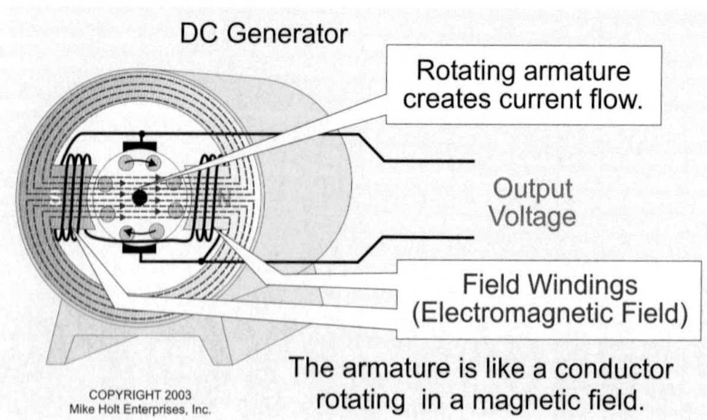

Figure 21–1

current, the generator is called a self-excited generator, **Figure 21–2**. If a separate dc power source is used to supply the excitation field, the generator is called a separately excited generator. **Figure 21–3**

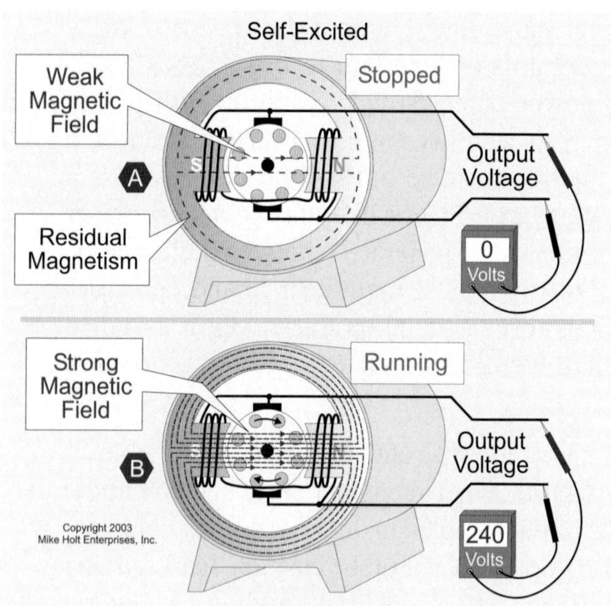

Figure 21–2

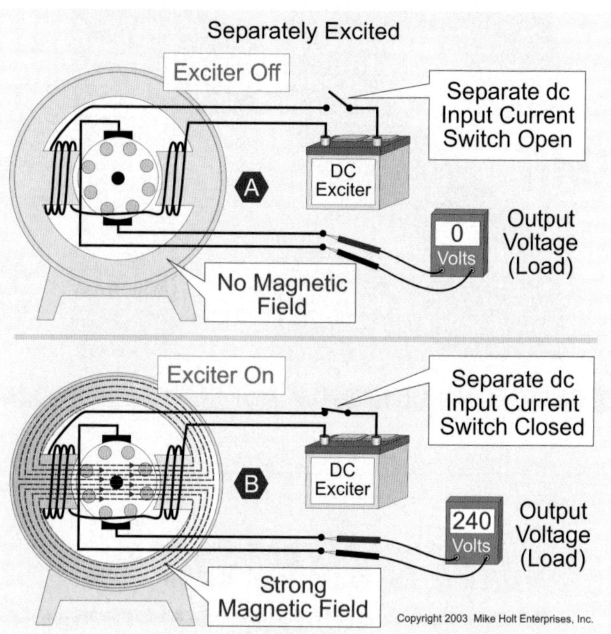

Figure 21–3

21.2 Alternating-Current Generator

The rotor of an ac generator contains the electromagnetic field, which develops the magnetic flux lines. When the rotor is made to rotate, the magnetic lines of force from the rotor electromagnet are made to cut through the stationary conductor coils. The relative motion between the lines of force and the conductor coils produces an electromotive force in the conductors. **Figure 21–4**

AUTHOR'S COMMENT: Some, very small, ac generators use permanent magnets for the magnetic field and the output voltage is taken off of the rotor's slip rings.

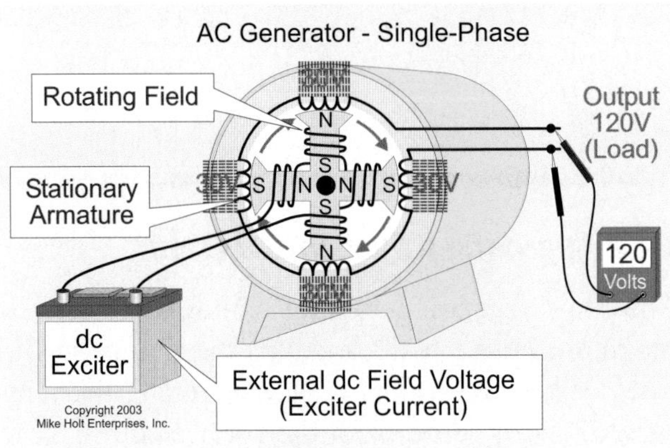

Figure 21–4

21.3 Three-Phase Generators

Three-phase ac generators have three equally spaced windings, all 120 degrees out-of-phase with each other. Figure 21–5

There are six leads from the windings of a three-phase generator which can be connected in series for delta connections or in parallel for wye connections.

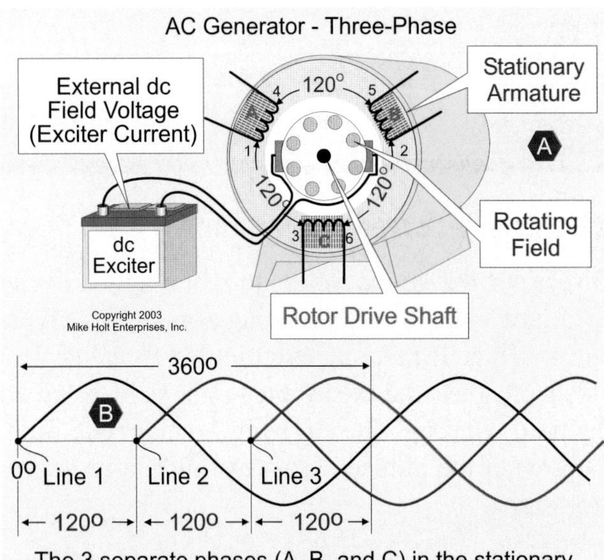

Figure 21–5

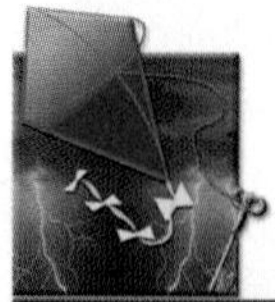

Unit 21 Summary

21.1 Direct-Current Generator

Direct-current generators require a magnetic field to induce voltage in the rotating armature to create current flow. If the magnetic field is created by an electromagnet, the electromagnetic field is called the field winding. The stronger the magnetic field, the greater the induced armature current or generator output.

Excitation Current

The current used for the field winding is called the excitation current and can be supplied from the dc generator output or by an external dc voltage source.

21.2 Alternating-Current Generator

The rotor of an ac generator contains the electromagnetic field which develops the magnetic flux lines. When the rotor is made to rotate, the magnetic lines of force from the rotor electromagnet are made to cut through the stationary conductor coils. The relative motion between the lines of force and the conductor coils produces an electromotive force in the conductors.

21.3 Three-Phase Generators

Three-phase ac generators have three equally spaced windings all 120 degrees out-of-phase with each other.

Unit 21 Conclusion

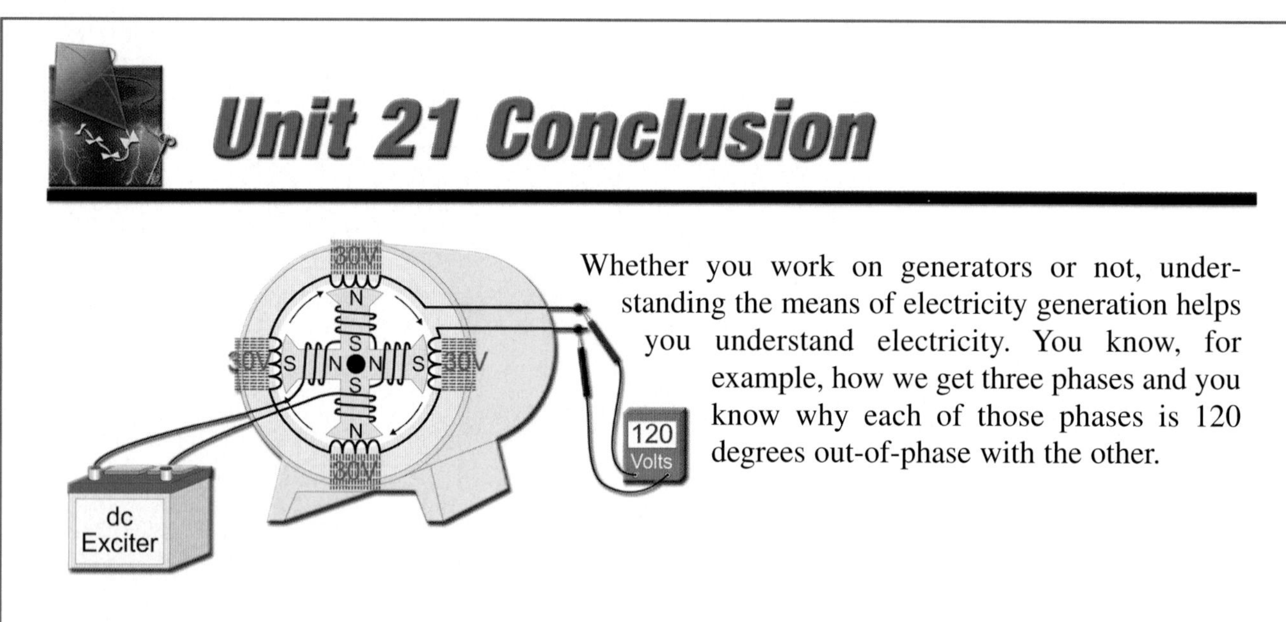

Whether you work on generators or not, understanding the means of electricity generation helps you understand electricity. You know, for example, how we get three phases and you know why each of those phases is 120 degrees out-of-phase with the other.

Words to Live By: *Take care of your character and your reputation will take care of itself.*

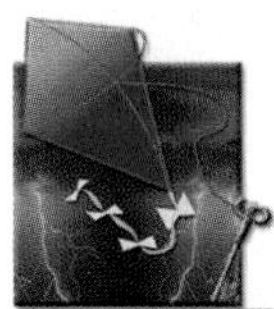

Unit 21 Practice Questions

21.1 Direct-Current Generator

1. Current for the field winding can be supplied from the dc generator output or by an external dc voltage source.

   (a) True (b) False

21.2 Alternating-Current Generator

2. The _____ of an ac generator contains the electromagnetic field, which cuts through the stationary conductor coils.

   (a) stator (b) rotor (c) coil (d) winding

21.3 Three-Phase Generators

3. Three-phase ac generators have three equally spaced windings, _____ out-of-phase with each other.

   (a) 90º (b) 120º (c) 180º (d) 360º

Notes

UNIT 22 Transformers

Introduction

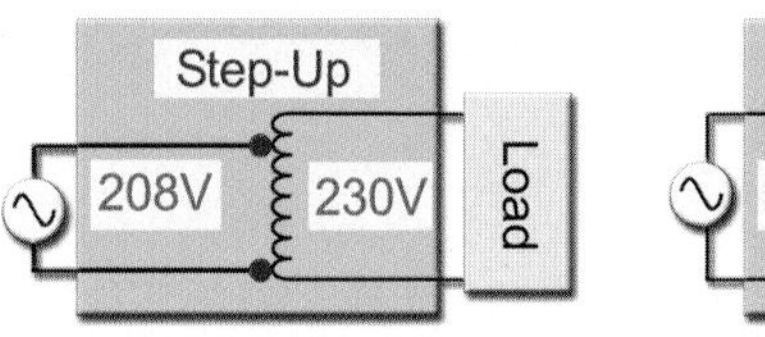

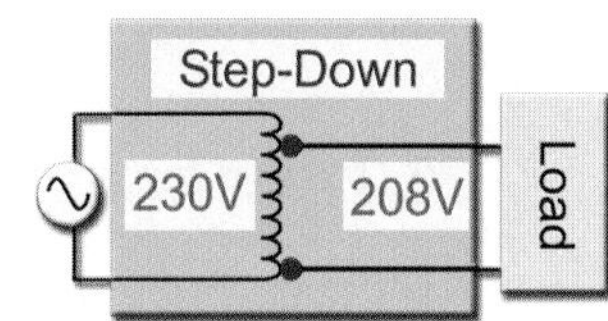

A transformer is a stationary device used to raise or lower voltage. It has the ability to transfer electrical energy (power) from one system to another with no physical connection between the two systems.

Some transformers, called isolation transformers, do not raise or lower the voltage. They are simply for the purpose of decoupling the primary from the secondary. This topic is beyond the scope of this textbook.

22.1 Transformer Basics

Primary Versus Secondary

The transformer winding connected to the voltage source is called the primary winding. The transformer winding connected to the load is called the secondary. Transformers are reversible, meaning that either winding can be used as the primary or secondary.

Mutual Induction

The energy transfer of a transformer is accomplished because the electromagnetic lines of force from the primary winding induce a voltage in the secondary winding. This process is called mutual induction. Figure 22–1

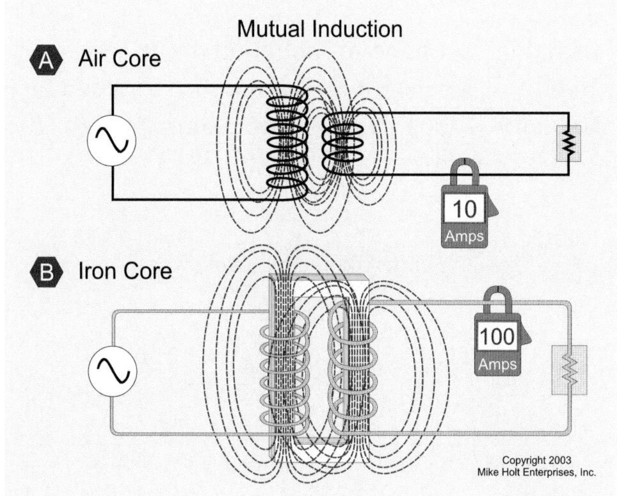

Figure 22–1

The voltage level that can be induced in the secondary winding, from the primary magnetic field, is a function of the number of secondary conductor loops (turns) that are cut by the primary electromagnetic field.

22.2 Secondary Induced Voltage

Voltage induced in the secondary winding of a transformer is equal to the sum of the voltages induced in each loop of the secondary winding.

For example, if a transformer had three windings on the secondary and each secondary winding had 80V induced, the secondary voltage would be 240V. Figure 22–2

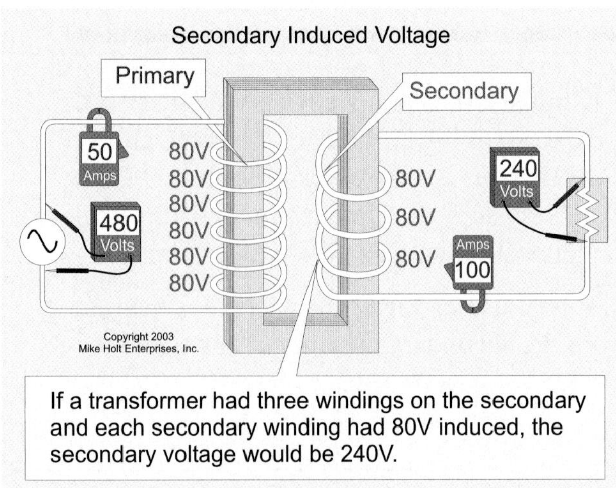

Figure 22–2

The induced voltage in each loop of the secondary winding is dependent on the number of secondary conductor loops (turns), as compared to the number of primary turns. Figure 22–3

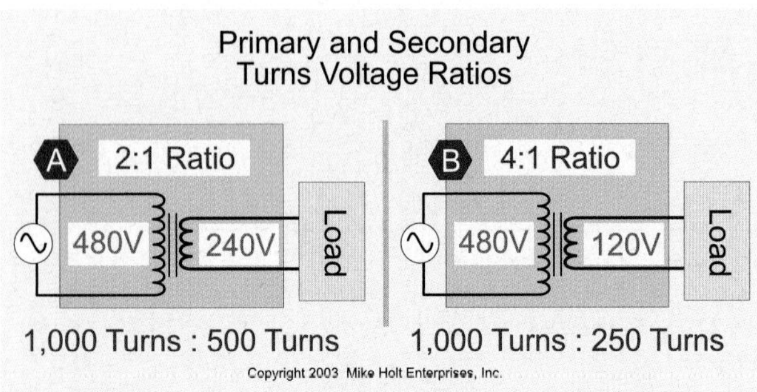

Figure 22–3

If both windings have the same number of turns, and if all of the magnetism set up by the primary passes through the secondary, the secondary will deliver the same voltage and power as the primary. Figure 22–4

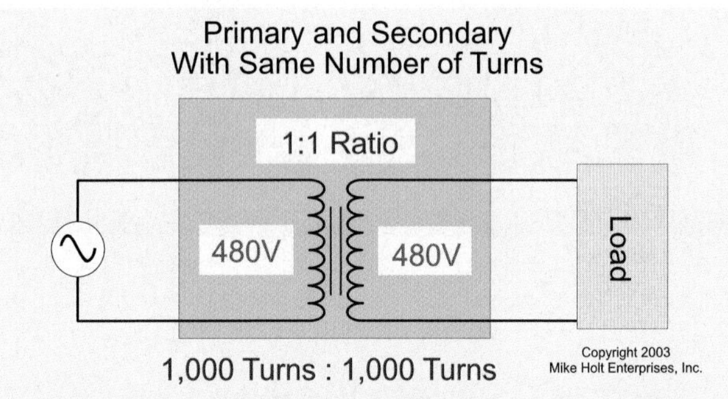

Figure 22–4

22.3 Autotransformers

Autotransformers use a common winding for both the primary and secondary and their purpose is to step the voltage up or down.

Autotransformers are often used to step the voltage up from 208V to 240V, or down from 240V to 208V. Figure 22–5

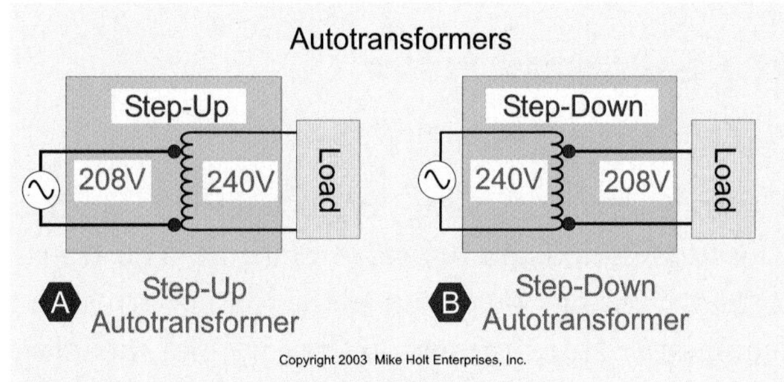

Figure 22–5

Step-Down Transformer

The secondary winding of a step-down transformer has fewer turns than the primary winding, resulting in a lower secondary voltage as compared to the primary.

Step-Up Transformer

The secondary winding of a step-up transformer has more turns than the primary winding, resulting in a higher secondary voltage as compared to the primary.

AUTHOR'S COMMENT: The disadvantage of an autotransformer is the lack of isolation between the primary and secondary conductors, but they are often used because they are inexpensive.

22.4 Power Losses

In an ideal transformer, all the primary power is transferred from the primary winding to the secondary winding, but real-world transformers have power losses because of conductor resistance, flux leakage, eddy currents, and hysteresis losses.

Conductor Resistance Loss

Transformer primary and secondary windings are generally made of many turns of copper. Conductor resistance is directly proportional to the length of the conductor and inversely proportional to the cross-sectional area of the conductor.

Primary Power Loss Example:

What is the primary conductor power loss of a 75 kVA transformer if the primary current rating is 90A and the winding has a resistance of 0.16Ω? **Figure 22–6A**

(a) 400W (b) 800W
(c) 1,100W (d) 1,300W

• Answer: (d) 1,300W

Power = $I^2 \times R$

I = 90A

R = 0.16Ω

P = $90A^2$ x 0.16Ω

P = 1,296W

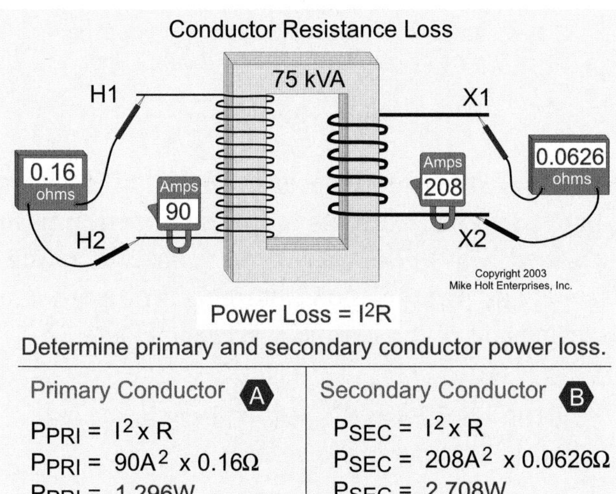

Figure 22–6

Secondary Power Loss Example:

What is the secondary conductor power loss of a 75 kVA transformer if the secondary current rating is 208A and the winding has a resistance of 0.0626Ω? **Figure 22–6B**

(a) 1,400W (b) 1,800W
(c) 2,100W (d) 2,700W

• Answer: (d) 2,700W

Power = $I^2 \times R$

I = 208A

R = 0.0626Ω

P = $208A^2$ x 0.0626Ω

P = 2,708W

Flux Leakage Loss

The leakage of the electromagnetic flux lines between the primary and secondary windings also represents wasted energy. **Figure 22–7**

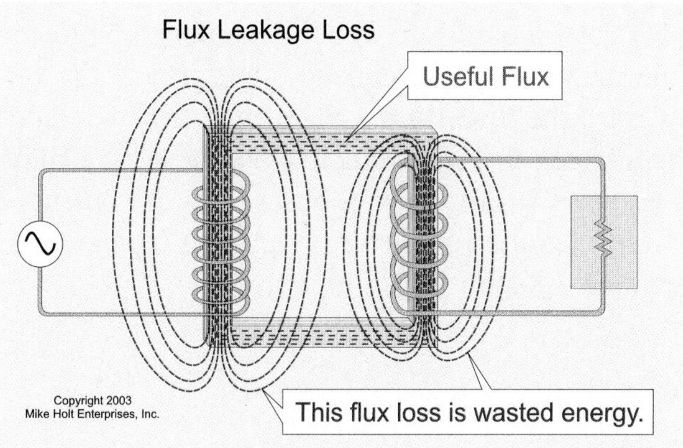

Figure 22–7

Eddy Currents

Iron is the only metal used for transformer cores because of the relative ease with which the material can be magnetized. However, the expanding and collapsing electromagnetic field from alternating current induces a voltage in the iron core. Wasteful circulating eddy currents in the iron core cause the core to heat up without any useful purpose. To reduce losses because of eddy currents, long laminated iron cores, separated by insulation (usually lacquer), are used. **Figure 22–8**

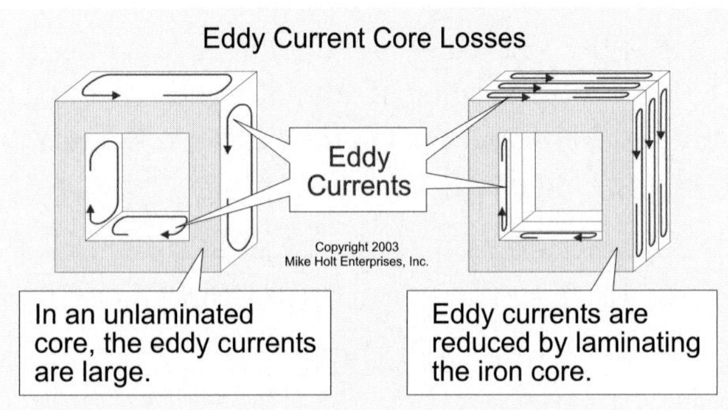

Figure 22–8

Hysteresis Losses

As current flows through the transformer, the iron core is temporarily magnetized by the electromagnetic field created by the alternating current. Each time the primary magnetic field expands and collapses, the core molecules realign themselves to the changing polarity of the electromagnetic field. The energy required to realign the core molecules to the changing electromagnetic field is called the hysteresis loss of the core. **Figure 22–9**

Hysteresis losses are directly proportional to the alternating-current frequency. The greater the frequency, the more times per second the molecules must realign. Hysteresis loss is one of the main reasons why iron-core transformers are not used in applications involving high frequencies and nonlinear loads.

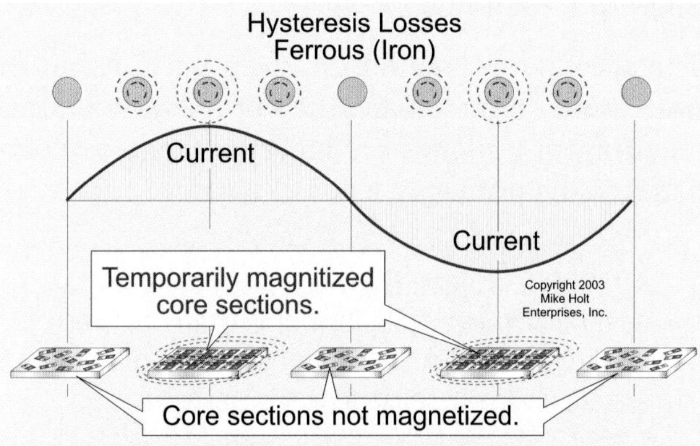

The molecules of the core material align and realign with the expanding and collapsing electromagnetic field. The energy that does this realignment is wasted energy and is called Hysteresis Loss.

Figure 22–9

22.5 Harmonic Current

Three-phase, 4-wire wye-connected systems, such as 120/208V or 277/480V that supply nonlinear line-to-neutral loads, can overheat because of circulating odd triplen harmonic currents (3rd, 9th, 15th, 21st, etc.). **Figure 22–10**

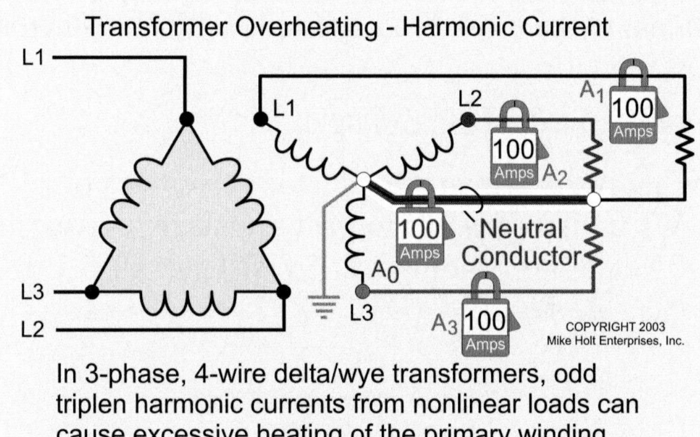

In 3-phase, 4-wire delta/wye transformers, odd triplen harmonic currents from nonlinear loads can cause excessive heating of the primary winding.

Figure 22–10

Additional losses may occur in some transformers where harmonic currents are present, resulting in increased heat in the transformer above its rating. The heating from harmonic currents is proportional to the square of the harmonic current. **Figure 22–11**

AUTHOR'S COMMENT: Both of these topics are beyond the scope of this textbook.

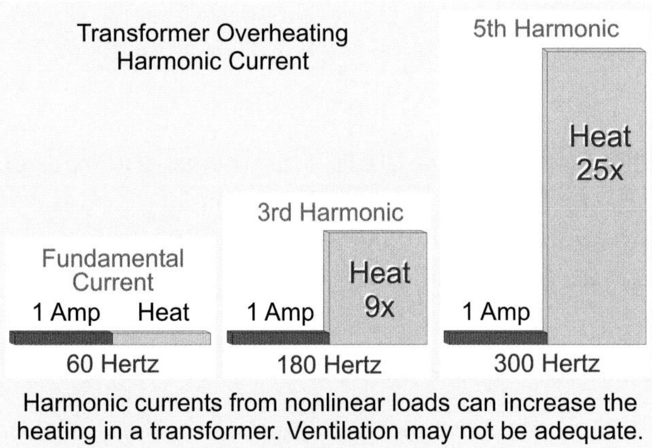

Figure 22–11

22.6 Efficiency

Because of conductor resistance, flux leakage, eddy currents, and hysteresis losses, not all of the input power is transferred to the secondary winding for useful purposes. **Figure 22–12**

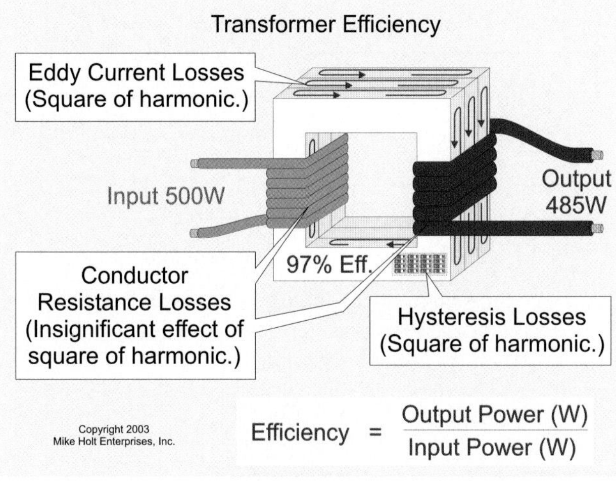

Figure 22–12

AUTHOR'S COMMENT: For most practical purposes, transformer efficiency can be ignored.

22.7 Transformer Turns Ratio

The relationship of the primary winding voltage to the secondary winding voltage is the same as the relationship between the number of turns of wire on the primary as compared to the number of turns on the secondary. This relationship is called turns ratio. **Figure 22–13**

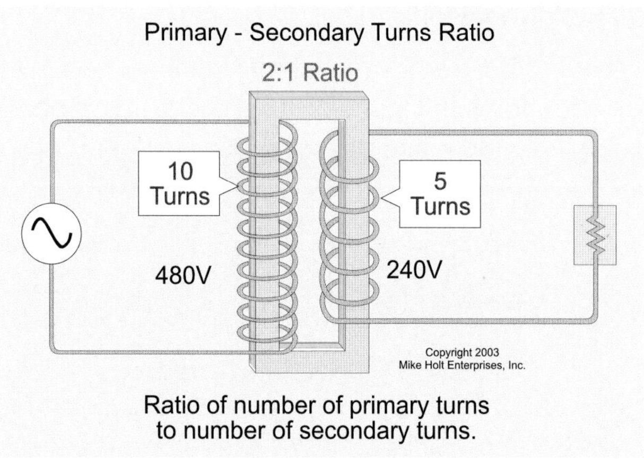

Figure 22–13

Delta/Wye Example

What is the turns ratio of the delta/wye transformer shown in **Figure 22–14** if the primary phase voltage is 480V and the secondary is 120V?

(a) 4:1 (b) 1:4
(c) 2:1 (d) 1:2

• Answer: (a) 4:1

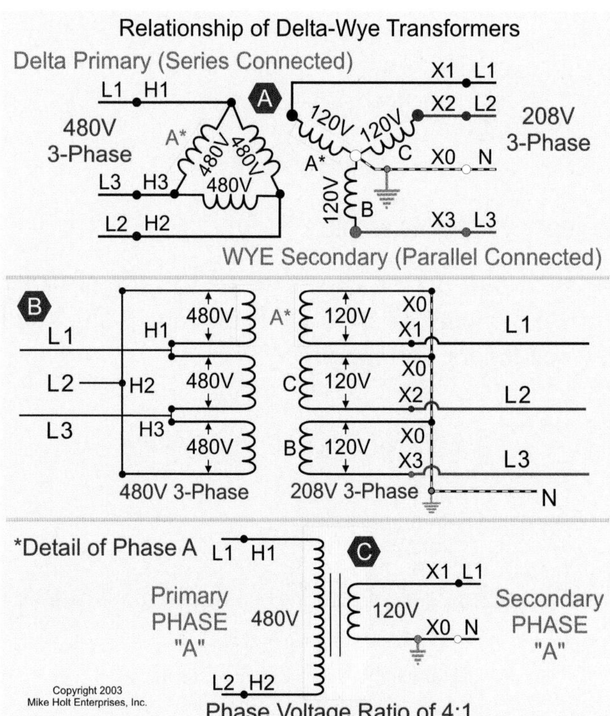

Figure 22–14

Delta/Delta Example

What is the turns ratio of the delta/delta transformer shown in Figure 22–15 if the primary phase voltage is 480V and the secondary is 240V?

(a) 4:1 (b) 1:4
(c) 2:1 (d) 1:2

• Answer: (c) 2:1

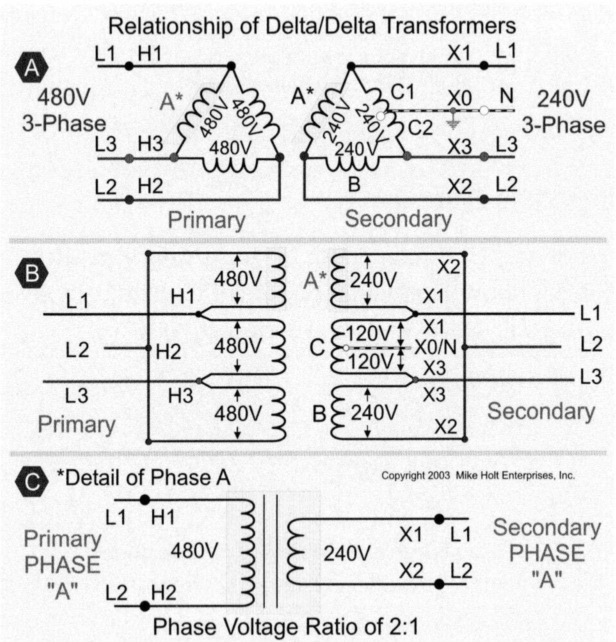

Figure 22–15

Primary Voltage Example

What is the primary voltage of the transformer shown in Figure 22–16 if the turns ratio is 20:1 and the secondary voltage is 6V?

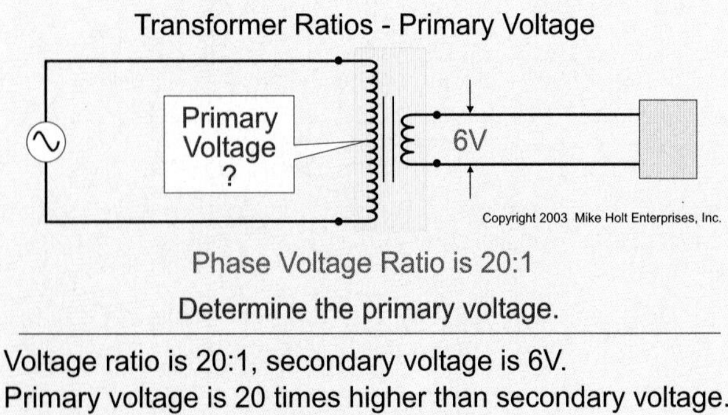

Transformer Ratios - Primary Voltage
Primary
Voltage
?
6V
Copyright 2003 Mike Holt Enterprises, Inc.
Phase Voltage Ratio is 20:1
Determine the primary voltage.
Voltage ratio is 20:1, secondary voltage is 6V.
Primary voltage is 20 times higher than secondary voltage.
6V x 20 = 120V on primary

Figure 22–16

(a) 6V (b) 24V
(c) 48V (d) none of these

• Answer: (d) none of these

The turns ratio is 20:1. This means the voltage ratio is also 20:1. Since the secondary voltage is 6V, the primary voltage is 20 times larger, 20 x 6V = 120V.

Secondary Voltage Example

What is the secondary voltage of the transformer shown in Figure 22–17 if the turns ratio is 10:1 and the primary voltage is 240V?

(a) 6V (b) 24V
(c) 48V (d) none of these

• Answer: (b) 24V

Since the primary voltage is 240V, the secondary voltage is 10 times smaller, 240V/10 = 24V.

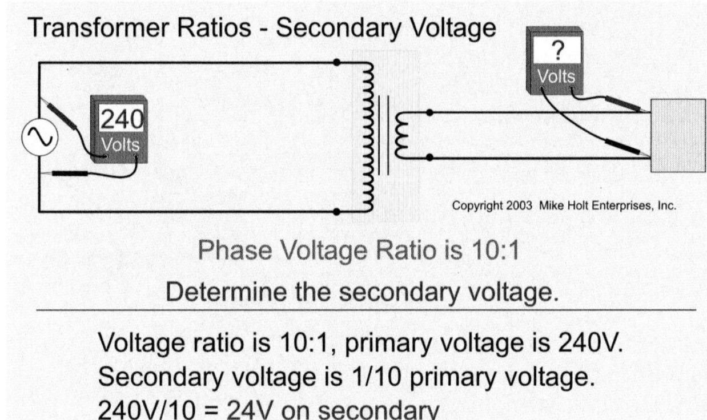

Figure 22–17

22.8 Transformer kVA Rating

Transformers are rated in kilovolt-amperes (kVA), where 1 kilovolt-ampere = 1,000 volt-amperes = 1,000 VA.

Figure 22–18 lists some standard transformer sizes, although some transformers get much, much larger than those listed in this figure.

22.9 Current Flow

The following steps explain the process of primary and secondary current flow in a transformer.

Standard Transformer Ratings - In kVA	
Single-Phase	Three-Phase
1.0	3.0
1.5	6.0
2.0	9.0
3.0	15.0
5.0	22.5
7.5	25.0
10.0	30.0
15.0	37.5
25.0	45.0
37.5	50.0
50.0	75.0
75.0	112.5
100.0	150.0
125.0	225.0

Figure 22–18

Step 1 When a load is connected to the secondary of a transformer, secondary voltage induced from the primary magnetic field will cause current to flow through the secondary conductor winding.

Step 2 The secondary current flow in the secondary winding creates an electromagnetic field that opposes the primary electromagnetic field.

Step 3 The flux lines from the secondary magnetic field effectively reduce the strength of the primary flux lines, and as a result, less CEMF is generated in the primary winding conductors. With less CEMF to oppose the primary applied voltage, the primary current increases in direct proportion to the secondary current. Figure 22–19

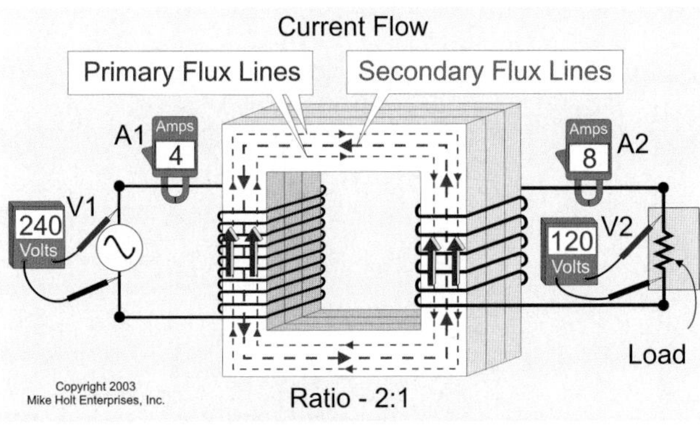

Figure 22–19

22.10 Current Rating

The primary current rating can be determined by the formulas:

Single-Phase

$$I = \frac{VA}{E}$$

Three-Phase

$$I = \frac{VA}{(E\sqrt{3})}$$

Single-Phase Example

What is the maximum primary and secondary line current at full load for a 480/240V, 25 kVA transformer? Figure 22–20

(a) 52/104A (b) 104/52A
(c) 104/208A (d) 208/104A

• Answer: (a) 52/104A

I primary $= \frac{VA}{E}$

I primary $= \frac{25{,}000 \text{ VA}}{480\text{V}}$

I primary = 52A

I secondary $= \frac{VA}{E}$

I secondary $= \frac{25{,}000 \text{ VA}}{240\text{V}}$

I secondary = 104A

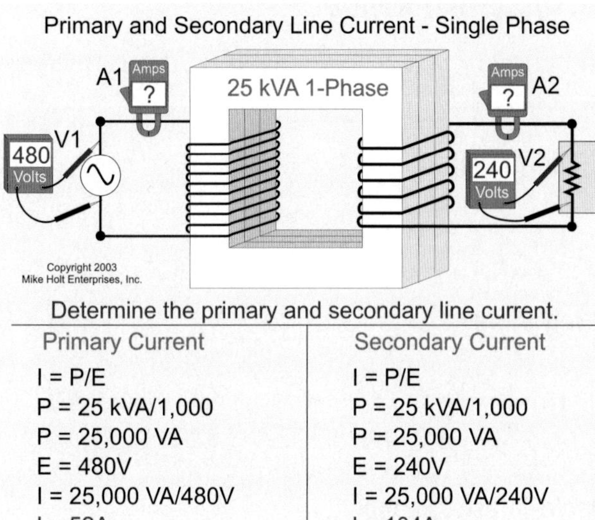

Figure 22–20

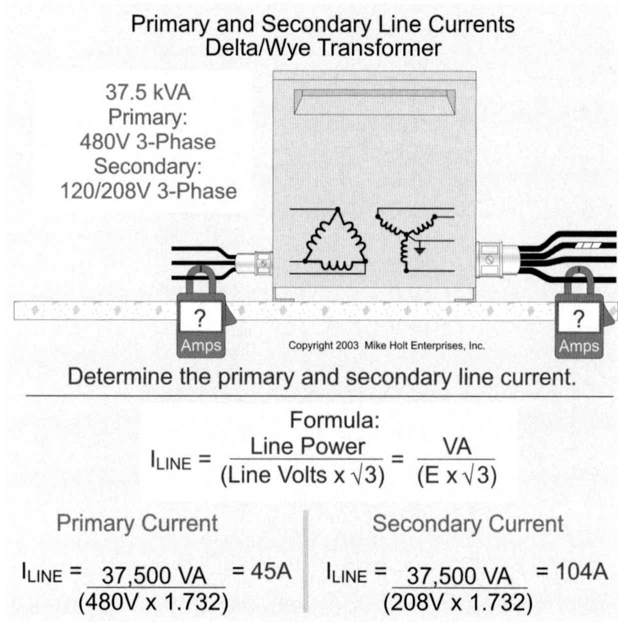

Figure 22–21

Three-Phase Example

What is the maximum primary and secondary line current at full load for a 480/208V, 37.5 kVA transformer? Figure 22–21

(a) 45/104A (b) 104/40A
(c) 208/140A (d) 140/120A

• Answer: (a) 45/104A

$$\textbf{I primary} = \frac{VA}{(E\sqrt{3})}$$

$$\text{I primary} = \frac{37{,}500\text{ VA}}{(480\text{V} \times 1.732)}$$

I primary = 45A

$$\textbf{I secondary} = \frac{VA}{(E\sqrt{3})}$$

$$\text{I secondary} = \frac{37{,}500\text{ VA}}{(208\text{V} \times 1.732)}$$

I secondary = 104A

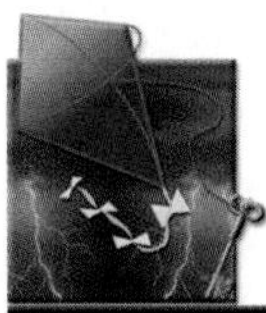

Unit 22 Summary

22.1 Transformer Basics

A transformer is a stationary device typically used to raise or lower voltage. It has the ability to transfer electrical energy from one system to another, with no physical connection between the two systems.

Primary Versus Secondary

The transformer winding connected to the voltage source is called the primary winding. The transformer winding connected to the load is called the secondary.

Mutual Induction

The energy transfer of a transformer is accomplished because the electromagnetic lines of force from the primary winding induce a voltage in the secondary winding.

The voltage level that can be induced in the secondary winding, from the primary magnetic field, is a function of the number of secondary conductor loops (turns) that are cut by the primary electromagnetic field.

22.2 Secondary Induced Voltage

Voltage induced in the secondary winding of a transformer is equal to the sum of the voltages induced in each loop of the secondary winding. The induced voltage in each loop of the secondary winding is dependent on the number of secondary conductor loops (turns), as compared to the number of primary turns.

22.3 Autotransformers

Autotransformers use a common winding for both the primary and secondary and their purpose is to step the voltage up or down. The secondary winding of a step-down transformer has fewer turns than the primary winding, and the secondary winding of a step-up transformer has more turns than the primary winding.

> **AUTHOR'S COMMENT:** The disadvantage of an autotransformer is the lack of isolation between the primary and secondary conductors, but they are often used because they are inexpensive.

22.4 Power Losses

In an ideal transformer, all the primary power is transferred from the primary winding to the secondary winding, but real-world transformers have power losses because of conductor resistance, flux leakage, eddy currents, and hysteresis losses.

Conductor Resistance Loss

Conductor resistance is directly proportional to the length of the conductor and inversely proportional to the cross-sectional area of the conductor.

Flux Leakage Loss

The leakage of the electromagnetic flux lines between the primary and secondary windings also represents wasted energy.

Eddy Currents

Wasteful circulating eddy currents in the iron core cause the core to heat up without any useful purpose. To reduce losses because of eddy currents, long laminated iron cores, separated by insulation (usually lacquer), are used.

Hysteresis Losses

As current flows through the transformer, the iron core is temporarily magnetized by the electromagnetic field created by the alternating current. Each time the primary magnetic field expands and collapses, the core molecules realign themselves to the changing polarity of the electromagnetic field. The energy required to realign the core molecules to the changing electromagnetic field is called the hysteresis loss of the core.

22.5 Harmonic Current

Three-phase, 4-wire, wye-connected systems that supply nonlinear line-to-neutral loads can overheat because of circulating odd triplen harmonic currents. In addition, the heating from harmonic currents is proportional to the square of the harmonic current.

22.6 Efficiency

Because of conductor resistance, flux leakage, eddy currents, and hysteresis losses, not all of the input power is transferred to the secondary winding for useful purposes.

22.7 Transformer Turns Ratio

The relationship of the primary winding voltage to the secondary winding voltage is the same as the relationship between the number of turns of wire on the primary as compared to the number of turns on the secondary.

22.8 Transformer kVA Rating

Transformers are rated in kilovolt-amperes (kVA), where 1 kilovolt-ampere = 1,000 volt-amperes = 1,000 VA.

22.9 Current Flow

The following steps explain the process of primary and secondary current flow in a transformer.

Step 1 When a load is connected to the secondary of a transformer, secondary voltage induced from the primary magnetic field will cause current to flow through the secondary conductor winding.

Step 2 The secondary current flow in the secondary winding creates an electromagnetic field that opposes the primary electromagnetic field.

Step 3 The flux lines from the secondary magnetic field effectively reduce the strength of the primary flux lines, and as a result, less CEMF is generated in the primary winding conductors. With less CEMF to oppose the primary applied voltage, the primary current increases in direct proportion to the secondary current.

22.10 Current Rating

The primary current rating can be determined by the formulas:

Single-Phase

$$I = \frac{VA}{E}$$

Three-Phase

$$I = \frac{VA}{(E\sqrt{3})}$$

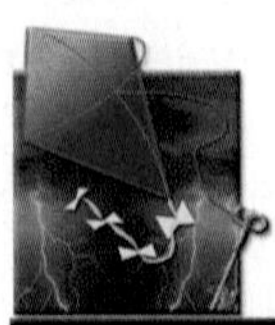

Unit 22 Conclusion

You now have a basic understanding of transformers, the various types, the standard sizes, how they're rated, and how they work. You will encounter transformers often in your work. What you have learned here will help determine how successful you are in that work.

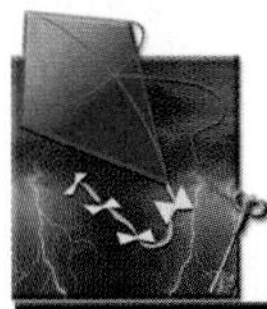

Unit 22 Practice Questions

22.1 Transformer Basics

1. A _____ is used to raise or lower voltage and it has the ability to transfer electrical energy from one system to another with no physical connection between the two systems.

   (a) capacitor (b) motor (c) relay (d) transformer

2. The transformer winding that is connected to the source is called the _____ winding and the transformer winding that is connected to the load is called the _____.

   (a) secondary, primary (b) primary, secondary
   (c) depends on the wiring (d) none of these

3. The energy transfer ability of a transformer is accomplished because the primary electromagnetic lines of force induce a voltage in the secondary winding.

   (a) True (b) False

22.2 Secondary Induced Voltage

4. Voltage induced in the secondary winding of a transformer is dependent on the number of secondary turns as compared to the number of primary turns.

   (a) True (b) False

22.3 Autotransformers

5. Autotransformers use separate windings for the primary and secondary.

   (a) True (b) False

22.4 Power Losses

6. Wasteful circulating _____ in the iron core cause(s) the core to heat up without any useful purpose.

   (a) conductor resistance (b) flux leakage
   (c) eddy currents (d) hysteresis losses

7. _____ can be reduced by dividing the core into many flat sections or laminations.

   (a) Conductor resistance (b) Flux leakage
   (c) Eddy currents (d) Hysteresis losses

8. As current flows through the transformer, the iron core is temporarily magnetized. The energy required to realign the core molecules to the changing electromagnetic field is called _____ loss.

(a) conductor resistance
(b) flux leakage
(c) eddy currents
(d) hysteresis

9. The leakage of the electromagnetic flux lines between the primary and secondary windings represents wasted energy.

(a) True
(b) False

22.5 Harmonic Current

10. Three-phase, _____ wye-connected systems can overheat because of circulating odd triplen harmonic currents.

(a) 2-wire
(b) 3-wire
(c) 4-wire
(d) none of these

11. The heating from harmonic currents is proportional to the square of the harmonic current.

(a) True
(b) False

22.6 Efficiency

12. Because of conductor resistance, flux leakage, eddy currents, and hysteresis losses, not all of the input power is transferred to the secondary winding for useful purposes.

(a) True
(b) False

13. For most practical purposes, transformer efficiency can be ignored.

(a) True
(b) False

22.7 Transformer Turns Ratio

14. The relationship of the number of turns of wire on the _____ as compared to the number of turns on the _____ is called turns ratio.

(a) primary, secondary
(b) secondary, primary
(c) primary, primary
(d) secondary, secondary

15. If the primary phase voltage is 480 and the secondary phase voltage is 240, the turns ratio is _____.

(a) 1:2
(b) 2:1
(c) 4:1
(d) 1:4

22.8 Transformer kVA Rating

16. Transformers are rated in _____.

(a) VA (b) kW (c) W (d) kVA

22.9 Current Flow

17. The primary electromagnetic field induces a voltage in the secondary. As the secondary current flows, it produces an electromagnetic field that reduces the strength of the primary flux lines. This results in an increase in primary current.

(a) True (b) False

18. Current flow in the secondary transformer winding creates an electromagnetic field that opposes the primary electromagnetic field resulting in less primary CEMF. The primary current automatically increases in direct proportion to the secondary current.

(a) True (b) False

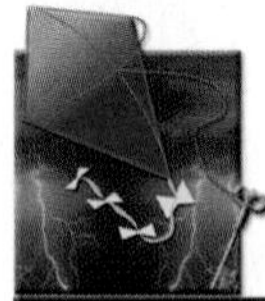

Chapter 6 Final Exam

Unit 20—Motors

PART A—MOTOR BASICS

20.1 Motor Principles

1. A motor must have two opposing magnetic fields in order to rotate. The stationary field winding is mounted on the stator, and the rotating part is referred to as the armature.

   (a) True (b) False

20.2 Dual-Voltage AC Motors

2. Dual-voltage ac motors are made with two field windings. The field windings are connected in _____ for low-voltage operation and in _____ for high-voltage operation.

   (a) series, parallel (b) parallel, series (c) series, series (d) parallel, parallel

20.3 Motor Horsepower Rating

3. Motors are used to convert electrical energy into mechanical work and the output mechanical work of a motor is rated in horsepower. 1 hp = _____.

   (a) 476W (b) 674W (c) 746W (d) none of these

20.4 Motor Current Ratings

4. The nameplate motor FLA rating describes the motor current rating when it carries its rated horsepower load at its rated _____.

   (a) power (b) resistance (c) CEMF (d) voltage

5. The actual motor current is dependent upon the load on the motor and the operating voltage at the motor terminals.

   (a) True (b) False

6. The motor FLA rating is used when sizing motor conductor size or circuit protection.

   (a) True (b) False

20.5 Calculating Motor FLA

7. What is the nameplate FLA for a 5 hp, 230V, 1Ø motor, with 93 percent power factor and 87 percent efficiency?

(a) 10A (b) 20A (c) 28A (d) 35A

8. What is the nameplate FLA of a 20 hp, 208V, 3Ø motor with 90 percent power factor and 80 percent efficiency?

(a) 51A (b) 58A (c) 65A (d) 80A

20.6 Motor-Starting Current

9. When a motor starts, the current drawn is at least _____ times the motor FLA; this is known as motor locked-rotor amperes (LRA).

(a) 1.25 (b) 0.8 (c) 3 (d) 6

20.7 Motor-Running Current

10. Once a motor begins turning, the rotor winding will be increasingly cut by the stationary magnetic field, resulting in an increasing counter-electromotive force.

(a) True (b) False

20.8 Motor Locked-Rotor Current (LRC)

11. If the rotating part of the motor winding is jammed so that it cannot rotate, no CEMF will be produced in the motor winding. Result—the motor operates at _____ and the windings will be destroyed by excessive heat.

(a) FLA (b) FLC (c) LRC (d) any of these

20.9 Motor Overload Protection

12. Motors must be protected against excessive winding heat by a properly sized overload protection device, based on the motor _____ current rating.

(a) FLA (b) FLC (c) LRC (d) any of these

PART C—ALTERNATING-CURRENT MOTORS

20.13 AC Induction Motor

13. In the ac induction motor, the stator produces a rotating magnetic field that induces current in the rotor windings. The rotor current generates a magnetic field in opposition to the magnetic field of the stator, thereby causing the rotor to turn.

(a) True (b) False

20.14 Alternating-Current Motor Types

14. In a(n) _____ motor, the rotor is actually locked in step with the rotating stator field and is dragged along at the speed of the rotating magnetic field.

(a) wound-rotor (b) induction (c) synchronous (d) squirrel-cage

15. _____ motors are fractional horsepower motors that operate equally well on ac and dc and are used for vacuum cleaners, electric drills, mixers, and light household appliances.

(a) AC (b) Universal (c) Wound-rotor (d) Synchronous

20.15 Reversing the Rotation of an AC Motor

16. Swapping _____ of the line conductors can reverse a 3Ø ac motor's rotation.

(a) one (b) two (c) three (d) none of these

Unit 21—Generators

21.2 Alternating-Current Generator

17. The _____ of an ac generator contains the electromagnetic field, which cuts through the stationary conductor coils.

(a) stator (b) rotor (c) coil (d) winding

21.3 Three-Phase Generators

18. Three-phase ac generators have three equally spaced windings, _____ out-of-phase with each other.

(a) 90º (b) 120º (c) 180º (d) 360º

Unit 22—Transformers

22.1 Transformer Basics

19. A _____ is used to raise or lower voltage and it has the ability to transfer electrical energy from one system to another with no physical connection between the two systems.

(a) capacitor (b) motor (c) relay (d) transformer

20. The energy transfer ability of a transformer is accomplished because the primary electromagnetic lines of force induce a voltage in the secondary winding.

(a) True (b) False

22.2 Secondary Induced Voltage

21. Voltage induced in the secondary winding of a transformer is dependent on the number of secondary turns as compared to the number of primary turns.

(a) True (b) False

22.3 Autotransformers

22. Autotransformers use separate windings for the primary and secondary.

(a) True (b) False

22.4 Power Losses

23. Wasteful circulating _____ in the iron core cause(s) the core to heat up without any useful purpose.

(a) conductor resistance (b) flux leakage
(c) eddy currents (d) hysteresis losses

24. _____ can be reduced by dividing the core into many flat sections or laminations.

(a) Conductor resistance (b) Flux leakage
(c) Eddy currents (d) Hysteresis losses

25. As current flows through the transformer, the iron core is temporarily magnetized. The energy required to realign the core molecules to the changing electromagnetic field is called _____ loss.

(a) conductor resistance (b) flux leakage
(c) eddy currents (d) hysteresis

26. The leakage of the electromagnetic flux lines between the primary and secondary windings represents wasted energy.

(a) True (b) False

22.5 Harmonic Current

27. Three-phase, _____ wye-connected systems can overheat because of circulating odd triplen harmonic currents.

(a) 2-wire (b) 3-wire (c) 4-wire (d) none of these

28. The heating from harmonic currents is proportional to the square of the harmonic current.

(a) True (b) False

22.6 Efficiency

29. Because of conductor resistance, flux leakage, eddy currents, and hysteresis losses, not all of the input power is transferred to the secondary winding for useful purposes.

(a) True (b) False

30. For most practical purposes, transformer efficiency can be ignored.

(a) True (b) False

22.7 Transformer Turns Ratio

31. If the primary phase voltage is 480V and the secondary phase voltage is 240V, the turns ratio is _____.

(a) 1:2 (b) 2:1 (c) 4:1 (d) 1:4

22.8 Transformer kVA Rating

32. Transformers are rated in _____.

(a) VA (b) kW (c) W (d) kVA

22.9 Current Flow

33. The primary electromagnetic field induces a voltage in the secondary. As the secondary current flows, it produces an electromagnetic field that reduces the strength of the primary flux lines. This results in an increase in primary current.

(a) True (b) False

34. Current flow in the secondary transformer winding creates an electromagnetic field that opposes the primary electromagnetic field resulting in less primary CEMF. The primary current automatically increases in direct proportion to the secondary current.

(a) True (b) False

Notes

Basic Electrical Theory
Final Exam Chapters 1-6

Chapter 1 - Electrical Fundamentals

Chapter 2 - Basic Electricity

Chapter 3 - Basic Electrical Circuits

Chapter 4 - Electrical Systems and Protection

Chapter 5 - Alternating Current

Chapter 6 - Motors, Generators, and Transformers

Final Conclusion

Notes

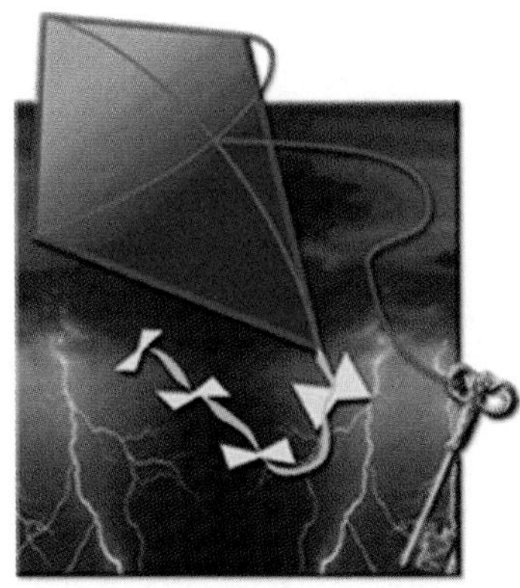

Basic Electrical Theory Final Exam

Chapter 1 Electrical Fundamentals

Unit 1—Matter

1.5 Charged Material (Static Charge)

1. Providing a path to the earth often helps reduce electrostatic charge.

   (a) True (b) False

1.7 Lightning

2. Lightning frequently terminates to a point of elevation and it strikes nonmetallic as well as metallic objects with the same frequency.

   (a) True (b) False

3. The termination of the lightning stroke is unlikely to ignite combustible materials.

   (a) True (b) False

1.8 Lightning Protection

4. Lightning protection is intended to protect the building structure itself, as well as the electrical equipment on or inside the building structure.

   (a) True (b) False

Unit 3—Magnetism

3.5 Magnetic Properties

5. Nonmagnetic metals are ferrous, meaning they do not contain any iron, and cannot be magnetized.

    (a) True (b) False

3.9 Magnetic Lines of Force

6. Magnetic lines of force can cross each other and they are called flux lines.

    (a) True (b) False

Unit 4—Electricity

4.2 Electricity

7. It is not the force of the magnetic field through a conductor that produces electricity; it is the relative motion of the field to the electrons within the conductor that produces the movement of electrons.

    (a) True (b) False

4.4 Danger of Electricity

8. People become injured and death occurs when voltage pushes electrons through the human body causing it to go into ventricular fibrillation.

    (a) True (b) False

9. The severity of an electric shock is dependent on the current flowing through the body, which is impacted by circuit voltage and contact resistance.

    (a) True (b) False

10. An electrical arc blast can approach _____, which vaporizes metal parts and produces an explosive and deadly pressure wave.

    (a) 10,000°F (b) 15,000°F (c) 25,000°F (d) 30,000°F

Unit 5—Electromagnetism

5.3 Field Interaction

11. If a conductor carrying current is next to another conductor carrying current in the opposite direction, the electromagnetic field attempts to pull the conductors apart.

    (a) True (b) False

Unit 6—Uses of Electromagnetism

6.1 Basic Electric Meters

12. A clamp-on ac ammeter has a coil that is clamped around the conductor and detects the rising and falling _____ field being produced due to the ac flow through the conductor.

    (a) static (b) current (c) power (d) magnetic

13. Ohmmeters measure the _____ or opposition to current flow of a circuit or component.

    (a) voltage (b) current (c) power (d) resistance

14. The megger is used to measure very high-_____ values, such as those found in cable insulation, or motor and transformer windings.

    (a) voltage (b) current (c) power (d) resistance

6.2 Electric Motor

15. The electric motor works on the principle of the attracting and repelling forces of _____ fields.

    (a) voltage (b) current (c) power (d) magnetic

6.3 Electrical Generator

16. The _____ of a generator is forced to rotate while it is being subjected to the magnetic field of the stator.

    (a) winding (b) rotor (c) stator (d) b or c

6.4 Electromagnetic Relay

17. A holding relay is primarily used for worker convenience.

    (a) True (b) False

Chapter 2
Basic Electricity

Unit 7—The Electrical Circuit

7.2 Electron Current Flow Theory

18. According to the electron current flow theory, electrons flow away from the negative terminal of the source, through the circuit and load, toward the positive terminal of the source.

    (a) True (b) False

7.3 Conventional Current Flow Theory

19. According to the conventional current flow theory, electrons travel from positive to negative.

(a) True (b) False

Unit 9—Electrical Formulas

9.2 Power Source

20. The major advantage of ac over dc is the ease of voltage regulation by the use of a transformer.

(a) True (b) False

9.3 Conductance

21. The best conductors, in order of their conductivity, are: gold, silver, copper, and aluminum.

(a) True (b) False

9.6 Ohm's Law and Alternating Current

22. In a dc circuit, the only opposition to current flow is the physical resistance of the material. This opposition is called reactance and it is measured in ohms.

(a) True (b) False

9.7 Ohm's Law Formula Circle

23. What is the voltage drop of two 12 AWG conductors supplying a 16A load, located 100 ft from the power supply? Formula: $E_{VD} = I \times R$, I = 16A, R = 0.4Ω

(a) 6.4V (b) 12.8V (c) 1.6V (d) 3.2V

24. What is the resistance of the circuit conductors when the conductor voltage drop is 7.2V and the current flow is 50A?

(a) 0.14Ω (b) 0.3Ω (c) 3Ω (d) 14Ω

9.8 PIE Formula Circle

25. What is the power loss in watts of a conductor that carries 24A and has a voltage drop of 7.2V?

(a) 175W (b) 350W (c) 700W (d) 2,400W

26. What is the approximate power consumed by a 10 kW heat strip rated 230V, when connected to a 208V circuit?

(a) 8 kW (b) 9 kW (c) 11 kW (d) 12 kW

9.9 Formula Wheel

27. The formulas in the power wheel apply to _____.

(a) dc
(b) ac with unity power factor
(c) dc or ac circuits
(d) a and b

9.11 Power Losses of Conductors

28. The total circuit resistance of two 12 AWG conductors (each 100 ft long) is 0.4Ω. If the current of the circuit is 16A, what is the power loss of the conductors in watts?

(a) 75W
(b) 100W
(c) 300W
(d) 600W

29. What is the conductor power loss in watts for a 120V circuit that has a 3 percent voltage drop and carries a current flow of 12A?

(a) 43W
(b) 86W
(c) 172W
(d) 1,440W

9.12 Cost of Power

30. What does it cost per year (at 8 cents per kWh) for the power loss of a 12 AWG circuit conductor (100 ft long) that has a total resistance of 0.4Ω and current flow of 16A?

(a) $30
(b) $50
(c) $70
(d) $90

9.13 Power Changes with the Square of the Voltage

31. What is the power consumed by a 10 kW heat strip rated 230V connected to a 115V circuit?

(a) 2.5 kW
(b) 5 kW
(c) 7.5 kW
(d) 15 kW

Chapter 3 Basic Electrical Circuits

Unit 10—Series Circuits

10.2 Understanding Series Calculations

32. The opposition to current flow results in voltage drop.

(a) True
(b) False

33. Kirchoff's Voltage Law states that in a series circuit, the sum of the voltage drops across all of the resistors will equal the applied voltage.

(a) True
(b) False

34. Kirchoff's Current Law states that in a series circuit, the current is _____ through the transformer, the conductors, and the appliance.

(a) proportional (b) distributed (c) additive (d) the same

Unit 11—Parallel Circuits

11.2 Understanding Parallel Calculations

35. According to Kirchoff's Current Law, the total current provided by the source to a parallel circuit will equal the sum of the currents of all of the branches.

(a) True (b) False

11.3 Circuit Resistance

36. The total resistance of a parallel circuit can be calculated by the _____ method.

(a) equal resistance (b) product-over-sum (c) reciprocal (d) any of these

11.5 Parallel-Connected Power Supplies

37. When power supplies are connected in parallel, the voltage remains the same, but the current or amp-hour capacity will be increased.

(a) True (b) False

Unit 13—Multiwire Circuits

13.3 Current Flow on the Grounded (Neutral) Conductor

38. A balanced 3-wire, 120/240V, 1Ø circuit is connected so that the ungrounded conductors are from different transformer phases (Line 1 and Line 2). The current on the grounded (neutral) conductor will be _____ of the ungrounded conductor current.

(a) 0% (b) 70% (c) 80% (d) 100%

39. If the ungrounded conductors of a multiwire circuit are not terminated to different phases, this can cause the neutral current to be in excess of the grounded (neutral) conductor rating.

(a) True (b) False

13.5 Unbalanced Current

40. The current flowing on the grounded (neutral) conductor of a multiwire circuit is called unbalanced current.

(a) True (b) False

13.7 Dangers of Multiwire Circuits

41. Improper wiring or mishandling of multiwire branch circuits can cause _____ connected to the circuit.

(a) overloading of the ungrounded conductors
(b) overloading of the grounded (neutral) conductors
(c) destruction of equipment because of overvoltage
(d) b and c

13.8 NEC Requirements

42. Because of the dangers associated with an open grounded (neutral) conductor, the continuity of the _____ conductor cannot be dependent upon the receptacle.

(a) ungrounded (b) grounded (c) a and b (d) none of these

Chapter 4 Electrical Systems and Protection

Unit 14—The Electrical System

14.1 Current Flow

43. Electrons leaving a power supply are always trying to return to the same power supply; they are not trying to go into the earth.

(a) True (b) False

14.4 Premises Neutral Current Path

44. To prevent fires and electric shock, the *NEC* specifies that neutral current can flow on metal parts of the electrical system.

(a) True (b) False

14.5 Premises Ground-Fault Current Path

45. Metal parts of premises wiring must be bonded to a low-impedance path designed so that the circuit protection device will quickly open and clear a ground fault.

(a) True (b) False

46. Because of the earth's high resistance to current flow, it cannot be used for the purpose of clearing a line-to-case ground fault for _____ wiring.

(a) utility (b) premises (c) a or b (d) none of these

Unit 15—Protection Devices

PART A—OVERCURRENT PROTECTION DEVICES

15.1 Overcurrent Protection

47. The purpose of overcurrent protection is to protect the conductors and equipment against excessive or dangerous temperatures because of overcurrent. Overcurrent is current in excess of the rated current of equipment or conductors. It may result from a(n) _____.

(a) overload (b) short circuit (c) ground fault (d) all of these

15.2 Clearing Faults

48. To protect against electric shock or to prevent a fire, a dangerous _____ must quickly be removed by opening the circuit's overcurrent protection device.

(a) overload (b) short circuit (c) ground fault (d) all of these

49. Inverse-time breakers operate on the principle that as the current decreases, the time it takes for the device to open decreases.

(a) True (b) False

15.5 Circuit Breaker Trip Elements

50. The _____ sensing element causes the circuit breaker to open when a predetermined calibration temperature is reached.

(a) magnetic (b) electronic (c) thermo (d) none of these

51. The magnetic time-delay circuit breaker operates on the solenoid principle where a movable core, held with a spring, is moved by the magnetic field of a(n) _____.

(a) overload (b) short circuit (c) ground fault (d) b or c

15.7 Available Short-Circuit Current

52. Available short-circuit current is the current in amperes that is available at a given point in the electrical system.

(a) True (b) False

53. Factors that impact the available short-circuit current include transformer _____.

(a) voltage (b) kVA rating (c) impedance (d) all of these

54. Factors that impact the available short-circuit current include circuit conductor _____.

(a) material (b) size (c) length (d) all of these

15.8 Interrupting Rating

55. Circuit breakers and fuses are intended to interrupt the circuit, and they shall have an ampere interrupting rating (AIR) sufficient for the available short-circuit current.

    (a) True (b) False

56. If the protection device is not rated to interrupt the current at the available fault values at its listed voltage rating, it could explode while attempting to clear the fault.

    (a) True (b) False

15.9 Short-Circuit Current Rating

57. Equipment must have a(n) _____ current rating that permits the protection device to clear a short circuit or ground fault without extensive damage to the components of the circuit.

    (a) overload (b) short circuit (c) ground fault (d) b or c

PART B—GROUND-FAULT CIRCUIT INTERRUPTERS

15.11 How a GFCI Works

58. A GFCI is designed to protect persons against electric shock. It operates on the principle of monitoring the imbalance of current between the circuit's _____ conductor.

    (a) ungrounded (b) grounded (c) equipment (d) a and b

15.12 Neutral-to-Case Detection

59. A GFCI protection device contains an internal monitor that prevents the device from being turned on if there is a neutral-to-case connection downstream of the device, but this only occurs if there is a load on the circuit.

    (a) True (b) False

15.13 Line-to-Neutral Shock Hazard

60. Severe electric shock or death can occur if a person touches the ungrounded and the grounded (neutral) conductors at the same time, even if the circuit is GFCI protected.

    (a) True (b) False

15.14 GFCI Fails—Circuit Remains Energized

61. Typically, when a GFCI protection device fails, the switching contacts remain closed and the device will continue to provide power without GFCI protection.

    (a) True (b) False

PART C—ARC-FAULT CIRCUIT INTERRUPTER

15.16 Arcing Definition

62. Arcing is defined as a luminous discharge of electricity across an insulating medium. Electric arcs operate at temperatures between _____ and expel small particles of very hot molten materials.

(a) 1,000 and 5,000°F
(b) 2,000 and 10,000°F
(c) 5,000 and 15,000°F
(d) 10,000 and 25,000°F

15.17 Series Versus Parallel Arc

63. Unsafe arcing faults can occur in one of two ways, as series arcing faults or as parallel arcing faults. The most dangerous is the parallel arcing fault.

(a) True
(b) False

15.19 AFCI—How They Operate

64. An AFCI protection device provides protection from an arcing fault by recognizing the characteristics unique to an arcing fault and by functioning to de-energize the circuit when an arc fault is detected.

(a) True
(b) False

Chapter 5 Alternating Current

Unit 16—Alternating Current

16.6 Sine Wave

65. A nonsinusoidal waveform is created when _____ loads distort the voltage and current sine wave.

(a) linear
(b) resistive
(c) inductive
(d) nonlinear

16.11 Lead or Lag

66. When describing the relationship between voltage and current, the reference waveform is always _____.

(a) current
(b) resistance
(c) voltage
(d) none of these

16.12 Values of Alternating Current

67. The effective value is equal to the peak value _____.

(a) times 0.707
(b) times 1.41
(c) times 2
(d) times $\sqrt{3}$

Unit 17—Capacitance

17.3 Discharging a Capacitor

68. Even when power is removed from the circuit, capacitors can store large amounts of energy for a long period of time. They can discharge and arc if inadvertently shorted or grounded out.

(a) True (b) False

17.6 Phase Relationship

69. The opposition offered to the flow of ac current by a capacitor is called capacitive reactance, which is expressed in ohms and abbreviated _____.

(a) X_C (b) X_L (c) Z (d) none of these

Unit 18—Induction

18.2 Induced Voltage and Applied Current

70. The induced voltage in a conductor carrying alternating current opposes the change in current flowing through the conductor. The induced voltage that opposes the current flow is called _____.

(a) CEMF (b) counter-electromotive force
(c) back-EMF (d) all of these

18.3 Conductor AC Resistance

71. For ac circuits, the ac _____ of a conductor must be taken into consideration.

(a) eddy currents (b) skin effect (c) resistance (d) all of these

72. The expanding and collapsing magnetic field within the conductor induces a voltage in the conductors (CEMF) that repels the flowing electrons toward the surface of the conductor. This is called _____.

(a) eddy currents (b) induced voltage (c) impedance (d) skin effect

18.4 Impedance

73. The total opposition to current flow in ac circuits is called _____ and it is measured in ohms.

(a) resistance (b) reactance (c) impedance (d) skin effect

74. The abbreviation for impedance is _____.

(a) X_L (b) X_C (c) Z (d) none of these

18.8 Current Flow

75. Self-induced voltage opposes the change in current flowing in the conductor. This is called inductive reactance and it is abbreviated _____.

(a) X_L (b) X_C (c) Z (d) none of these

Unit 19—Power Factor and Efficiency

PART A—POWER FACTOR

19.3 Power Factor

76. AC inductive or capacitive reactive loads cause the voltage and current to be in-phase with each other.

(a) True (b) False

19.7 Effects of Power Factor

77. What size transformer is required for a 100A, 240V, 1Ø noncontinuous load that has a power factor of 85 percent?

(a) 15 kVA (b) 25 kVA (c) 37.5 kVA (d) 50 kVA

78. How many 20A, 120V circuits are required for forty-two, 300W luminaires (noncontinuous load) that have a power factor of 85 percent?

(a) 4 circuits (b) 5 circuits (c) 7 circuits (d) 8 circuits

PART B—EFFICIENCY

19.9 Efficiency Formulas

79. If the output is 1,600W and the equipment is 88 percent efficient, what are the input amperes at 120V?

(a) 10A (b) 15A (c) 20A (d) 25A

Chapter 6
Motors, Generators and Transformers

Unit 20—Motors

PART A—MOTOR BASICS

20.2 Dual-Voltage AC Motors

80. Dual-voltage ac motors are made with two field windings. The field windings are connected in _____ for low-voltage operation and in _____ for high-voltage operation.

(a) series, parallel (b) parallel, series (c) series, series (d) parallel, parallel

20.4 Motor Current Ratings

81. The motor FLA rating is used when sizing motor conductor size or circuit protection.

(a) True (b) False

20.5 Calculating Motor FLA

82. What is the nameplate FLA of a 20 hp, 208V, 3Ø motor with 90 percent power factor and 80 percent efficiency?

(a) 51A (b) 58A (c) 65A (d) 80A

20.6 Motor-Starting Current

83. When a motor starts, the current drawn is at least _____ times the motor FLA; this is known as motor locked-rotor amperes (LRA).

(a) 1.25 (b) 0.8 (c) 3 (d) 6

20.8 Motor Locked-Rotor Current (LRC)

84. If the rotating part of the motor winding is jammed so that it cannot rotate, no CEMF will be produced in the motor winding. Result—the motor operates at _____ and the windings will be destroyed by excessive heat.

(a) FLA (b) FLC (c) LRC (d) any of these

PART C—ALTERNATING-CURRENT MOTORS

20.13 AC Induction Motor

85. In the ac induction motor, the stator produces a rotating magnetic field that induces current in the rotor windings. The rotor current generates a magnetic field in opposition to the magnetic field of the stator, thereby causing the rotor to turn.

(a) True (b) False

20.14 Alternating-Current Motor Types

86. In a(n) _____ motor, the rotor is actually locked in step with the rotating stator field and is dragged along at the speed of the rotating magnetic field.

(a) wound-rotor (b) induction (c) synchronous (d) squirrel-cage

87. _____ motors are fractional horsepower motors that operate equally well on ac and dc and are used for vacuum cleaners, electric drills, mixers, and light household appliances.

(a) AC (b) Universal (c) Wound-rotor (d) Synchronous

20.15 Reversing the Rotation of an AC Motor

88. Swapping _____ of the line conductors can reverse a 3Ø ac motor's rotation.

(a) one (b) two (c) three (d) none of these

Unit 21—Generators

21.2 Alternating-Current Generator

89. The _____ of an ac generator contains the electromagnetic field, which cuts through the stationary conductor coils.

(a) stator (b) rotor (c) coil (d) winding

21.3 Three-Phase Generators

90. Three-phase ac generators have three equally spaced windings, _____ degrees out-of-phase with each other.

(a) 90 (b) 120 (c) 180 (d) 360

Unit 22—Transformers

22.1 Transformer Basics

91. The energy transfer ability of a transformer is accomplished because the primary electromagnetic lines of force induce a voltage in the secondary winding.

(a) True (b) False

22.2 Secondary Induced Voltage

92. Voltage induced in the secondary winding of a transformer is dependent on the number of secondary turns as compared to the number of primary turns.

(a) True (b) False

22.4 Power Losses

93. Wasteful circulating _____ in the iron core cause(s) the core to heat up without any useful purpose.

(a) conductor resistance (b) flux leakage
(c) eddy currents (d) hysteresis losses

94. _____ can be reduced by dividing the core into many flat sections or laminations.

(a) Conductor resistance (b) Flux leakage
(c) Eddy currents (d) Hysteresis losses

95. As current flows through the transformer, the iron core is temporarily magnetized. The energy required to realign the core molecules to the changing electromagnetic field is called _____ loss.

(a) conductor resistance
(b) flux leakage
(c) eddy currents
(d) hysteresis

22.5 Harmonic Current

96. Three-phase, _____ wye-connected systems can overheat because of circulating odd triplen harmonic currents.

(a) 2-wire
(b) 3-wire
(c) 4-wire
(d) none of these

97. The heating from harmonic currents is proportional to the square of the harmonic current.

(a) True
(b) False

22.6 Efficiency

98. Because of conductor resistance, flux leakage, eddy currents, and hysteresis losses, not all of the input power is transferred to the secondary winding for useful purposes.

(a) True
(b) False

22.7 Transformer Turns Ratio

99. If the primary phase voltage is 480V and the secondary phase voltage is 240V, the turns ratio is _____.

(a) 1:2
(b) 2:1
(c) 4:1
(d) 1:4

22.8 Transformer kVA Rating

100. Transformers are rated in _____.

(a) VA
(b) kW
(c) W
(d) kVA

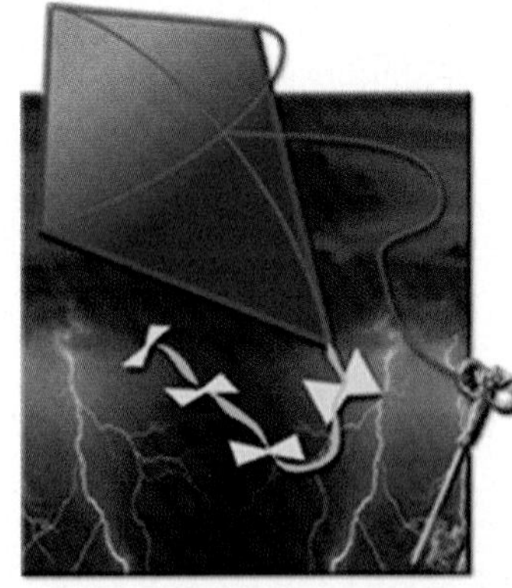

Basic Electrical Theory Final Conclusion

Our journey through 22 units of electrical theory began with studying basic laws of physics. We then moved through the fundamentals based on those laws of physics; electron theory, electricity, magnetism, and electromagnetism.

Next we studied the various types of electrical circuits, circuit protection, and some power quality basics. After studying capacitance and inductance, we took the final leg of our journey by learning about the three kinds of inductive devices electricians work with today—motors, generators, and transformers.

It was a long trip, but well worth the effort. I hope you are not at your final destination. You now have a solid understanding of electrical theory, but there is so much more to learn. The practical application of electricity is not something you master from one, two, or even several courses. It takes years of dedicated study and effort. Be sure to use our other training resources to help you along the way.

ANNEX

Grounding and Bonding

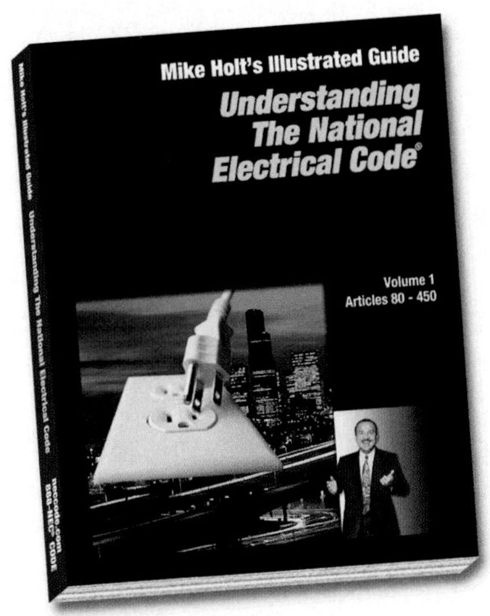

The following text and graphics were extracted from Mike Holt's Illustrated Guide to Understanding the *National Electrical Code* textbook.

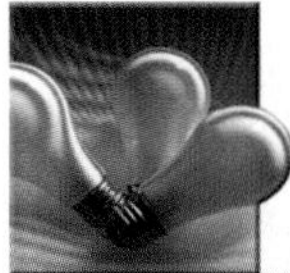

Introduction to Article 250—Grounding and Bonding

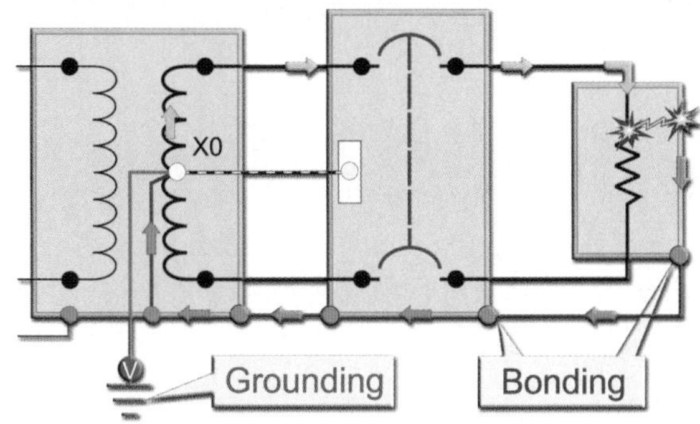

The purpose of the *National Electrical Code* is the practical safeguarding of persons and property from hazards arising from the use of electricity [90.1(A)]. In addition, the *NEC* contains provisions that are considered necessary for safety. Compliance with the *NEC,* combined with proper maintenance, shall result in an installation that is essentially free from hazard [90.1(B)].

Understanding the Basics of Electrical Systems

Contrasting the electric utility system wiring, which is governed by the *National Electrical Safety Code (NESC),* with those of premises wiring which are covered by the *NEC*, should be helpful to enhance an understanding of some basic electrical principles such as current flow, neutral and fault-current paths.

Utility Current Flow

Electrons leaving a power supply are always trying to return to the same power supply; they are not trying to go into the earth. When alternating current is applied to the primary of a transformer, it induces a voltage in the secondary. This induced secondary voltage causes electrons to leave one end of the transformer's secondary, travel over the circuit's conductors through the load and return over the remaining circuit's conductors to the other end of the transformer's secondary. Figure 250–1

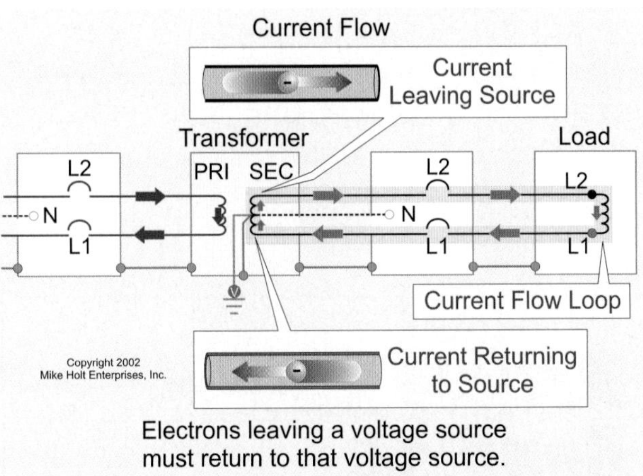

Electrons leaving a voltage source must return to that voltage source.

Figure 250–1

Utility Neutral Current Path

The electric utility grounds the primary and secondary neutral conductor to the earth at multiple locations to create a parallel path so as to reduce the impedance of the return neutral current path. This multipoint grounded utility neutral helps in reducing primary utility neutral voltage drop, the clearing of utility line-to-neutral faults, and in reducing elevated line-to-ground voltages caused by ground faults. Figure 250–2

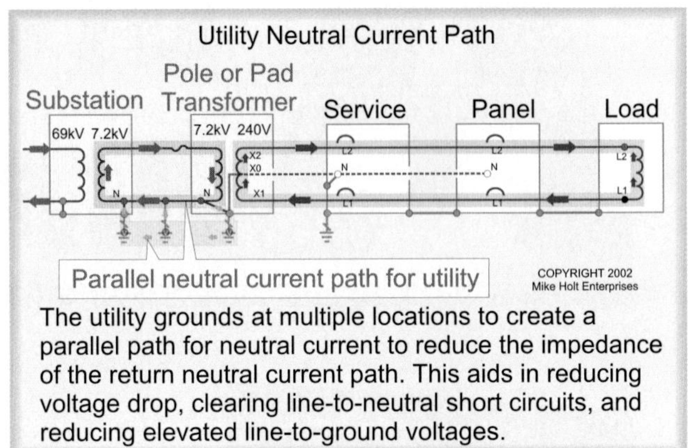

The utility grounds at multiple locations to create a parallel path for neutral current to reduce the impedance of the return neutral current path. This aids in reducing voltage drop, clearing line-to-neutral short circuits, and reducing elevated line-to-ground voltages.

Figure 250–2

Utility Ground-Fault Current Path

Metal parts of the electric utility equipment (transformer and capacitor cases, guy wires, luminaires, etc.) are grounded to the earth and bonded to the grounded (neutral) conductor to provide a low-impedance parallel path for the purpose of clearing a line-to-case ground fault. If the utility grounded (neutral) conductor is inadvertently opened, the earth itself should still have sufficiently low impedance to permit sufficient fault current to flow to blow the fuse, thereby clearing the high-voltage ground fault.

For example, a 7,200V line is typically protected by a 3 to 5A fuse (depending on wire size). The earth, having an impedance of 25Ω, would have no problem carrying sufficient fault current to blow a 5A fuse. (I = E/Z, I = 7,200V/25Ω, I = 288A). Figure 250–3

Premises Neutral Current Path

Neutral current should only flow on the grounded (neutral) conductor, not on metal parts of the electrical installation [250.6]. Figure 250–4

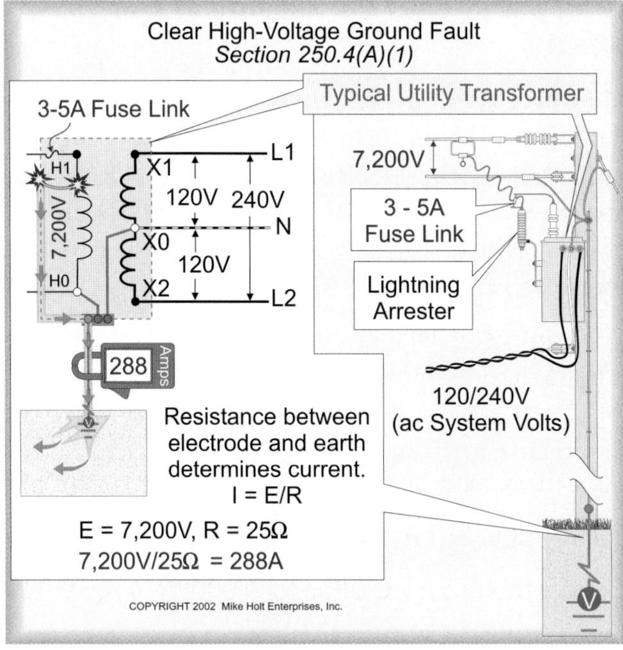

Figure 250–3

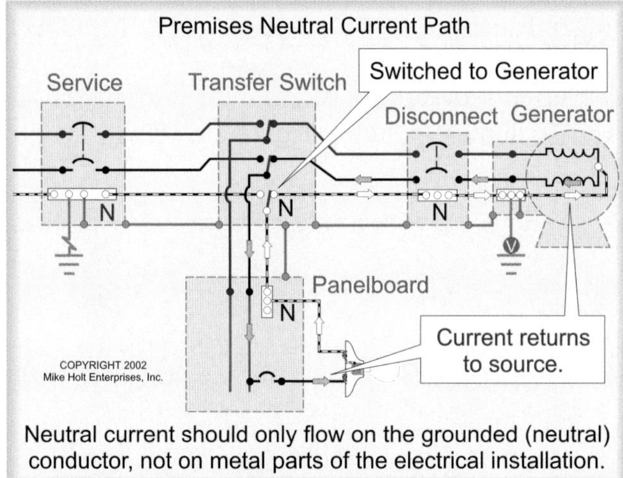

Figure 250–4

Premises Ground-Fault Current Path

Metal parts of premises wiring are bonded to a low-impedance path designed and intended to carry fault current from the point of a line-to-case fault on a wiring system to the grounded (neutral) conductor at the electrical supply source. This low-impedance fault-current path ensures that the ground fault will be quickly cleared by the opening of the circuit protection device. **Figure 250–5**

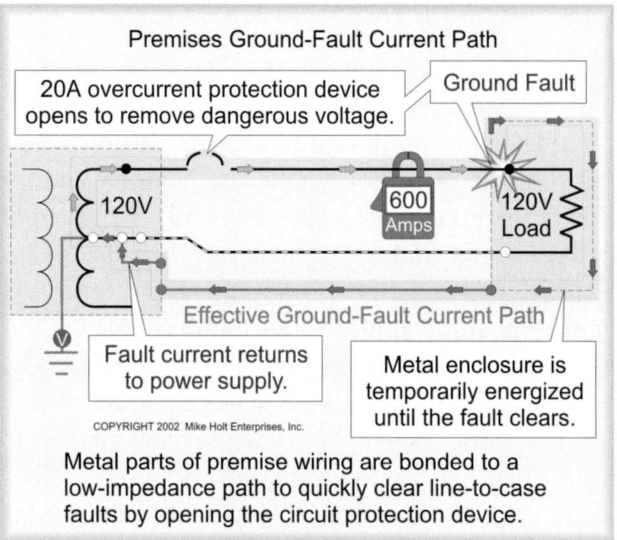

Figure 250–5

For systems operating at 600V or less, the earth will not carry sufficient fault current to clear a line-to-case ground fault. For example, a 120V fault to the earth of 25Ω will only draw 4.8A (I = E/Z, I = 120V/25Ω, I = 4.8A), not enough to open a 15A protection device [250.4(A)(5)]. **Figure 250–6**

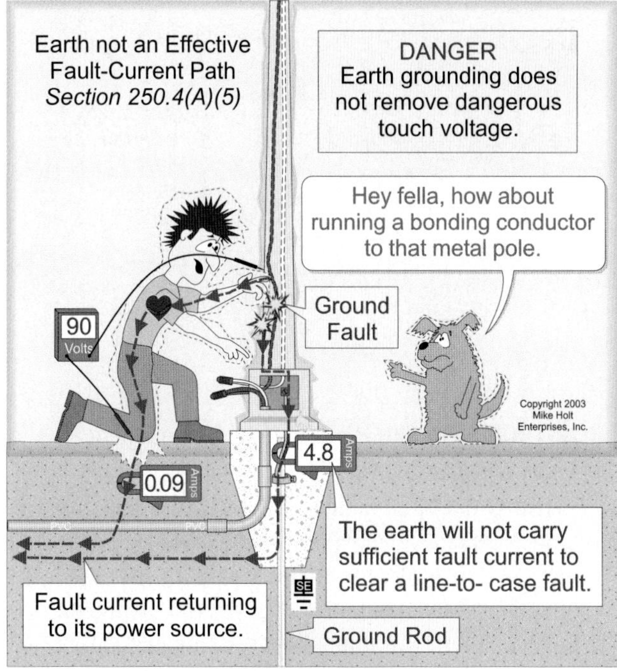

Figure 250–6

Understanding Electrical Shock Hazard

If an electrical system is not properly wired to remove dangerous voltage from a ground fault, persons can be subjected to electric shock, which can result in injury or death. The National Safety Council estimates that approximately 300 people in the United States die each year because of an electric shock from 120V and 277V circuits. People become injured and death occurs when voltage pushes electrons through the human body, particularly through the heart. An electrical shock from as little as 30V alternating current for as little as one second can disrupt the heart's electrical circuitry, causing it to go into ventricular fibrillation. Ventricular fibrillation prevents the blood from circulating through the brain, resulting in death in a matter of minutes. **Figure 250–7**

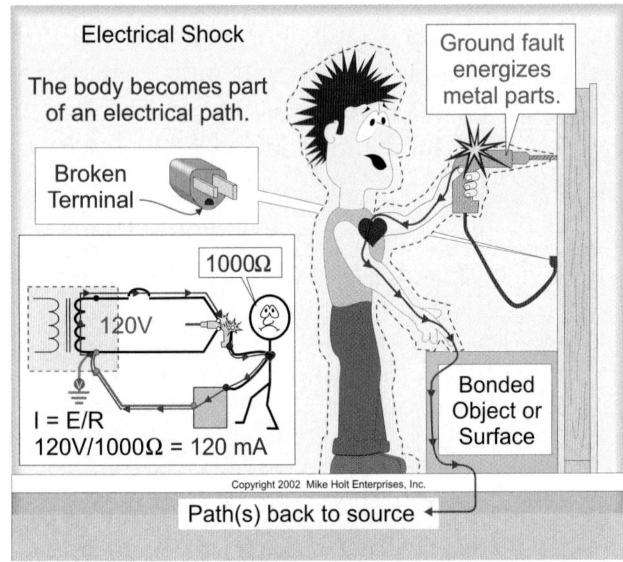

Figure 250–7

AUTHOR'S COMMENT: According to the American Heart Association, ventricular fibrillation (VF) is a life-threatening condition in which the heart no longer beats but "quivers" or fibrillates very rapidly — 350 times per minute or more. To avoid sudden cardiac death, the person must be treated with a defibrillator immediately. Cardiopulmonary resuscitation (CPR) provides some extra time, but defibrillation is essential for surviving ventricular fibrillation.

What Determines the Severity of Electric Shock?

The severity of an electric shock is dependent on the current flowing through the body, which is impacted by the electromotive force (E), measured in volts, and the contact resistance (R), measured in ohms. Current can be determined by the formula I = E/R.

The typical resistances of individual elements of human circuits include:

	Dry	Wet
Foot Immersed in Water		100Ω
Hand Immersed in Water		300Ω
Hand Around $1^1/_2$ in. Pipe	1,000Ω	500Ω
Hand Holding Pliers	8,000Ω	1,000Ω
Finger-Thumb Grasp	30,000Ω	8,000Ω
Finger Touch	100,000Ω	12,000Ω

The effects of 60 Hz alternating current on an average human includes: **Figure 250–8**

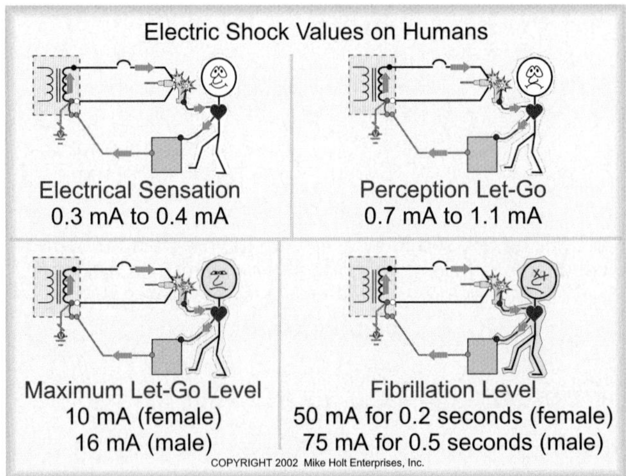

Figure 250–8

- Electrical Sensation. Tingle sensation occurs at about 0.3 mA to 0.4 mA for an adult female and 0.5 mA for an adult male.
- Perception Let-Go. Current over 0.7 to 1.1 mA is very uncomfortable to both sexes.

- Maximum Let-Go Level. The maximum let-go threshold level for a female is approximately 10 mA and for a male it is about 16 mA.

AUTHOR'S COMMENT: The "let-go threshold" is the current level where we lose control of our muscles and the electricity causes muscles to contract until the current is removed.

- Fibrillation Level – 50 mA for 0.2 seconds (female) and 75 mA for 0.5 seconds (male).

According to IEEE Std. 80, *IEEE Guide for Safety in AC Substations,* the maximum safe shock duration can be determined by the formula:

Seconds = 0.116/(E/R), where "R" (the resistance of a person) is assumed to be 1,000Ω.

Example

For a 120V circuit, the maximum shock duration = 0.116/(120V/1,000Ω) = 1 second.

For a 277V circuit, the maximum shock duration = 0.116/(277V/1,000Ω) = 0.43 seconds.

Clearing a Ground Fault

To protect against electric shock from dangerous voltages on metal parts of electrical equipment, a ground fault must quickly be removed by opening the circuit's overcurrent protection device. The time it takes for an overcurrent protection device to open is inversely proportional to the magnitude of the fault current. Thus, the higher the ground-fault current value, the less time it will take for the protection device to open and clear the fault. For example, a 20A circuit with an overload of 40A (two times the rating) would trip a breaker in 25 to 150 seconds. At 100A (five times the rating) the breaker would trip in 5 to 20 seconds. **Figure 250–9**

To remove dangerous touch voltage on metal parts from a ground fault, the fault-current path must have sufficiently low impedance to allow the fault current to quickly rise to facilitate the opening of the branch-circuit overcurrent protection device.

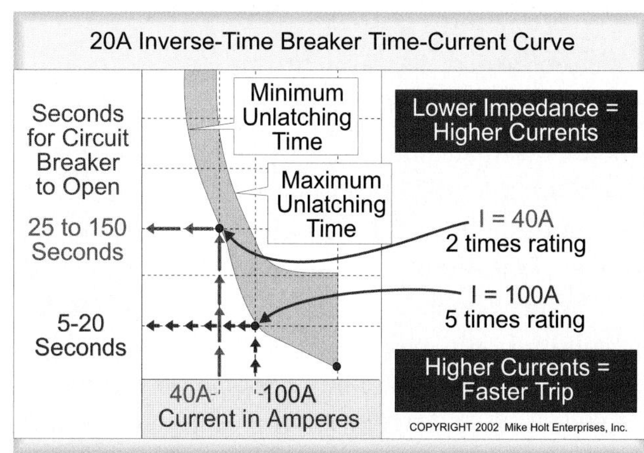

Figure 250–9

Example

Approximately how much ground-fault current can flow in a 100A circuit, which consists of:

Ungrounded Conductors:
200 ft of 3 AWG at 0.05Ω

Equipment Grounding (bonding) Conductor:
200 ft of 8 AWG at 0.156Ω, **Figure 250–10**

(a) 100A (b) 200A
(c) 600A (d) 800A

- Answer: (c) 600A

Fault Current = E/Z

E = 120V

Z = 0.05Ω + 0.156Ω

Z = 0.206Ω

Fault Current = 120V/0.206Ω

Fault Current = 583A

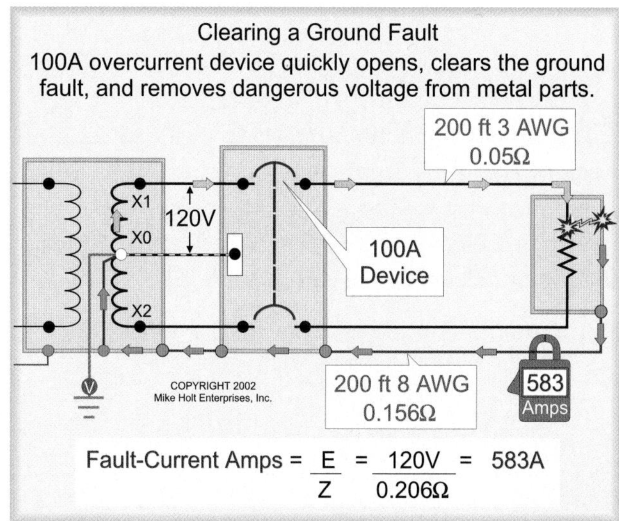

Figure 250–10

Why Grounding is Often Difficult to Understand

The reason it's difficult to understand the rules contained in Article 250 – Grounding, is because many do not understand that this article applies to both grounding and bonding. In addition, the proper definitions of many important terms such as "bond, bonded, bonding, ground, grounded, grounding, and effectively grounded," and their intended application is not understood or improperly used. So before we get too deep into this subject, let's review the differences between grounding and bonding.

Bond, Bonded or Bonding (Article 100)

The permanent joining of metallic parts to form an electrically conductive path that ensures electrical continuity, and the capacity to conduct safely any fault current that is likely to be imposed. Bonding is intended to create a low-impedance path for the purpose of removing dangerous touch voltage from metal parts from a ground fault by quickly opening the overcurrent protection device.

Bonding is generally accomplished by properly mechanically terminating metal raceways and cables to enclosures. It is also accomplished by properly bonding electrical devices to enclosures. Figure 250–11

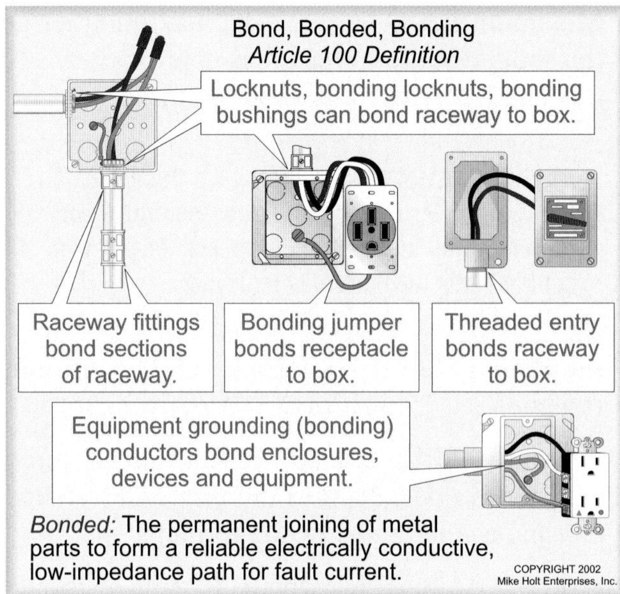

Figure 250–11

Ground (100 Definition)

The earth. Figure 250–12

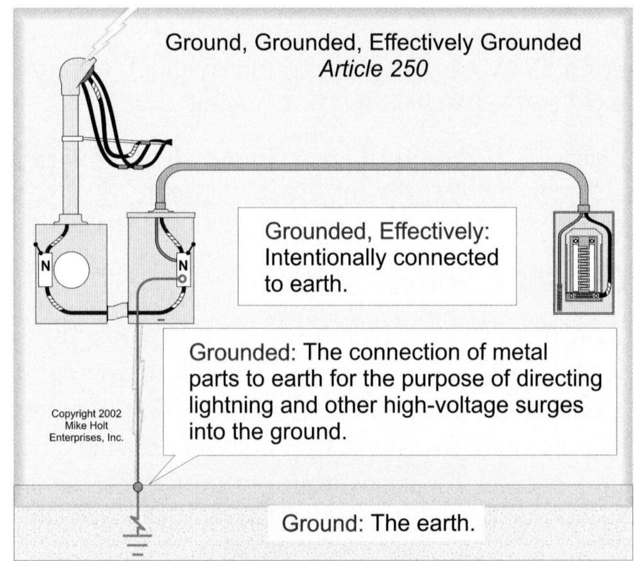

Figure 250–12

Grounded (100 Definition)

The connection of metal parts to earth for the purpose of directing lightning and other high-voltage surges into the ground. See Figure 250–12.

Grounded, Effectively (100 Definition)

Intentionally connected to earth. See Figure 250–12.

AUTHOR'S COMMENT: In addition, electrical power-supply systems over 1,000 VA are grounded to earth to stabilize the system voltage [250.4(A)(1)].

Grounded Conductor (100 Definition)

The conductor that is intentionally grounded to earth at a power supply. Typically, this conductor is called the neutral wire and it is identified with the color white or gray [200.6]. Figure 250–13

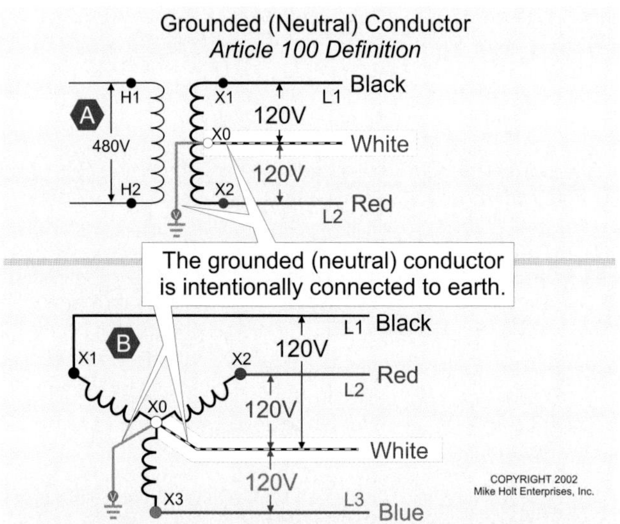

Grounded Conductor: The conductor that is intentionally connected to earth at a power supply. Typically, this is called the neutral wire and it is identified by a white color.

Figure 250–13

AUTHOR'S COMMENT: In this textbook, the "grounded conductor" will be identified as the "grounded (neutral) conductor."

Grounding Electrode Conductor (100 Definition)

The conductor that connects the equipment grounding (bonding) conductor, the grounded (neutral) conductor, or both, to the grounding electrode at the service equipment, at separately derived systems, and at each building or structure in accordance with Article 250. **Figure 250–14**

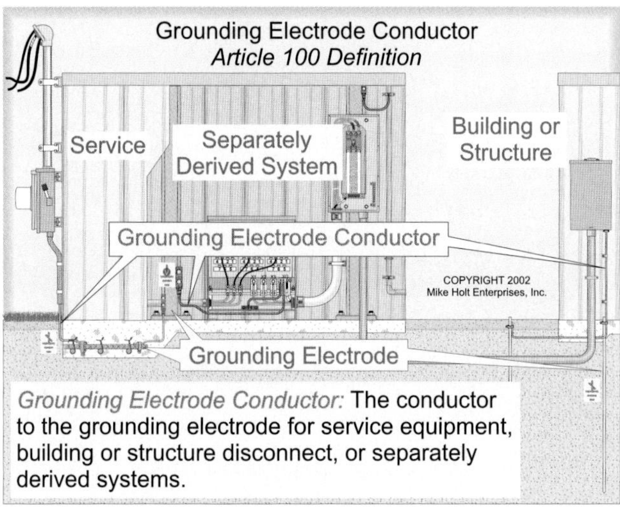

Grounding Electrode Conductor: The conductor to the grounding electrode for service equipment, building or structure disconnect, or separately derived systems.

Figure 250–14

CAUTION: *Often the term ground or grounded is used when the proper term would be bond or bonded. For example, 404.9(B) specifies that "snap switches, including dimmer and similar control switches, shall be effectively grounded." Naturally, we are not expected to intentionally connect the switch to earth; we shall "bond" the metal yoke of the switch to a low-impedance path so that dangerous voltage from a ground fault can be quickly removed by opening the circuit-protection device.* **Figure 250-15**

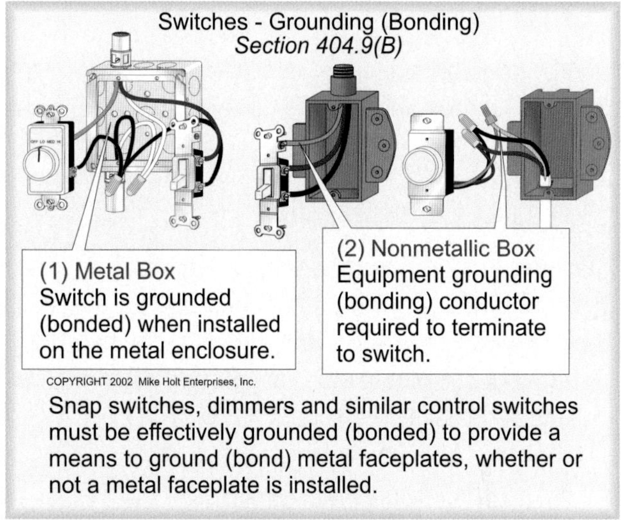

Switches - Grounding (Bonding)
Section 404.9(B)
(1) Metal Box
Switch is grounded (bonded) when installed on the metal enclosure.
(2) Nonmetallic Box
Equipment grounding (bonding) conductor required to terminate to switch.
COPYRIGHT 2002 Mike Holt Enterprises, Inc.

Snap switches, dimmers and similar control switches must be effectively grounded (bonded) to provide a means to ground (bond) metal faceplates, whether or not a metal faceplate is installed.

Figure 250–15

AUTHOR'S COMMENT: One of the key points in understanding the difference between grounding and bonding is that grounding provides a path to earth for lightning, whereas bonding provides the low-impedance path necessary to quickly remove dangerous voltage from metal parts by quickly opening the circuit protection device.

Special Textbook Helps

Figure Graphics

To help keep the subjects straight, the figure graphics in this unit have a color-coded border:

- Dark orange border indicates that the graphic relates to grounding.
- Green border indicates that the graphic relates to bonding.
- Yellow border indicates an improper installation where neutral return current flows on the metal parts of the electrical system.
- No color border indicates important information but not specifically about grounding or bonding.

Grounding Electrode Symbol

Where a grounding electrode symbol is displayed in the graphic, it will indicate its purpose as to whether it is a lightning electrode, a voltage stabilization electrode, or a supplemental or signal reference electrode. Figure 250–16

AUTHOR'S COMMENT: Grounding electrodes serve no part in clearing ground faults of premises wiring systems operating at under 600V.

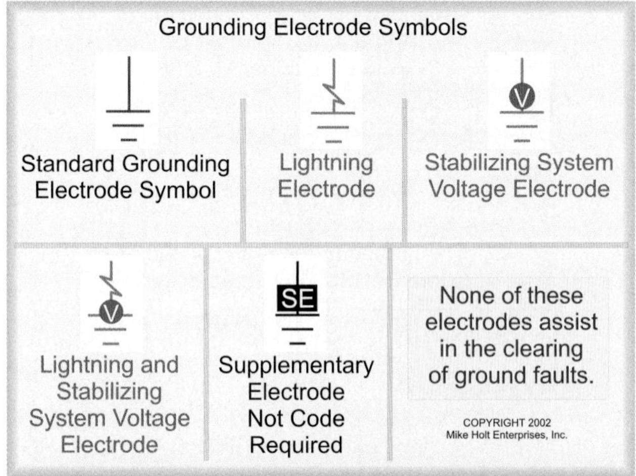

Figure 250–16

NEC "Ground" Terms

Throughout this book, where the *NEC* references the terms "ground," "grounded," or "grounding" and the intent is "bond," "bonded" or "bonding," I will add (bond), (bonded), or (bonding) to help make the rule easier to understand. For example, snap switches, including dimmer and similar control switches, shall be effectively grounded (bonded).

Article 250— Grounding and Bonding

The purpose and objective of "Article 250 – Grounding" is to ensure that electrical installations are safe from electric shock and fires by limiting voltage imposed by lightning and line surges. Though not listed in the title of Article 250, yet included in the requirement, "bonding" is the intentional connection of metal parts to form a low-impedance effective ground-fault current path to remove dangerous voltage from metal parts from a ground fault.

AUTHOR'S COMMENT: The grounding and bonding rules covered in this unit apply to solidly grounded alternating-current systems under 600V, such as 120/240V, 120/208V and 277/480V. Other system configurations, such as 3-wire corner-grounded delta systems, ungrounded systems, or high-impedance grounded neutral systems are permitted by the *National Electrical Code*, but they are typically limited to three-phase industrial applications and not covered in this unit.

PART I. GENERAL

250.1 Scope

Part I contains the general requirements for grounding and bonding. The remaining parts contain specific grounding and bonding requirements such as:

(1) Systems and equipment required, permitted, or not permitted to be grounded.

(2) Which circuit conductor is required to be grounded on grounded systems.

(3) The location of grounding (bonding) connections.

(4) How to size grounding and bonding conductors.

(5) Methods of grounding and bonding.

250.2 Definitions

Effective Ground-Fault Current Path

An intentionally constructed, permanent, low-impedance conductive path designed to carry fault current from the point of a ground fault on a wiring system to the grounded (neutral) point at the electrical supply source. Figure 250–17

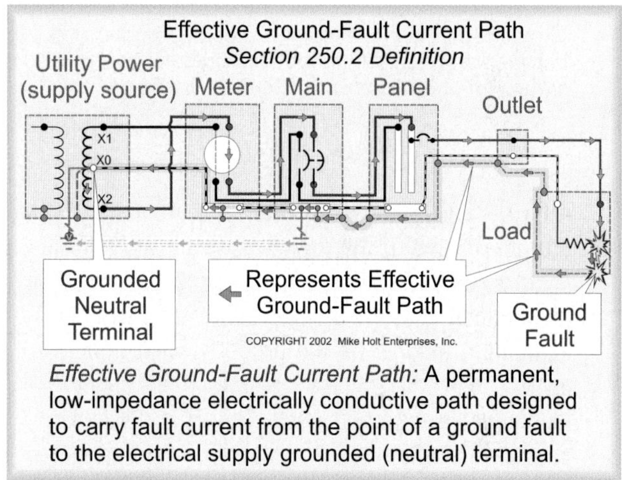

Figure 250–17

An effective ground-fault current path is created when all noncurrent-carrying electrically conductive materials of an electrical installation are bonded together and to the grounded (neutral) conductor at the electric supply. Effective bonding is accomplished through the use of equipment grounding (bonding) conductors, metallic raceways, connectors, couplings, metallic-sheathed cable with approved fittings and other approved devices recognized for this purpose [250.18].

AUTHOR'S COMMENT: A ground-fault current path is only effective when it is properly sized so that it will safely carry the maximum fault current likely to be imposed on it. See 250.4(A)(5) and 250.122 for additional details.

Ground Fault (Line-to-Case Fault)

An unintentional, electrically conducting connection between an ungrounded conductor of an electrical circuit and metallic enclosures, metallic raceways, or metallic equipment. **Figure 250–18**

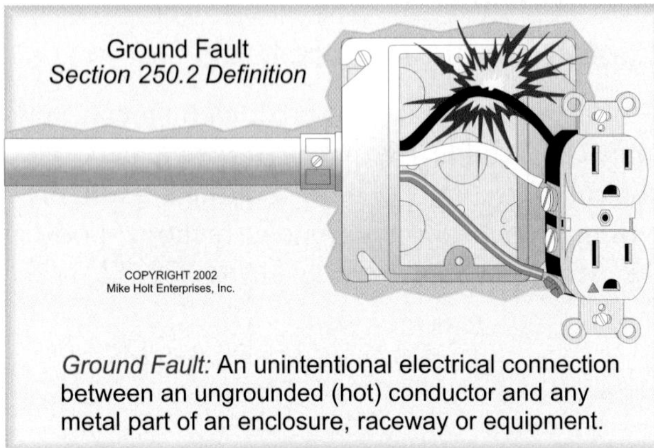
Ground Fault
Section 250.2 Definition
COPYRIGHT 2002
Mike Holt Enterprises, Inc.
Ground Fault: An unintentional electrical connection between an ungrounded (hot) conductor and any metal part of an enclosure, raceway or equipment.

Figure 250–18

AUTHOR'S COMMENT: Line-to-case ground faults are not always of the low-impedance type; they might be of the high-impedance arcing type, which are difficult to clear before a fire destroys the equipment as well as the property. High impedance, in this case, occurs when improper bonding techniques have been used. This is a particular problem for 480V solidly grounded systems and that is why the *NEC* requires equipment ground-fault protection for larger installations. See 230.95. Another way of reducing this hazard is by the installation of high-impedance grounded systems. See 250.36 for the use of current-limiting fuses.

Ground-Fault Current Path

An electrically conductive path from the point of a ground fault (line-to-case fault) on a wiring system through conductors, or equipment extending to the grounded (neutral) terminal at the electrical supply source.

FPN: The ground-fault current paths could consist of grounding and bonding conductors, metallic raceways, metallic cable sheaths, electrical equipment and other electrically conductive material, such as metallic water and gas piping, steel framing members, stucco mesh, metal ducting, reinforcing steel, or shields of communications cables.

AUTHOR'S COMMENT: The difference between an "effective ground-fault current path" and a "ground-fault current path" is that the effective ground-fault current path is "intentionally" made for the purpose of clearing a fault. The ground-fault current path is simply the path that ground-fault current will flow on to the power supply during a ground fault.

250.3 Other Code Sections

Other rules that contain additional grounding and bonding requirements listed in Table 250.3 include:

- Agricultural Building Equipotential Planes, 547.9 and 547.10. **Figure 250–19**

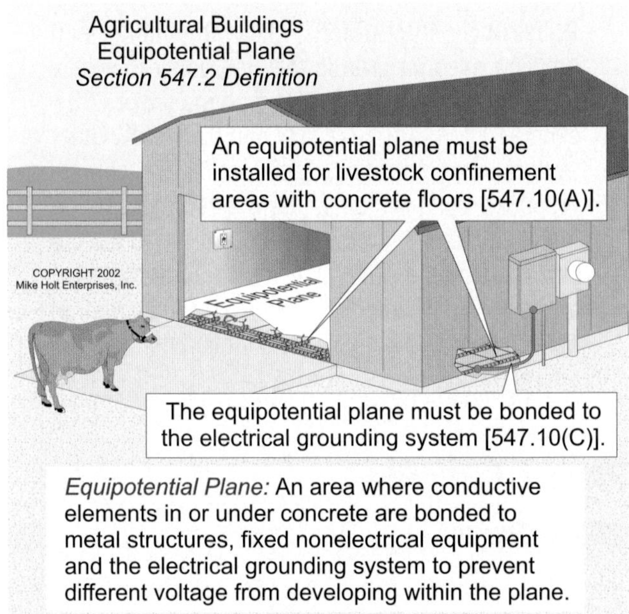
Agricultural Buildings
Equipotential Plane
Section 547.2 Definition
An equipotential plane must be installed for livestock confinement areas with concrete floors [547.10(A)].
COPYRIGHT 2002
Mike Holt Enterprises, Inc.
Equipotential Plane
The equipotential plane must be bonded to the electrical grounding system [547.10(C)].
Equipotential Plane: An area where conductive elements in or under concrete are bonded to metal structures, fixed nonelectrical equipment and the electrical grounding system to prevent different voltage from developing within the plane.

Figure 250–19

- Audio Equipment, 640.7
- Hazardous (classified) Locations, 501.16, 502.16 and 503.16
- Panelboards, 408.20
- Receptacles, 406.3, 406.9, 517.13
- Receptacle Cover Plates, 406.5
- Swimming Pools and Spas, 680.23(F)(2), 680.24(D) and 680.25(B)
- Switches, 404.9(B) and 517.13

250.4 General Requirements for Grounding and Bonding

The following explains the purpose of the grounding and bonding of electrical systems and equipment to ensure a safe installation.

AUTHOR'S COMMENT: The term "electrical system" as used in the subsection that follows refers to the "power source" such as a transformer, generator or photovoltaic system, not the circuit wiring and/or the equipment.

(A) Grounded Systems

(1) **Grounding of Electrical Systems.** Electrical power supplies such as the utility transformer shall be grounded to earth to help limit high voltage imposed on the system windings from lightning or line surges. Figure 250–20

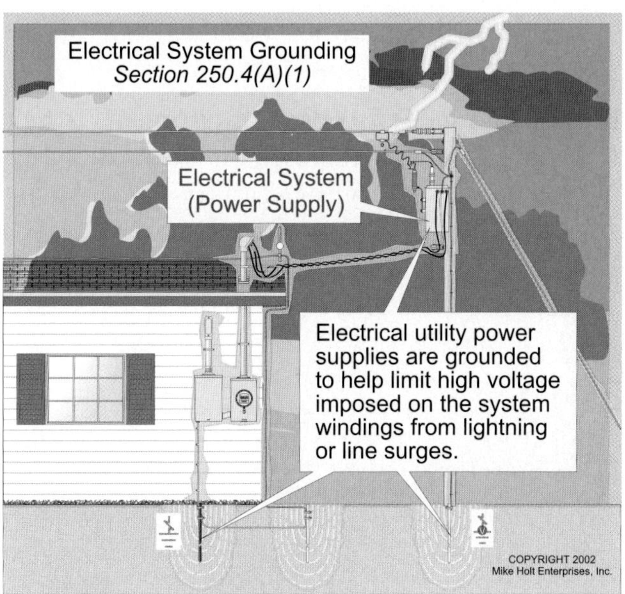

Figure 250–20

AUTHOR'S COMMENT: Grounding System for Lightning – The electric discharge from lightning is typically from a negative charged cloud to a positive charged earth surface, but it can be from the earth's surface to a cloud, or it can be from cloud to cloud as well as cloud to space. When the negative capacitive voltage charge of a cloud exceeds the dielectric strength of the air between the cloud and the earth, an arc will occur between the clouds and the earth in an attempt to equalize the difference of potential between the two objects. When this occurs, high voltages, often over 20,000V, drive high amperages of current (as much as 40,000A) into the earth for a fraction of a second. Figure 250-21

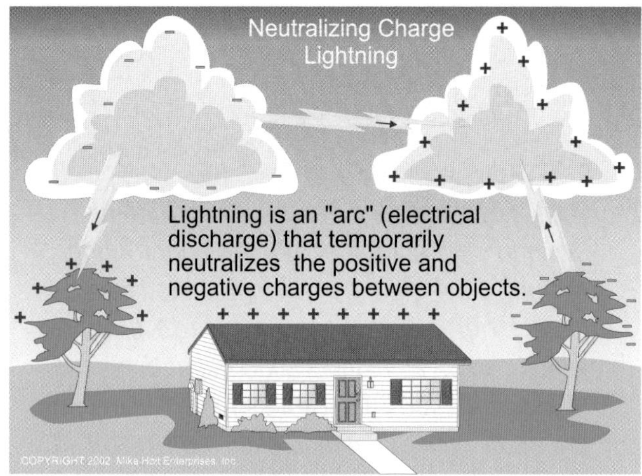

Figure 250–21

Typically, utility wiring outside will be struck by lightning and it's critical that these systems be grounded to the earth to assist the flow of lightning into the earth.

Grounding System for Line Surges – When a utility high-voltage ground fault occurs, the voltage on the other phases will rise for the duration of the fault (typically 3 to 12 cycles). This voltage surge during the utility ground fault will be transformed into an elevated surge voltage on the secondary, which can cause destruction of electrical and particularly electronic equipment in the premises. Studies have shown that the lower the resistance of the utility grounding system, the lower the voltage surge.

Electrical systems (power supplies) are grounded and bonded to stabilize the system voltage during normal operation. Figure 250–22

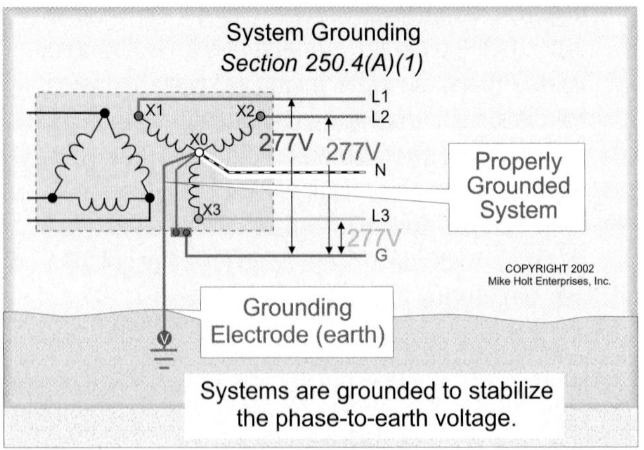

Figure 250–22

CAUTION: *According to IEEE Std. 242 "Buff Book," if a ground fault is intermittent or allowed to continue on an ungrounded system, the system could be subjected to possible severe system overvoltage-to-ground, which can be as high as six or eight times the phase voltage. This excessive voltage can puncture conductor insulation and result in additional ground faults. System overvoltage-to-ground is caused by repetitive charging of the system capacitance or by resonance between the system capacitance and the inductances of equipment in the system.*

In addition, IEEE Std. 142 "Green Book" states that "Field experience and theoretical studies have shown that arcing, restriking, or vibrating ground faults on ungrounded systems (actually unbonded systems) can, under certain conditions, produce surge voltages as high as six times normal. Neutral (system) grounding (actually bonding) is effective in reducing transient voltage build up from such intermittent ground faults by reducing neutral displacement from ground potential and reducing destructive effectiveness of any high-frequency voltage oscillations following each arc initiation or restrike." Figure 250-23

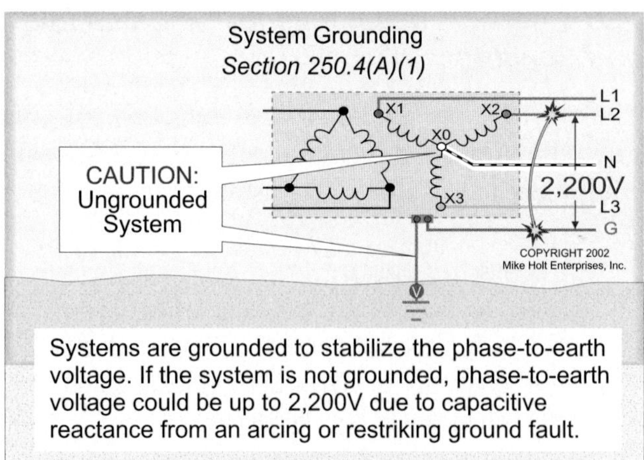

Figure 250–23

AUTHOR'S COMMENT: The danger of overvoltage occurs in systems that are intended to be ungrounded as well as those systems that were supposed to be grounded but were not. Elevated voltage-to-ground is beyond the scope of this unit. To obtain more information on this subject, visit http://www.mikeholt.com/Newsletters/highvolt.htm.

(2) Grounding of Electrical Equipment. To help limit the voltage imposed on metal parts from lightning, noncurrent-carrying conductive metal parts of electrical equipment in or on a building or structure shall be grounded to earth. Figure 250–24

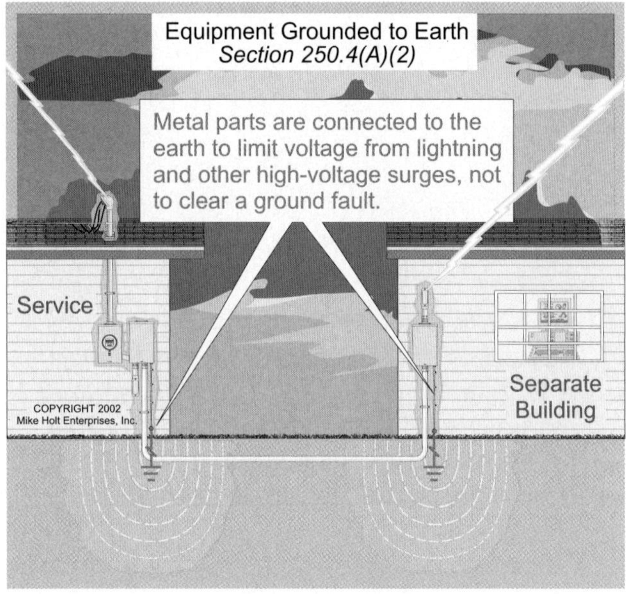

Figure 250–24

AUTHOR'S COMMENT: Grounding of electrical equipment to earth is not for the purpose of clearing a ground fault.

Metal parts of electrical equipment in a building or structure are grounded to earth by electrically connecting the building or structure disconnecting means [225.31 or 230.70] with a grounding electrode conductor [250.64(A)] to an appropriate grounding electrode (earth) identified in 250.52 [250.24(A) and 250.32(B)].

DANGER: ***Failure to ground the metal parts of electrical equipment to earth could result in elevated voltage from lightning entering the building or structure, via metal raceways or cables, seeking a path to the earth. The high voltage on the metal parts from lightning can result in electric shock and fires, as well as the destruction of electrical equipment from lightning.*** **Figure 250-25**

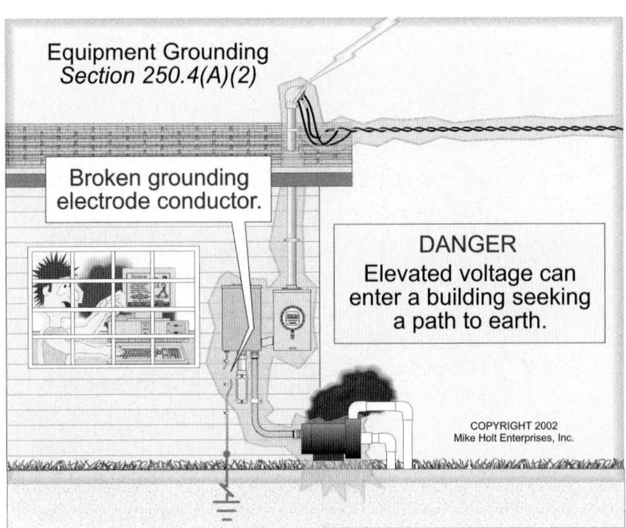

Figure 250–25

Grounding of metal parts of electrical equipment also helps prevent the build up of high-voltage static charges on metal parts. Grounding is often required in areas where the discharge (arcing) of the voltage build up could cause failure of electronic equipment being assembled on a production line, or a fire and explosion in a hazardous classified area. See 500.4 FPN 3.

AUTHOR'S COMMENT: Grounding metal parts of electrical equipment to earth does not protect electrical or electronic equipment from lightning voltage transients (high-frequency voltage impulses) on the circuit conductors inside the building or structure. To protect electronic and electrical equipment from high-voltage transients, proper transient voltage surge-protection devices should be installed in accordance with Article 280 at service equipment and Article 285 at the panelboards.

To provide proper operation of transient voltage surge-protection devices, the resistance of the grounding electrode (earth) should be as low as practicable. Most specifications for communications systems installations (cell towers) require the ground resistance to be 5Ω, sometimes as little as 3Ω and on some rare occasions 1Ω! To achieve and maintain a low resistive ground, special grounding configurations, design, equipment and measuring instruments must be used. This is beyond the scope of this unit.

(3) **Bonding of Electrical Equipment.** To remove dangerous voltage caused by ground faults, the metal parts of electrical raceways, cables, enclosures or equipment shall be bonded together. In addition, the metal parts shall be bonded to the grounded (neutral) terminal of the electrical supply source in accordance with 250.142. **Figure 250–26**

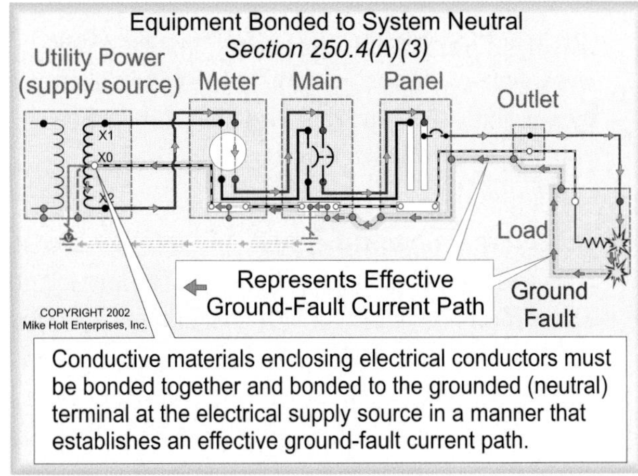

Figure 250–26

AUTHOR'S COMMENT: An effective ground-fault current path [250.2] is created when all non-current-carrying electrically conductive materials are bonded together and to the grounded (neutral) terminal at the electric supply.

(4) **Bonding of Electrically Conductive Materials.** To remove dangerous voltage caused by ground faults, electrically conductive metal water piping, sprinkler piping, metal gas piping, and other metal piping as well as exposed structural steel members that are likely to become energized shall be bonded in accordance with 250.104. **Figure 250–27**

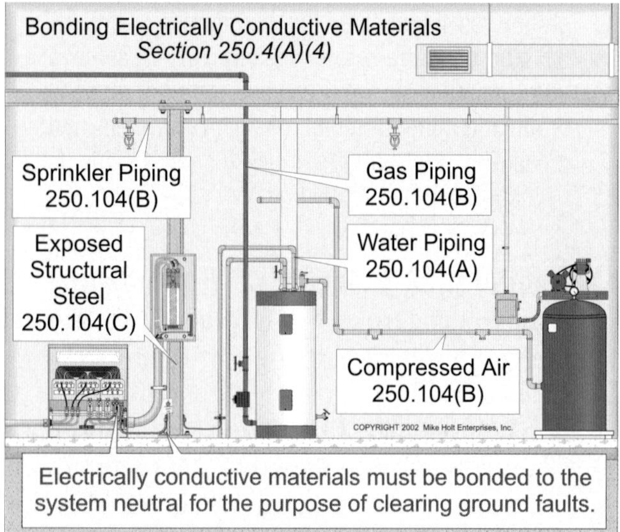
Bonding Electrically Conductive Materials
Section 250.4(A)(4)
Sprinkler Piping 250.104(B)
Gas Piping 250.104(B)
Exposed Structural Steel 250.104(C)
Water Piping 250.104(A)
Compressed Air 250.104(B)
COPYRIGHT 2002 Mike Holt Enterprises, Inc.
Electrically conductive materials must be bonded to the system neutral for the purpose of clearing ground faults.

Figure 250–27

AUTHOR'S COMMENT: The phrase "that are likely to become energized" is subject to interpretation by the Authority Having Jurisdiction (AHJ). See 250.104 for additional details.

(5) **Effective Ground-Fault Current Path.** Electrical raceways, cables, enclosures and equipment as well as other electrically conductive material "likely to become energized" shall be installed in a manner that creates a permanent, low-impedance path that has the capacity to safely carry the maximum ground-fault current likely to be imposed on it [110.10]. The purpose of this path is to facilitate the operation of overcurrent devices if a ground fault occurs to the metal parts. Clearing ground faults is accomplished by bonding all of the metal parts of electrical equipment and conductive material likely to become energized to the power-supply grounded (neutral) terminal. **Figure 250–28**

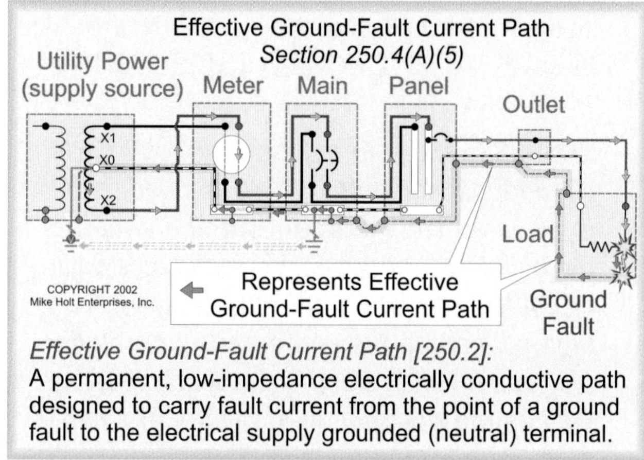
Effective Ground-Fault Current Path
Section 250.4(A)(5)
Utility Power (supply source)
Meter
Main
Panel
Outlet
X1
X0
X2
Load
COPYRIGHT 2002 Mike Holt Enterprises, Inc.
Represents Effective Ground-Fault Current Path
Ground Fault
Effective Ground-Fault Current Path [250.2]:
A permanent, low-impedance electrically conductive path designed to carry fault current from the point of a ground fault to the electrical supply grounded (neutral) terminal.

Figure 250–28

The *NEC* does permit a ground rod at a pole [250.54] but the *Code* does not allow the earth to be used as the sole equipment grounding (bonding) conductor. An equipment grounding (bonding) conductor of a type specified in 250.118 is ALWAYS required. **Figure 250–29**

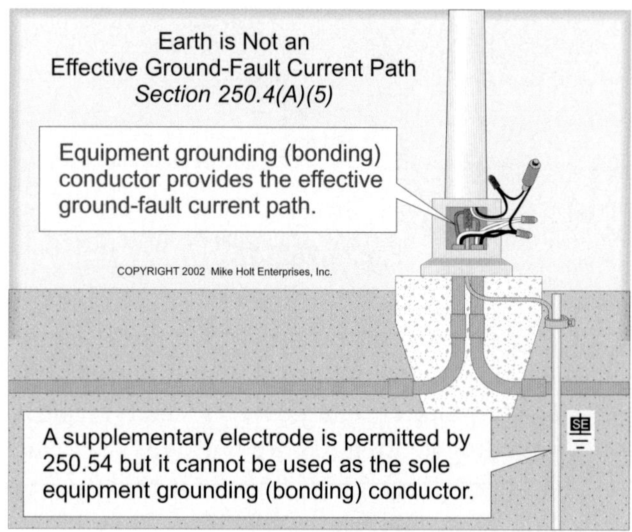
Earth is Not an Effective Ground-Fault Current Path
Section 250.4(A)(5)
Equipment grounding (bonding) conductor provides the effective ground-fault current path.
COPYRIGHT 2002 Mike Holt Enterprises, Inc.
A supplementary electrode is permitted by 250.54 but it cannot be used as the sole equipment grounding (bonding) conductor.

Figure 250–29

CAUTION: *Because the earth is a poor conductor whose resistivity does not permit sufficient fault current to flow back to the power supply [IEEE Std. 142 Section 2.2.8], a ground rod will not serve to clear a ground fault and dangerous touch voltage will remain on metal parts if an effective ground-fault current path is not provided. For more information on this topic visit www.mikeholt.com.* Figure 250-30

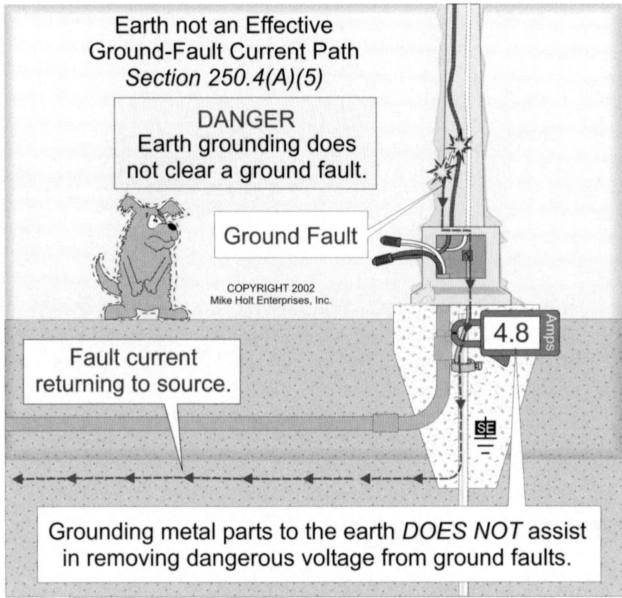
Earth not an Effective
Ground-Fault Current Path
Section 250.4(A)(5)
DANGER
Earth grounding does
not clear a ground fault.
Ground Fault
COPYRIGHT 2002
Mike Holt Enterprises, Inc.
4.8
Amps
Fault current
returning to source.
Grounding metal parts to the earth DOES NOT assist
in removing dangerous voltage from ground faults.

Figure 250–30

Question: What is the maximum current that could flow through a ground rod if the ground rod has an impedance of 25Ω and the system voltage is 120/240V?

(a) 4.8A (b) 24A
(c) 48A (d) 96A

- Answer: (a) 4.8A

I = E/Z

E = 120V

Z = 25Ω

I = 120V/25Ω

I = 4.8A

DANGER: *Because the resistance of the earth is so great (10 to 500 Ω), very little current will return to the power supply via the earth if the earth is the only ground-fault return path. The result is that the circuit overcurrent protection device will not open and metal parts will remain energized at a lethal level waiting for someone to make contact with them and the earth. Therefore, a ground rod cannot be used to lower touch voltage to a safe value for metal parts that are not bonded to an effective ground-fault current path. To understand how a ground rod is useless in reducing touch voltage to a safe level, let's review the following:*

- *What is touch voltage?*
- *At what level is touch voltage hazardous?*
- *How earth surface voltage gradients operate.*

1. Touch Voltage – The IEEE definition of touch voltage is "the potential (voltage) difference between a grounded (bonded) metallic structure and a point on the earth 3 ft from the structure."

2. Hazardous Level – NFPA 70E – Standard for Electrical Safety Requirements for Employee Workplaces, cautions that death and/or severe electric shock can occur whenever the touch voltage exceeds 30V.

3. Surface Voltage Gradients – According to IEEE Std. 142 "Green Book" [4.1.1], the resistance of the soil outward from a ground rod is equal to the sum of the series resistances of the earth shells. The shell nearest the rod has the highest resistance and each successive shell has progressively larger areas and progressively lower resistances. The following table lists the percentage of total resistance and the touch voltage based on a 120V fault. The table's percentage of resistance is based on a 10 ft ground rod having a diameter of 5/8 inches.

Don't worry if you don't understand the above statement, just review the table below with Figure 250-31.

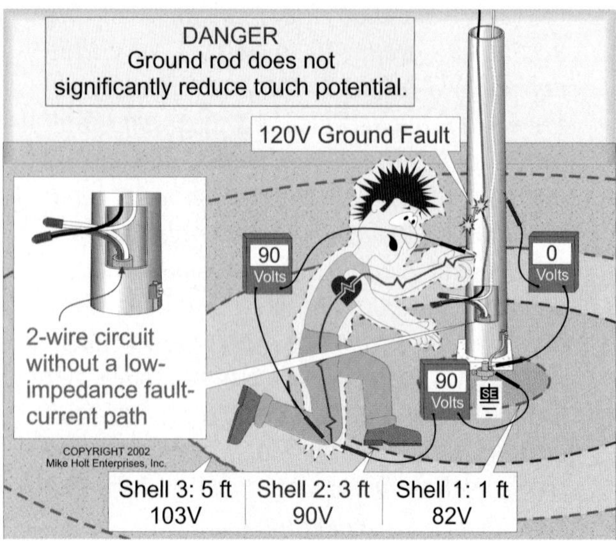

Figure 250–31

Distance from Rod	Resistance	Touch Voltage
1 Foot (Shell 1)	68%	82V
3 Feet (Shells 1 and 2)	75%	90V
5 Feet (Shells 1, 2 and 3)	86%	103V

With the intention of providing a safer installation, many think a ground rod can be used to reduce touch voltage. However, as we can see in the previous table, the voltage gradient of the earth drops off so rapidly that a person in contact with an energized object can receive a lethal electric shock one foot away from an energized object if the metal parts are not bonded to an effective ground-fault current path.

Scary as it might be, the accepted grounding practice for street lighting and traffic signaling for many parts of the United States was to use the ground rod as the only ground-fault current return path. That is, the metal pole of a light fixture or traffic signal is grounded to a ground rod and an effective ground-fault current path is not provided (no equipment grounding conductor)! I'm sure there are thousands of energized metal poles, just waiting for someone to make contact with them and this is one of the reasons so many people get killed with street lighting and traffic signal poles in the United States. For a case study on this subject, visit www.mikeholt.com/Newsletters/dadecounty.

AUTHOR'S COMMENT: Another factor necessary to help ensure a low-impedance ground-fault path is that all circuit conductors, ungrounded, grounded and the equipment grounding (bonding) conductor shall be grouped together in the same raceway, cable or trench [300.3(B), 300.5(I), 300.20(A)]. **Figure 250-32**

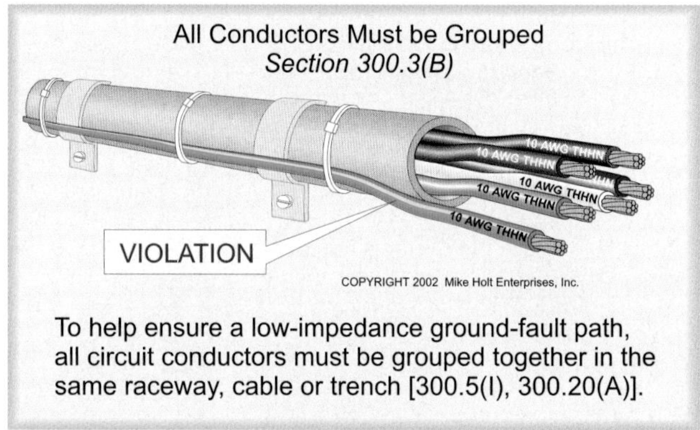

To help ensure a low-impedance ground-fault path, all circuit conductors must be grouped together in the same raceway, cable or trench [300.5(I), 300.20(A)].

Figure 250–32

250.4(A) Summary

(1) An electrical power supply shall be grounded to stabilize the system voltage.

(2) Metal parts of electrical equipment at a building or structure disconnect shall be grounded to assist lightning to earth.

(3) Electrically bonding noncurrent-carrying parts of the electrical wiring system to an effective ground-fault current path is required so that a ground fault can be quickly cleared by opening the circuit overcurrent protection device.

(4) Electrically bonding conductive piping and structural steel that may become energized to the effective ground-fault current path is required so that a ground fault can be quickly cleared by opening the circuit overcurrent protection device.

(5) Create an effective ground-fault current path for metal parts of equipment enclosures, raceways, and equipment as well as metal piping

and structural steel. The effective ground-fault current path shall be sized to withstand high fault current [110.10 and 250.122].

The following shaded text is not part of the NEC itself, but it is provided to help you better understand the requirements contained within 250.6 Objectionable (Neutral) Current.

Objectionable (Neutral) Current

Objectionable current on grounding and bonding paths occurs when:

1. Improper neutral-to-case bonds are made.
2. There are errors in the wiring installation.
3. Using the equipment grounding conductor to carry neutral current.

Improper Neutral-to-Case Bond [250.142]

Panelboards. Bonding of the neutral terminal to the case of a panelboard that is not part of service equipment, or a separately derived system, creates a parallel path which allows objectionable neutral current to flow on the metal parts of electrical equipment, as well as the grounding and bonding conductors. Figure 250–33

Disconnects. Where an equipment grounding (bonding) conductor is run with the feeder conductors to a separate building [250.32(B)(1)], a common and dangerous mistake is to make a neutral-to-case bond in the separate building disconnect, which allows objectionable neutral current to flow on the metal parts of electrical equipment as well as on the grounding and bonding conductors. Figure 250–34

Separately Derived Systems. The neutral-to-case bonding jumper for a separately derived system, such as that derived from a transformer, generator, or uninterruptible power supply (UPS) shall be installed either at the source of the separately derived system or at the first disconnect electrically downstream, but not at both locations, in accordance with 250.30(A)(1).

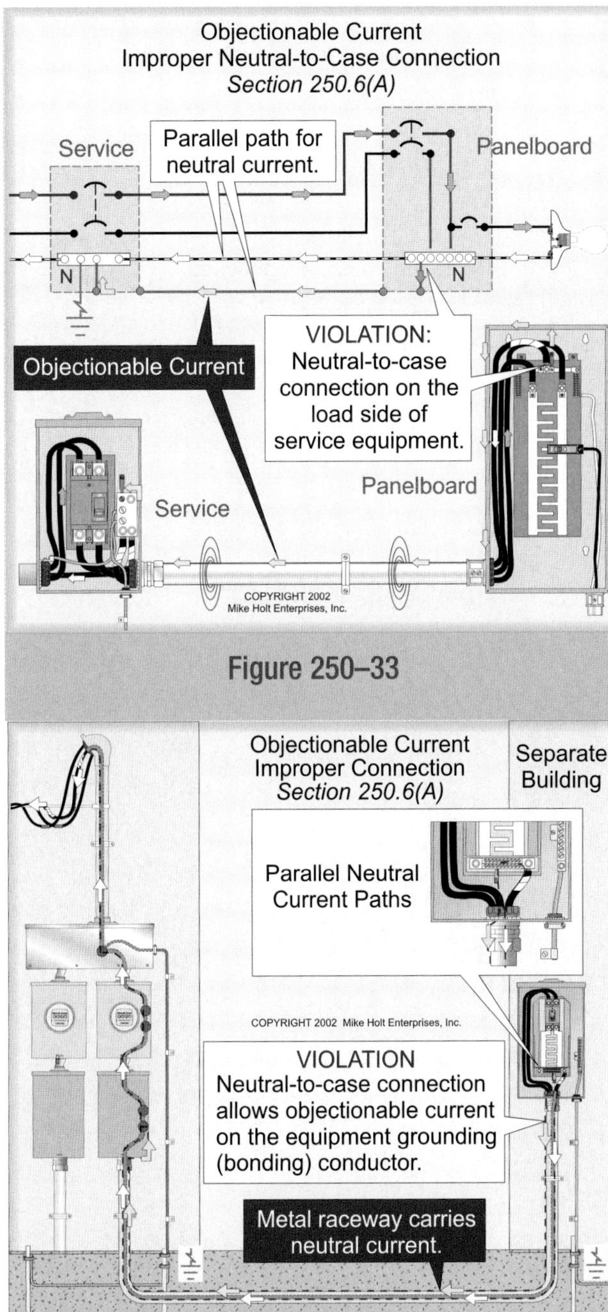

Objectionable Current
Improper Neutral-to-Case Connection
Section 250.6(A)
Service
Parallel path for neutral current.
Panelboard
N
N
Objectionable Current
VIOLATION:
Neutral-to-case connection on the load side of service equipment.
Panelboard
Service
COPYRIGHT 2002
Mike Holt Enterprises, Inc.

Figure 250–33

Objectionable Current
Improper Connection
Section 250.6(A)
Separate Building
Parallel Neutral Current Paths
COPYRIGHT 2002 Mike Holt Enterprises, Inc.
VIOLATION
Neutral-to-case connection allows objectionable current on the equipment grounding (bonding) conductor.
Metal raceway carries neutral current.

Figure 250–34

Transformers. If a neutral-to-case bond is made at both the transformer and at the secondary panelboard/disconnect, then objectionable neutral current will flow on the metal parts of electrical equipment as well as the grounding and bonding conductors. Figure 250–35

Generator. If the grounded (neutral) conductor in a transfer switch is not opened with the ungrounded conductors, then the grounded

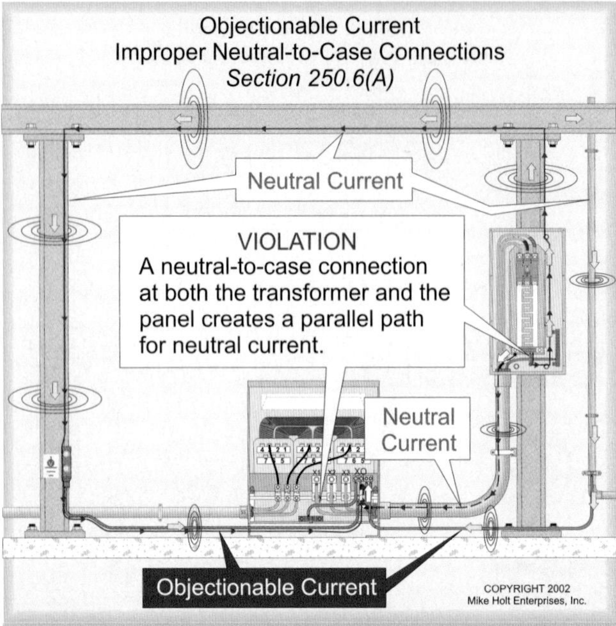

Figure 250–35

(neutral) from the generator will be solidly connected to the utility's service grounded (neutral) conductor. Under this condition, the generator is not a separately derived system, and a neutral-to-case bond shall not be made at the generator or at the generator disconnect [250.20(D) FPN 1]. If a neutral-to-case bond is made at the generator or generator disconnect, then objectionable neutral current will flow on the metal parts of electrical equipment as well as on the grounding and bonding conductors. Figure 250–36

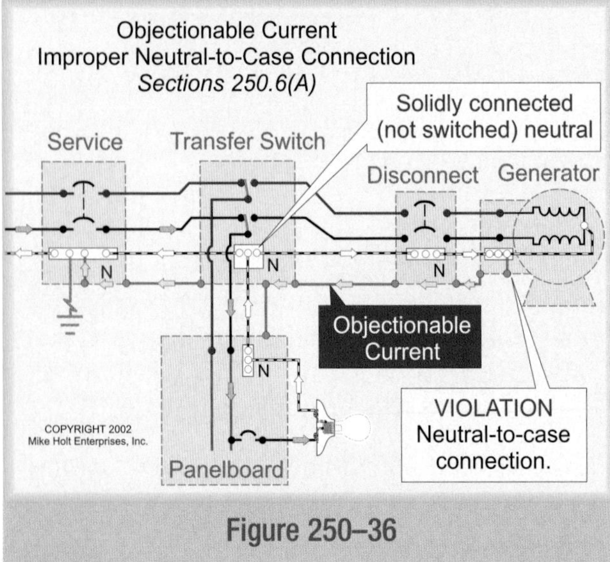

Figure 250–36

Errors in the Wiring Installation

Mixing Neutrals. The *NEC* does not prohibit the mixing of circuit conductors from different systems in the same raceway or enclosure [300.3(C)(1)]. As a result, mistakes can be made where the grounded (neutral) conductors from different systems are crossed (mixed). When this occurs, the grounding and bonding path will carry objectionable neutral current, even when it appears that all circuits have been de-energized. Figure 250–37

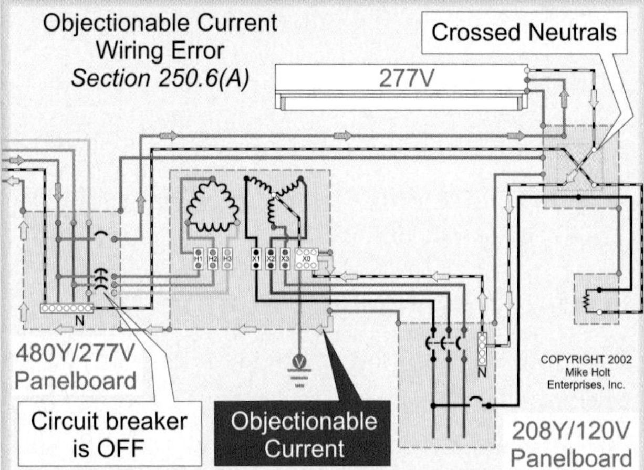

Figure 250–37

Using Equipment Grounding (Bonding) Conductor for Neutral Current

This often happens when a 120V circuit is required at a location where a neutral conductor is not available. Example: A 240V time clock motor is replaced with a 120V time clock motor and the equipment grounding conductor is used to feed one side of the 120V time clock. Another example is a 120V water filter wired to a 240V well-pump motor circuit and the equipment grounding conductor is used for the neutral. Figure 250–38

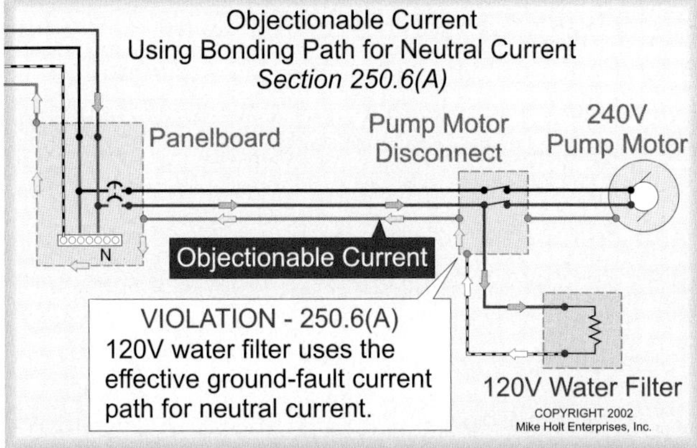

Figure 250–38

Using the bonding path for the neutral is also seen in ceiling fan installations where the equipment grounding (bonding) conductor is used as a neutral and the white wire is used as the switch leg for the light, or where a receptacle is added to a switch outlet that doesn't have a neutral conductor. Figure 250–39

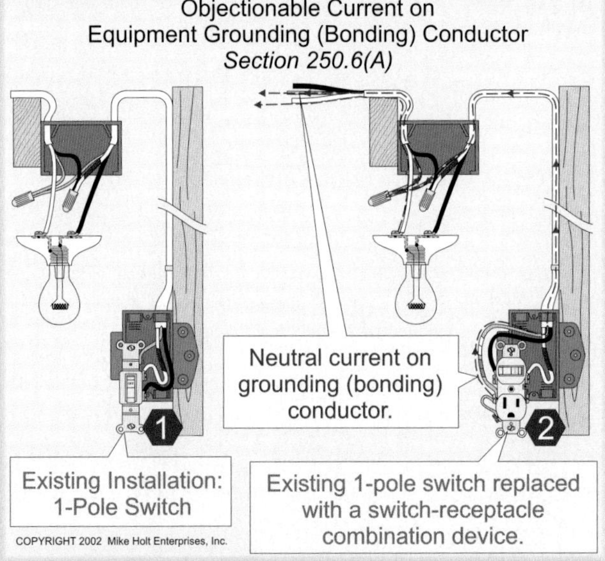

Figure 250–39

AUTHOR'S COMMENT: Neutral currents always flow on a community metal underground water-piping system where the water service to all of the buildings is metallic. This occurs because the underground water pipe and the service neutral conductors are in parallel with each other. Figure 250–40

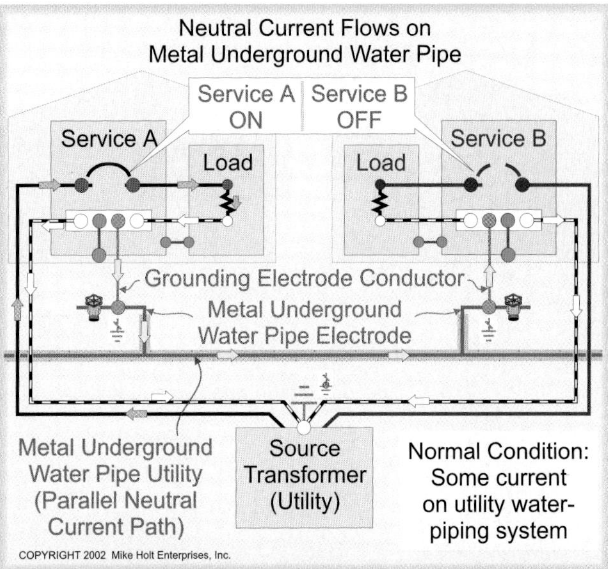

Figure 250–40

Dangers of Objectionable (Neutral) Current

Objectionable neutral current can cause shock hazard, fire hazard, improper operation of sensitive electronic equipment, and improper operation of circuit protection devices.

Shock Hazard

Objectionable current on metal parts of electrical equipment can create a condition where electric shock and even death from ventricular fibrillation can occur. Figure 250–41 shows an example where a person becomes in series with the neutral current path of a 120V circuit.

Fire Hazard

Fire occurs when the temperature rises to a level sufficient to cause ignition of adjacent combustible material in an area that contains sufficient oxygen. In an electrical system, heat is generated whenever current flows. Improper wiring, resulting in the flow of neutral current on grounding and bonding paths can cause the temperature at loose connections to rise to a level that can cause a fire. In addition, arcing at loose connections is particularly dangerous in areas that contain easily ignitible and explosive gases, vapors, or dust. Figure 250–42

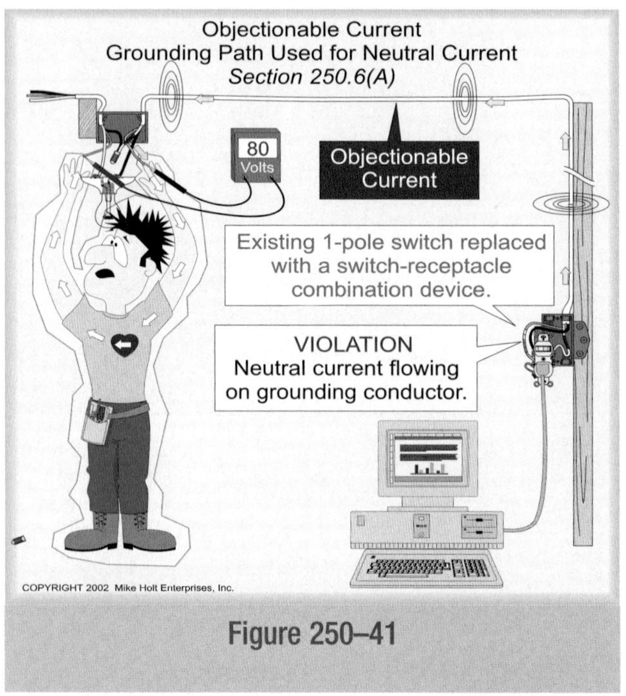

Figure 250–41

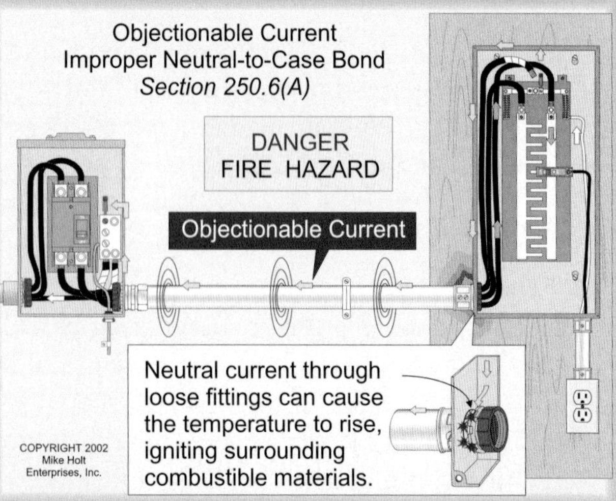

Objectionable Current
Improper Neutral-to-Case Bond
Section 250.6(A)
DANGER
FIRE HAZARD
Objectionable Current
Neutral current through
loose fittings can cause
the temperature to rise,
igniting surrounding
combustible materials.
COPYRIGHT 2002
Mike Holt
Enterprises, Inc.

Figure 250–42

Improper Operation of Circuit Protection Devices

Nuisance tripping of a protection device equipped with ground-fault protection can occur if neutral current returns on the equipment grounding (bonding) conductor, instead of the neutral conductor because of improper neutral-to-case bonds. A circuit breaker with ground-fault protection (277/480V, three-phase system over 1,000A per 230.95) uses either the residual current method or the zero sequence method to detect a ground fault. For the zero sequence method, the ground-fault trip unit sums the currents in the three-phase conductors and the neutral. When no ground fault is present, the summation of currents flowing on A+B+C+N will equal zero. Any current flow not equal to zero is considered a ground fault. The residual method is used only at the service as it measures current flowing through the main bonding jumper.

Where improper neutral-to-case bonds have been made, objectionable neutral current will flow on the equipment grounding (bonding) conductor in parallel with the grounded (neutral) conductor. Depending on the impedance of this path versus the neutral conductor path, the ground-fault protective relay may see current flow above its pickup point and cause the protective device to open the circuit.

If a ground fault occurs and there are improper neutral-to-case bonds, the protection relay might not operate because some of the ground-fault current will return on the neutral conductor bypassing the ground-fault protective device.

Improper Operation of Sensitive Electronic Equipment

When objectionable neutral current travels on the metal parts of electrical equipment, the electromagnetic field generated from alternating-circuit conductors will not cancel. This uncancelled current flowing on metal parts of electrical equipment and conductive building parts causes elevated electromagnetic fields in the building. These low frequency electromagnetic fields can negatively impact the performance of sensitive electronic devices, particularly video monitors and medical equipment. For more information visit: www.mikeholt.com/Powerquality/Powerquality. Figure 250–43

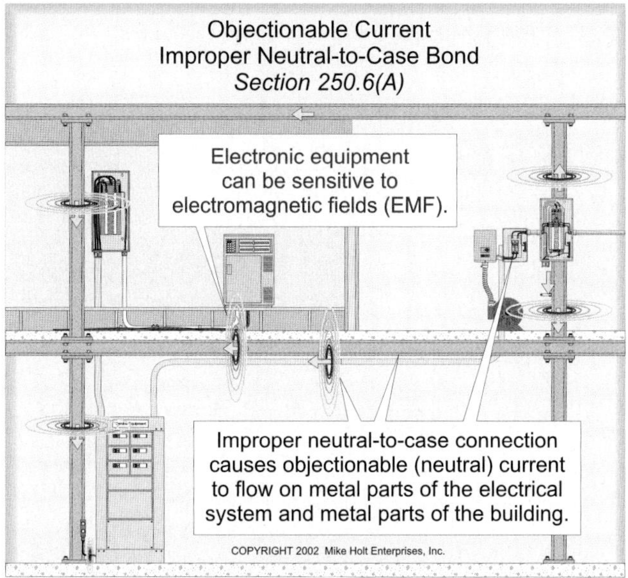
Objectionable Current
Improper Neutral-to-Case Bond
Section 250.6(A)
Electronic equipment can be sensitive to electromagnetic fields (EMF).
Improper neutral-to-case connection causes objectionable (neutral) current to flow on metal parts of the electrical system and metal parts of the building.
COPYRIGHT 2002 Mike Holt Enterprises, Inc.

Figure 250–43

250.6 Objectionable (Neutral) Current

(A) Preventing Objectionable Current

To prevent a fire, electric shock, improper operation of circuit protection devices, as well as improper operation of sensitive equipment, the grounding of electrical systems and the bonding of equipment shall be done in a manner that prevents objectionable (neutral) current from flowing on conductive materials, electrical equipment, or on grounding and bonding paths.

(B) Stopping Objectionable Current

If improper neutral-to-case bonds result in an objectionable flow of current on grounding or bonding conductors, simply remove or disconnect the improper neutral-to-case bonds.

(C) Temporary Currents Not Classified as Objectionable Currents

Temporary ground-fault current on the effective ground-fault current path, until the circuit overcurrent protection device opens removing the fault, is not classified as objectionable current. Figure 250–44

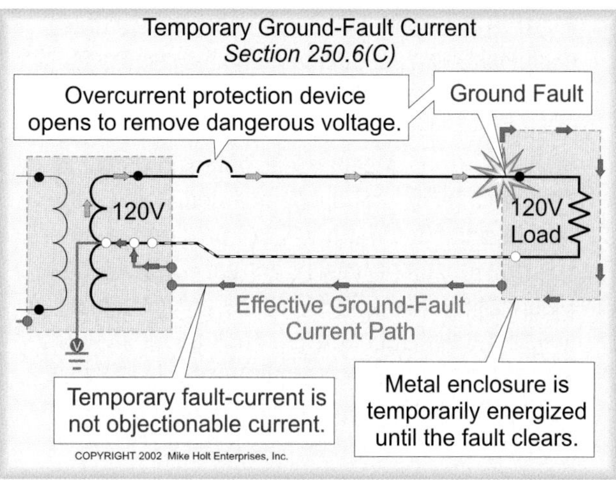
Temporary Ground-Fault Current
Section 250.6(C)
Overcurrent protection device opens to remove dangerous voltage.
Ground Fault
120V
120V Load
Effective Ground-Fault Current Path
Temporary fault-current is not objectionable current.
Metal enclosure is temporarily energized until the fault clears.
COPYRIGHT 2002 Mike Holt Enterprises, Inc.

Figure 250–44

(D) Electromagnetic Interference (Electrical Noise)

Currents that cause noise or data errors in electronic equipment are not considered objectionable currents. Figure 250–45

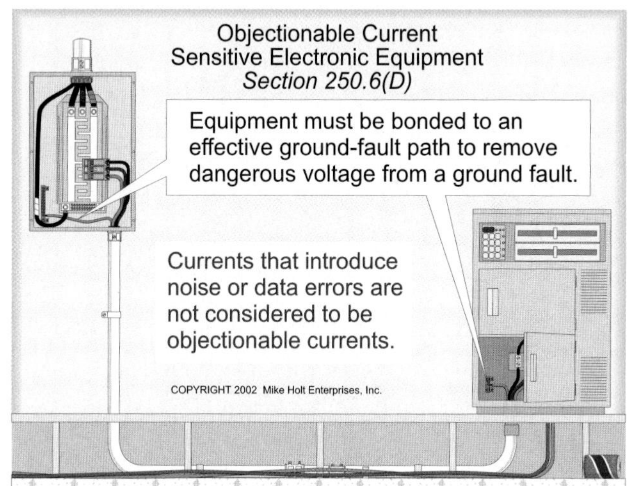
Objectionable Current
Sensitive Electronic Equipment
Section 250.6(D)
Equipment must be bonded to an effective ground-fault path to remove dangerous voltage from a ground fault.
Currents that introduce noise or data errors are not considered to be objectionable currents.
COPYRIGHT 2002 Mike Holt Enterprises, Inc.

Figure 250–45

AUTHOR'S COMMENT: Some sensitive electronic equipment manufacturers require their equipment to be isolated from the equipment bonding conductor, yet they require the equipment to be grounded to an independent grounding system. This practice is very dangerous and violates the *NEC* because the earth will not provide the low-impedance path necessary to clear a ground fault [250.4(A)(5)]. See 250.54 for the proper application of a supplementary electrode and 250.96(D) and 250.146(D) for the requirements of isolated equipment grounding (bonding) conductors for sensitive electronic equipment. **Figure 250–46**

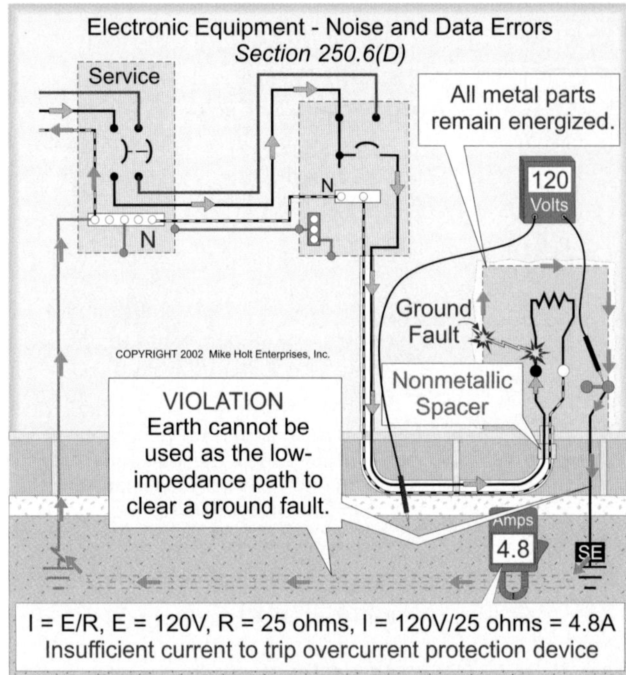
Electronic Equipment - Noise and Data Errors
Section 250.6(D)
Service
N
N
All metal parts remain energized.
120 Volts
Ground Fault
Nonmetallic Spacer
COPYRIGHT 2002 Mike Holt Enterprises, Inc.
VIOLATION
Earth cannot be used as the low-impedance path to clear a ground fault.
Amps
4.8
SE
I = E/R, E = 120V, R = 25 ohms, I = 120V/25 ohms = 4.8A
Insufficient current to trip overcurrent protection device

Figure 250–46

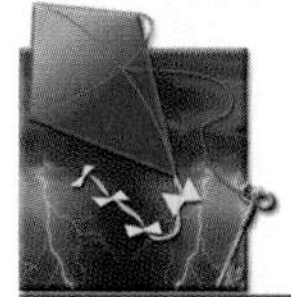

Index

Notes